A Collection of Readings

COLLECTION 5

Silver Burdett Ginn
A Division of Simon & Schuster
160 Gould Street
Needham Heights, MA 02194

Acknowledgments appear on pages 590–592, which constitute an extension of this copyright page.

ISBN: 0-663-61226-8 2 3 4 5 6 7 8 9 10 VHP 03 02 01 00 99 98 97 96

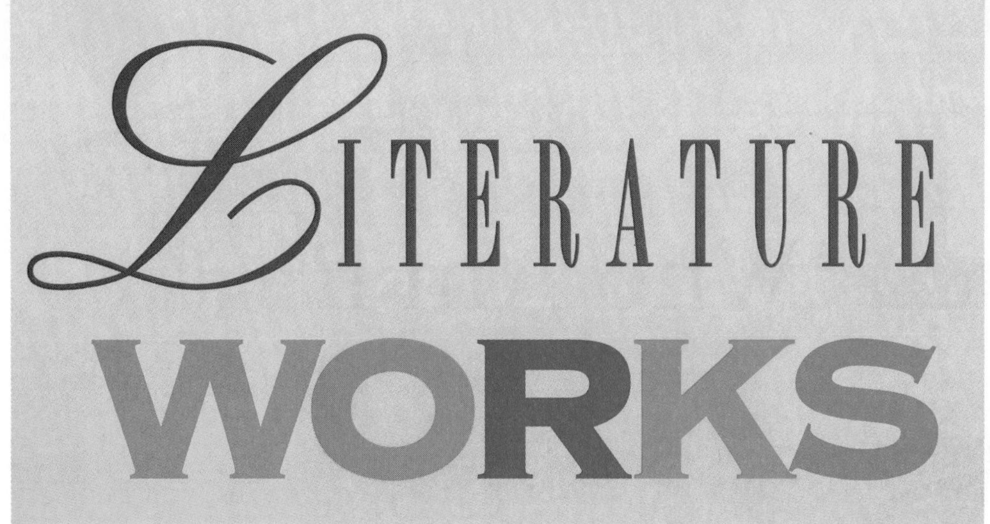

A Collection of Readings

COLLECTION 5

THEMES

Who Am I?

Moving On

Looking Below the Surface

Images and Imaginings

Learning from Nature

Voices from America's Past

SILVER BURDETT GINN

Needham, MA Parsippany, NJ
Atlanta, GA Deerfield, IL Irving, TX Santa Clara, CA

Who Am I?

Theme Trade Books

Theme 2

Moving On

Theme Trade Books

Looking Below the Surface

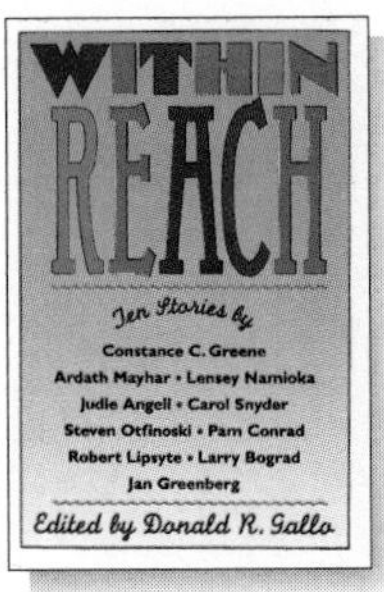

Theme Trade Books

Images and Imaginings

Theme Trade Books

Theme 5

Learning from Nature

Theme Trade Books

Theme 6

Voices from America's Past

★ Award-winning authors

Theme Trade Books

Who Am I?

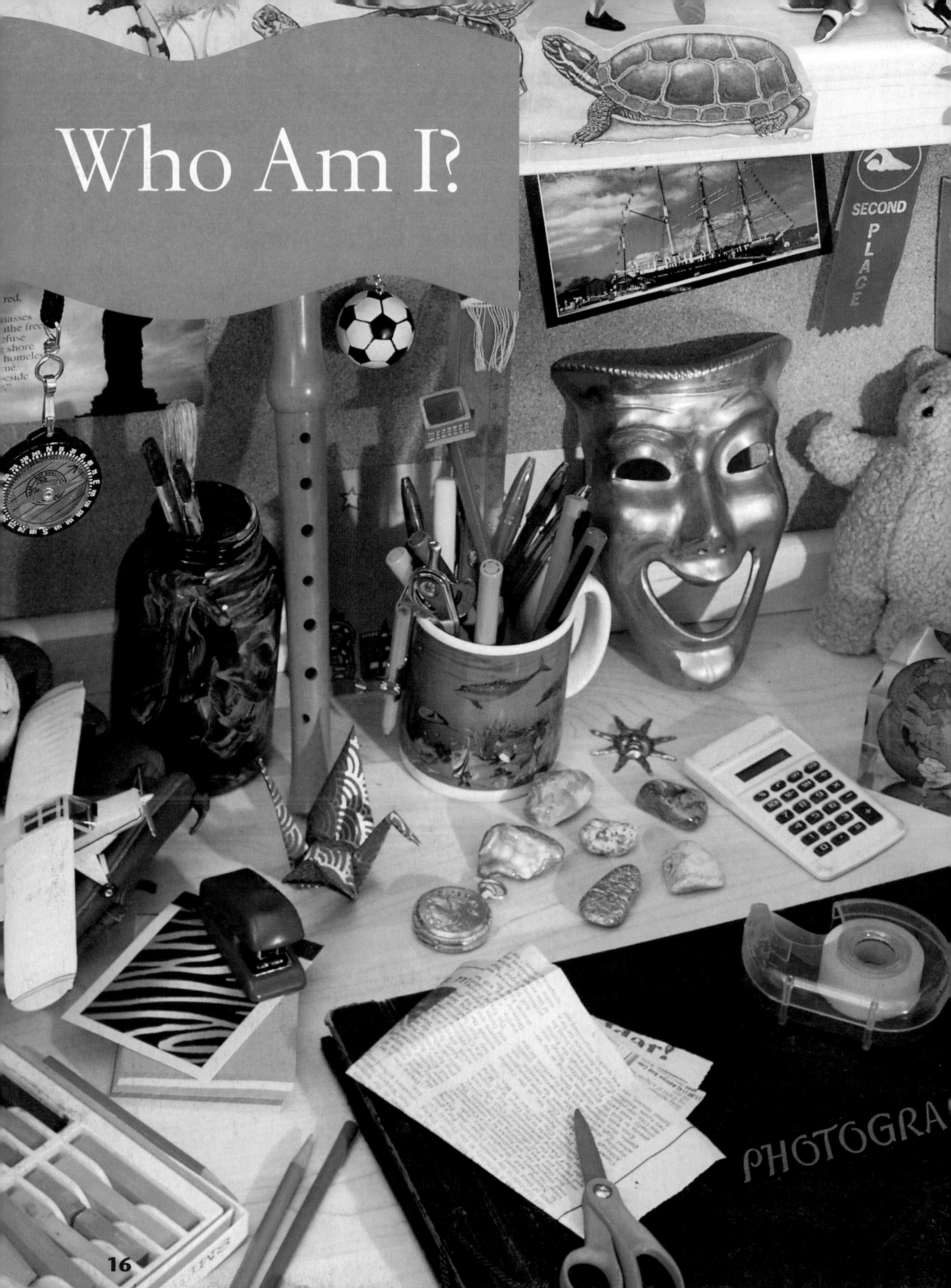

Theme

1

"Hey world, here I am!"

—Jean Little
Hey World, Here I Am!

Theme 1

Who Am I?

CONTENTS

Theme Trade Books

A Book of Your Own

by Carla Stevens

Carla Stevens tells you everything you need to know about starting and keeping a diary or journal. She also shares examples from the diaries of famous people.

The Singing Man

by Angela Shelf Medearis

Young Balzar wants to become a musician. The elders in his village disapprove and force the young man to leave home. This West African folk tale follows Balzar as he travels and sings about the people of Africa. When Balzar sees his family again, he has many successes to share.

Theme Magazine

Are you shy or showy? What do the things you collect say about who you are? Find the answers in the Theme Magazine *My Own Zone*.

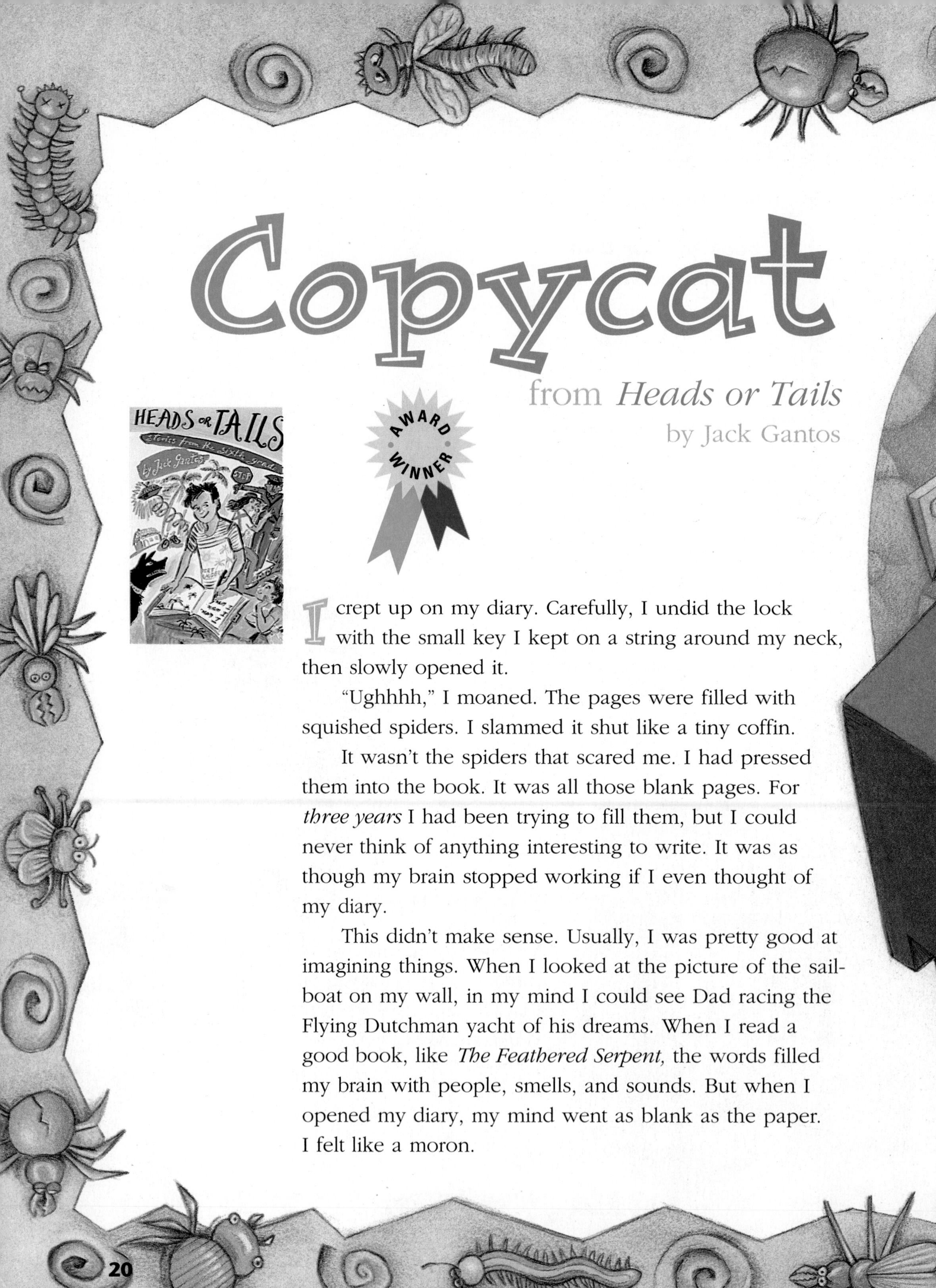

Copycat

from *Heads or Tails*

by Jack Gantos

I crept up on my diary. Carefully, I undid the lock with the small key I kept on a string around my neck, then slowly opened it.

"Ughhhh," I moaned. The pages were filled with squished spiders. I slammed it shut like a tiny coffin.

It wasn't the spiders that scared me. I had pressed them into the book. It was all those blank pages. For *three years* I had been trying to fill them, but I could never think of anything interesting to write. It was as though my brain stopped working if I even thought of my diary.

This didn't make sense. Usually, I was pretty good at imagining things. When I looked at the picture of the sailboat on my wall, in my mind I could see Dad racing the Flying Dutchman yacht of his dreams. When I read a good book, like *The Feathered Serpent,* the words filled my brain with people, smells, and sounds. But when I opened my diary, my mind went as blank as the paper. I felt like a moron.

It started the afternoon Mom came home from work and gave my older sister, Betsy, a diary. The year was stamped in gold on the flowery front cover. The hundreds of pages were made of thick, glossy paper. But what amazed me most was the lock. A strap from the back cover fit into a lock sewn onto the front cover, and there was a tiny key that only Betsy would be able to use.

"You can write anything that comes to your mind in this book," Mom told her. "A diary is for keeping all your secrets, and nobody is allowed to read it but you."

I looked up at my mother. "Where's mine?" I asked.

"I'll get you one when you're old enough to have secrets," she said.

"I do have secrets," I shot back.

"Not *grownup* secrets," she replied.

"I *want* a diary," I shouted and stomped my foot as hard as I could.

Mom didn't budge so I had to go all the way. I threw myself down on the floor and cried and bucked up and down. "I *want* a diary! I *want* a diary!"

"Don't be such an immature little brat," Betsy said and walked off to her bedroom, probably to start filling her diary with secrets. I howled even louder and kicked the floor with my heels.

"Okay, cut the theatrics," Mom said. "I'll get you a diary, but you must promise to write in it every day."

I promised. But I did not keep my promise.

At first, I just wrote down what day it was and the weather. Then I started listing everything I ate. But when it came to writing about what I was doing or what I was thinking and feeling, I couldn't seem to get it down. I could lie in bed and remember everything I had seen and said during the day, but when I opened the diary my thoughts vanished.

Still, I fought back and began to fill my diary with *stuff.* Each day, I searched for interesting things. I captured all kinds of bugs and squished them between the pages. I stapled in my baseball cards. I kept my stamp collection neatly arranged in rows. I used the diary as a photo album and mounted all my pictures inside. When I taped in my fortune-cookie fortunes, they looked like tiny telegrams from a foreign land. One of them read, "You Are Brave And Have Many Friends." I didn't believe it. I was covering over the empty white space of the pages in the same way I covered my eyes with my hands when I watched a monster movie.

It was no good. Even though the diary was filled with stuff, it was stuff someone else had thought up, someone else's *stuff.*

This evening was no different. Without writing much of anything, I locked the diary, grabbed a deck of cards and fled my bedroom. Betsy was sitting at the dining-room table playing a hand of solitaire. I sat down across from her and began to lay out my cards.

"Stop that," she said sharply.

"What?" I said.

"Stop copying me," she said. "Mom, tell him to stop copying me. He's driving me crazy."

"Leave your sister alone," Mom said, "and come help me work on this jigsaw puzzle. I'm having trouble."

Betsy slapped her cards down on the table. "Don't let him help you, Mom," she said. "Make him think of something to do on his own. Everything I do, he wants to do. Everything you do, he wants to do. He doesn't have a brain in his head. He's like some kind of dumb animal. Monkey see, monkey do."

"That's enough," Mom said. But we knew Betsy was right. I couldn't come up with any great ideas of my own. Nothing seemed interesting until I saw another person do it first. When Betsy started a shell collection, I started a shell collection. When she put PEACE posters on her bedroom wall, so did I. I wanted to be friends with all her friends. It seemed as if I could only do what she did first. I'll never be the President, I thought, just the Vice President. I won't be a gangster kingpin, just his stooge. I won't be the sole survivor in any humongous disaster, just another victim along with all the other losers. Believe it or not, I hate feeling sorry for myself. It makes me feel like an idiot, which makes me feel even sorrier for myself.

"Why don't you go fishing with your father," Mom suggested.

Dad was in the back yard, fishing in the canal for mullet and reading his favorite magazine, *Popular Mechanics.* But a few days before, I had seen our left-side next-door neighbor, Mr. Velucci, feeding spoiled pork chops to the alligators in the canal and I didn't want to go near that brown water. And I didn't want to get into a dumb discussion with Dad on how to transform his truck into a cabin cruiser or the washing machine into a helicopter. *Popular Mechanics* gave him the strangest ideas.

“Dad and I have nothing in common,” I said, repeating a line I had heard Betsy say the previous week.

“Don’t you have any homework to do?” Mom asked.

I did. I was avoiding my math homework because I wasn’t sure of the assignment. My teacher terrorized me and I was afraid to ask her after school for an explanation. I didn’t know the other kids that well and I was afraid to ask them. They might call me *stupid.* And once you get that name you’re stuck with it for the rest of the year.

My teacher's name was Mrs. Marshall and I thought she was more dense than I was. *She* certainly didn't have an original thought in her head. Each day, after she took roll, she turned to us and announced, "All students take out your copybooks." We reached under the seats of our desks for our black-and-white composition books. But we didn't dare open them until she said so. She had threatened to mash our fingers between the pages if we disobeyed.

From a desk drawer she removed a pair of white cotton gloves and put them on. Next she got a fresh box of white chalk from her supply closet and loaded five new sticks into her wire chalk holder which drew five lines at a time. She pressed it against the chalkboard in front of the class and scratched a stack of lines from left to right. The screeching was so loud I thought my head would explode. Then she scratched more lines across the blackboards that ran along the entire right side of the room and

across the back. Along the left side of the class, we had windows. But Mrs. Marshall wheeled two portable blackboards in front of the windows and our room became gloomy. She covered them with lines, too. I was surrounded by walls of blackboards, and from where I sat the gray lines of chalk looked like miles of barbed wire.

She removed a textbook from her desk and opened it to the page where we had left off the day before. She held the book in her left hand and raised a piece of chalk with her right. "Students, prepare to copy," she ordered. We opened our copybooks and twenty-five ballpoint pens clicked into position. "Go," she shouted and began to write. She copied onto the board exactly what was written in the book. If I only had known what the title of the book was, or who wrote it, I would have bought it so I could copy it at home. But she kept the book wrapped in a brown-paper cover.

"Egyptian history begins with the reign of King Menes," I scribbled.

She wrote like a sewing machine. Her handwriting looked even better than my mother's. All the letters were perfectly formed and they all slanted to the right at exactly the same angle. My handwriting was a mess. I wrote mostly straight up and down. My letters were always squashed together or too large and loopy. But, worst of all, I was slow. Every day I tried to keep up with Mrs. Marshall, but when she finished filling up the front blackboard I was only halfway down. She made us keep our desks clustered together in the center of the room so she had space to use the boards. When she finished the front, she hollered, "Shift!" and we scooted our desks a quarter turn to the right and faced the long side blackboard. Because I hadn't finished the front, I left a section of my copybook blank and began with the new board. I figured that maybe I could get caught up later.

"Shift!" she hollered when she finished the side board and moved to the back, and again we scooted our desks to the right. When I looked around, it seemed that all the other kids were keeping up with her. Then she began on the portable blackboards.

"Shift!" she commanded. We did, and once again I left extra space in my copybook as I leaped ahead of myself, trying to keep up. But I was still scribbling away when she finished the portable blackboards. She put down her book and chalk and quickly began to erase her writing as I desperately scrambled to fill the blank spots in my book. When all the boards were erased, she said, "Everyone put down your pens and stretch out your fingers and hands." As the class stretched, a team of honor students jumped into action. They wet sponges in the back sink, then madly washed the chalkboards. The room was so hot the water evaporated in a flash, and once again we were ready to go.

"Okay," she announced after drawing fresh lines. "Everyone pick up your pens and let's begin." She changed books and we began to copy a chapter on earth science.

All day long we copied chapters from her books, but I never remembered a thing I wrote. I was too frazzled with trying to keep up. At the end of the day she had overlapped me a dozen times. I felt even more tortured each Friday, when we turned in our copybooks. She passed them out to us on Monday and each time I read the same comments: "Write more neatly and quickly. Don't daydream. Keep your mind on your work." What mind, I asked myself. I didn't have a thought of my own.

Betsy scooped up her playing cards. "You can play cards," she said. "I'll do some homework." She got up and went to her bedroom.

I picked my cards up, too, and ran to my bedroom. I grabbed my book bag and dashed back to the dining-room table before Betsy had returned. I took out a clean sheet of paper and a book.

When Betsy returned she slapped her books down on the table. "Copycat," she sneered. She spread her homework out while I copied a page from my history book. After a while I peeked up at her to see what she was doing. She was writing a letter to a friend. It occurred to me that I should be writing a letter to a friend. Then I noticed that she was writing differently than usual. Her handwriting slanted to the left instead of to the right. I thought it was a neat idea and so I started to do it, too. I was peeking up at her again to see if I was missing out on some new trick when she saw me.

"You're copying my new handwriting," she said. "I caught you."

"I am not," I cried. She snapped up my paper before I could grab her hand. "Give it back," I hollered. "I'll call Mom."

"Call her," Betsy said calmly, "so I can show her what a moron you are. Not only are you copying my handwriting but you are copying your homework word for word out of the book. A trained monkey could do what you do."

"Leave me alone," I said.

"Gladly." She sighed and gathered up her books. "If you try to follow me into my room, I'll knock you cold and sell you to a zoo."

I didn't care what she said. I was excited with the new handwriting style. It seemed to work really well for me. My letters were clear and I thought I was writing faster. I couldn't wait to try it out in class.

The next morning I got up early and started to get dressed. Everyone at school was wearing blue jeans and T-shirts. But Mom had other ideas. At the beginning of the school year she took me to Sears and bought five new pairs of slacks, five matching shirts, five pairs of matching socks, and a pair of brown lace-up shoes. Then she organized my closet so that on Monday I wore the green slacks and green-and-yellow plaid shirt with green socks. On Tuesday, I wore the brown slacks with the brown-and-white stripes and brown socks. This was Friday, so I put on my blue slacks and the blue-and-white checkered shirt with dark blue socks. Getting dressed was like being on an assembly line. I couldn't wait until I was old enough to pick out my own clothes. Mom said it had nothing to do with being old enough. "When you can *pay* for them," she said, "you can wear whatever you want. You can go to class dressed in a clown suit."

Today I'm going to have an idea of my own, I promised myself as I rode my bike to school. I'm not going to copy Betsy. I'm going to do exactly what I want to do, no matter what anyone thinks of me. I can either be a copycat for the rest of my life or I can be a one-of-a-kind.

I passed the drive-in theater at the end of our street. They showed only old movies and *The Sound of Music* was still playing. It was playing when we moved into the neighborhood, and that was four months ago. On some nights when the wind was blowing just right, I could hear the music through my bedroom window. Because of that movie, I caught myself singing, " . . . The hills are alive . . . " about a million times a day. I heard it in my brain when I was sitting in class. I heard it when I was playing kickball. I heard it when I was eating breakfast. I hated that movie. Maybe that's why I don't have an original thought in my head, I guessed. I'm being brainwashed by that movie all night long.

I got to school early. The place looked as strange as ever. It was made out of eight separate rectangular wooden trailers. There was one trailer for each grade, first through sixth. One trailer was for the office and one trailer was split in half for the girls' and boys' bathrooms. All the trailers were fitted with wheels and the entire school could be pulled away in the middle of the night. I could imagine all of us arriving one morning to find nothing but the asphalt paths left behind in the sandy field which was hot and large as a desert.

When Mrs. Marshall gave us the order to "start copying," I was ready for her. My new slant-to-the-left handwriting *was* faster. As she circled the room I was almost right behind her. And because I wasn't so afraid of being overlapped by her all the time, I could think about what I was writing. The Egyptians were great. Maybe I'll be an archaeologist when I grow up and study ancient Egypt, I thought. That was an original idea for me.

I went home for lunch and unlocked my diary with the key I kept around my neck. Yesterday I had scrawled above a line of flattened ants that I was "the stupidest kid on the planet." Today I wrote: "There is hope for me after

all." The discovery of my new slant-left writing would change my life, like the discovery of electricity had changed the world, I decided. I closed the diary and heard the delicious crunching of a juicy palmetto bug that hadn't yet dried out.

At the end of the week, Mrs. Marshall collected our copybooks. I was excited because I had almost kept up with her the last two days, now that I was using my new handwriting. I expected praise for doing better. Maybe she'd even make me an honor student.

On Monday morning Mrs. Marshall handed out the copybooks. I flipped through the pages, and when I reached my new writing, I saw a big red X across every page. "DO YOUR OWN WORK," she had written. "SEE ME AFTER CLASS." My heart was pounding. I tried not to cry, but I could feel the tears filling my eyes. I put my head down on my desk as Mrs. Marshall began to draw lines around the room.

At lunchtime I waited until everyone left the classroom before I went up to her desk.

"I don't respect cheaters," she said to me.

"But I did write this," I protested. "I changed my writing."

"Don't argue with me," she replied, "I've already made up my mind. I don't know who copied this into your book, but you can't fool me."

I didn't know what else to say. I was being cheated by my teacher and there was nothing I could do about it. I turned and walked to my desk.

"I expect from now on you'll do your own work," she scolded. "Let this be a lesson to you."

The rest of the afternoon I copied her as best I could in my old handwriting. She overlapped me five times. I imagined myself failing sixth grade because I was unable to write fast enough. Betsy was right. A trained monkey could do what I do, only better.

When I returned home I went straight to Betsy's bedroom. "You've got to help me," I blurted out. "Look at this." I opened the notebook and showed her Mrs. Marshall's comments.

"Well, that's what you get for being a copycat," she said.

"But I did do the work," I cried.

"What do you want me to do?" she asked.

"Write her a note and tell her I copied you," I begged. "She'll believe you."

"I'm not your mother," said Betsy. "You copied me, now suffer the consequences."

"But I promise never to copy you again. Cross my heart and hope to die."

"Even your promises are copies of promises," she said scornfully. "Beat it."

I retreated to my bedroom. I thought I could take a book and copy it in my new handwriting and prove to Mrs. Marshall that it was my work. But she could say someone else had done it, and fail me. I knew what I had to do. I unlocked my diary and with my new handwriting began to write down anything that came into my mind. I wrote between the bugs and stamps and cards and fortunes. At first, my writing didn't make sense. No two sentences had much in common. Then I suddenly began to write out all the lyrics to *The Sound of Music.* There were a lot of those songs stuck in my head. After I cleared them out, I settled down and started to write all about my lousy school year.

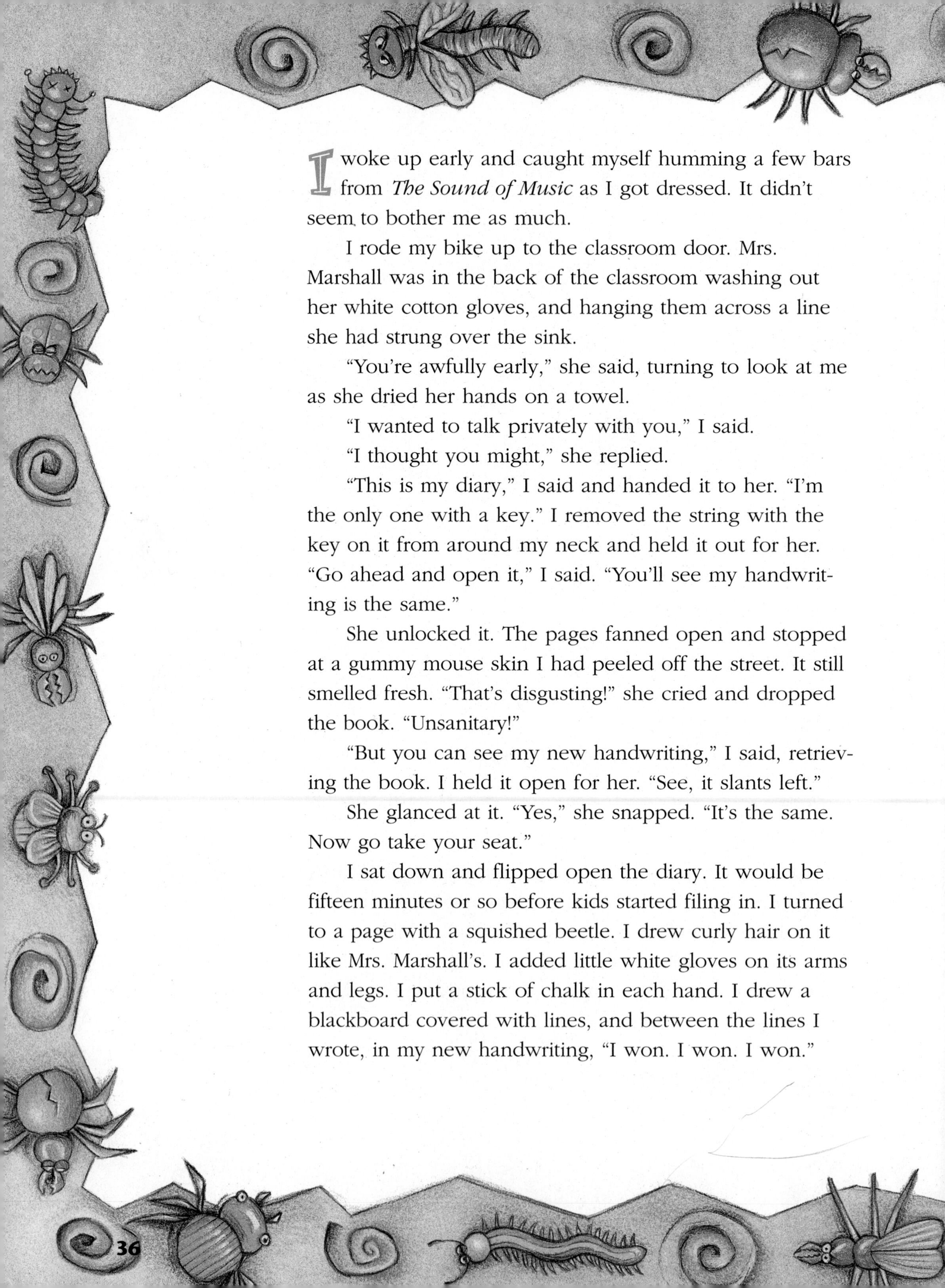

I woke up early and caught myself humming a few bars from *The Sound of Music* as I got dressed. It didn't seem to bother me as much.

I rode my bike up to the classroom door. Mrs. Marshall was in the back of the classroom washing out her white cotton gloves, and hanging them across a line she had strung over the sink.

"You're awfully early," she said, turning to look at me as she dried her hands on a towel.

"I wanted to talk privately with you," I said.

"I thought you might," she replied.

"This is my diary," I said and handed it to her. "I'm the only one with a key." I removed the string with the key on it from around my neck and held it out for her. "Go ahead and open it," I said. "You'll see my handwriting is the same."

She unlocked it. The pages fanned open and stopped at a gummy mouse skin I had peeled off the street. It still smelled fresh. "That's disgusting!" she cried and dropped the book. "Unsanitary!"

"But you can see my new handwriting," I said, retrieving the book. I held it open for her. "See, it slants left."

She glanced at it. "Yes," she snapped. "It's the same. Now go take your seat."

I sat down and flipped open the diary. It would be fifteen minutes or so before kids started filing in. I turned to a page with a squished beetle. I drew curly hair on it like Mrs. Marshall's. I added little white gloves on its arms and legs. I put a stick of chalk in each hand. I drew a blackboard covered with lines, and between the lines I wrote, in my new handwriting, "I won. I won. I won."

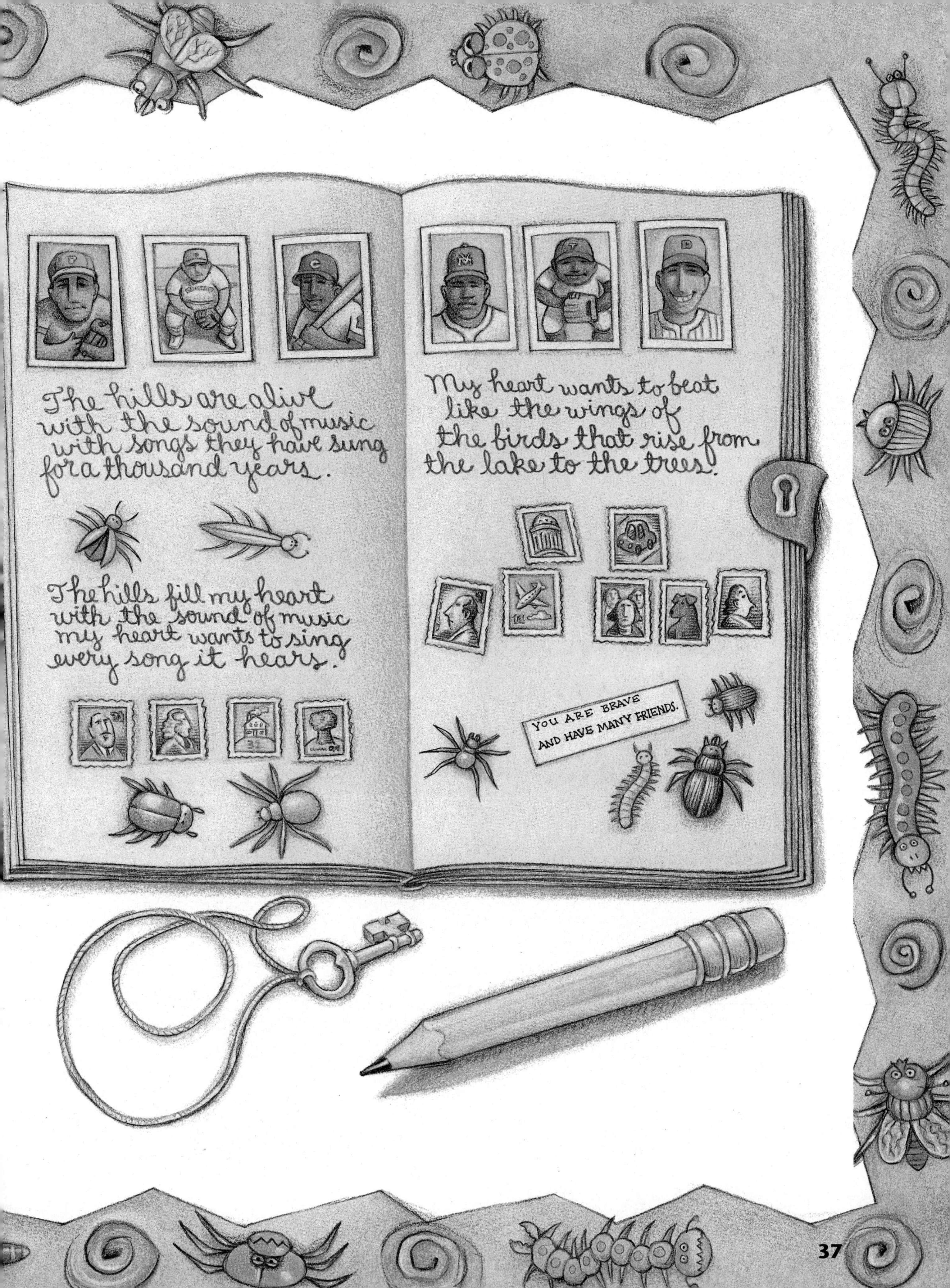
The hills are alive
with the sound of music
with songs they have sung
for a thousand years.
The hills fill my heart
with the sound of music
my heart wants to sing
every song it hears.
My heart wants to beat
like the wings of
the birds that rise from
the lake to the trees.
YOU ARE BRAVE
AND HAVE MANY FRIENDS.

IN RESPONSE

Copycats Can Change

"I can either be a copycat for the rest of my life or I can be a one-of-a-kind," the main character says. How does the character change in the story? List at least three words or phrases that describe him early in the story. Then write three words or phrases that describe him at the end.

Help Out a Friend

Imagine that you are the main character's best friend. With a partner, role-play a talk between the friend and the boy's teacher, Mrs. Marshall. Tell her how he feels about himself and his work. Suggest how Mrs. Marshall can help make him more successful in school and at home.

A Future Interview

The main character thinks his new handwriting will change his life. Suppose you were to interview him one year later. You want to ask how his life is different in school and at home. Write three or four questions for the interview. Look back at the story for ideas. Then invite a partner to answer your questions based on clues the story gives.

AUTHOR AT WORK

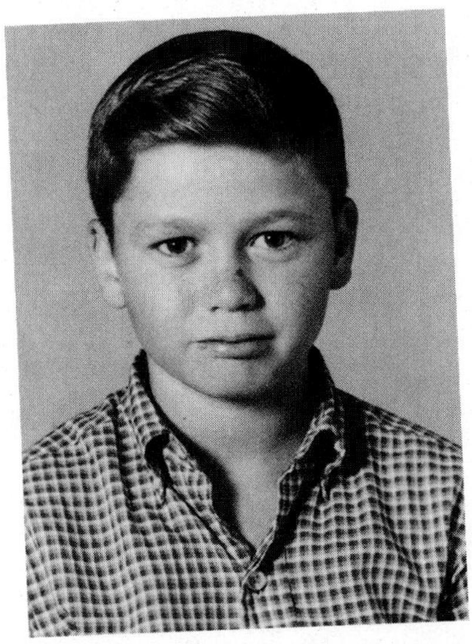

Jack Gantos as a grade school student

Jack Gantos remembers being in grade school. He also recalls keeping a diary with a collection of squished bugs inside! His childhood memories help him understand what children like to read. "I remember my childhood and write to please it," he says.

Mr. Gantos's first book, *Rotten Ralph,* was about "a rotten cat who does rotten things to his owner." Since then, he has written several books about Ralph and other characters.

Library Link This story was taken from *Heads or Tails* by Jack Gantos. You might enjoy reading the entire book to see what happens to the boy in "Copycat."

★ Award-winning Author

Other Books by . . .

Jack Gantos

Rotten Ralph by Jack Gantos, illustrated by Nicole Rubel, Houghton Mifflin, 1976

Not So Rotten Ralph by Jack Gantos, illustrated by Nicole Rubel, Houghton Mifflin, 1994

Jack Gantos the adult, with a picture of himself as a sixth grader.

A Work in Progress

Just as a writer jots ideas in a journal, an artist makes sketches. An artist may work a long time before deciding a picture is finished. Sketches often show how an idea or image gets its start. Mary Cassatt made several versions of this picture.

Drawing by Mary Cassatt (United States) for *The Letter,* 1890–1891

Etching (first state) for *The Letter,* 1890–1891

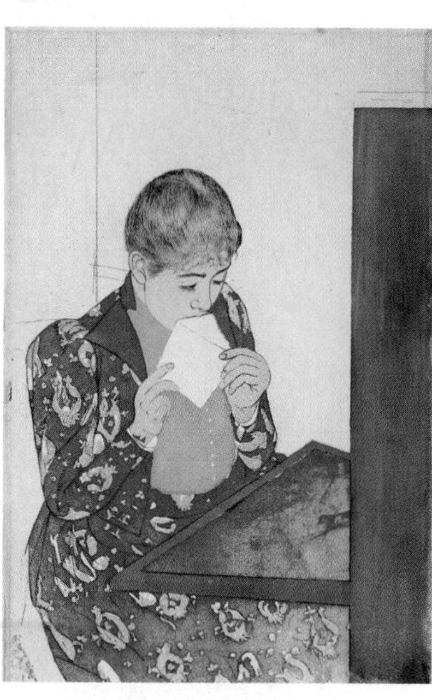

Etching (second state) for *The Letter,* 1890–1891

Describe the woman in the picture. What do you think she is doing? How does the artist draw your attention to the letter?

Describe the changes from one picture to the next. What do you see in the last picture that you don't see in the first?

Etching (fourth state) for *The Letter*, 1890–1891

About Notebooks

by Jean Little

I love the first page of a new notebook.
I write the date crisply.
My whole name marches exactly along the line.
The spaces are always even.
The commas curl just so.
I never have to erase on the first page.
Never!

When I get to the middle, there are lots of eraser holes.
The corners are dog-eared.
Whole paragraphs have been crossed out.
My words slide off the lines and crowd together.
I wish it was done.

I have a dream that, someday, someone will say,
"Here, give me that beat-up old notebook.
You needn't bother filling in all those other zillion pages.
Start a new one this instant
—Because it's February, because today's not Wednesday,
Because everybody deserves beginning again more often."

Yet, crazy as it sounds,
I always like to write the number 8,
Even on the third last page of a messy notebook.
It meets itself so neatly it's almost magic.
And I love swooping big E's and looping small z's.
If, for some reason, I get to write a word
Like "quintessence" maybe or something with lots of m's
Or "balloon" or "rainbow" or "typhoon" or "lollipop"
I forget I'm sick of the book with its stupid margins
And, while I'm writing, I hum inside my head.

It Started with Miss Ibbotson

from *Little by Little*

by Jean Little

AWARD WINNER

Me, age 12, on a family holiday. (Mother took picture to send Dad, who was in the Navy.)

In the fall I went into Miss Ibbotson's class. We had to learn about decimals and percents. I disliked grade six till the day Miss Ibbotson started us writing journals.

When she passed out the notebooks, they did not look special. They had blue paper covers and lined pages with a thin red margin. I could not see those faint lines when I was writing.

"For the last half hour, every day this month," Miss Ibbotson told us, "you will keep a diary. You will write in them what happened in your life that day and how you felt."

She talked on for a few minutes, but I was not listening. I could hardly wait to begin.

That first afternoon, I did write down what had actually happened in my life that day. I may even have stuck to the truth till page three or four. But long before the first week was up, I had begun fancying things up a little.

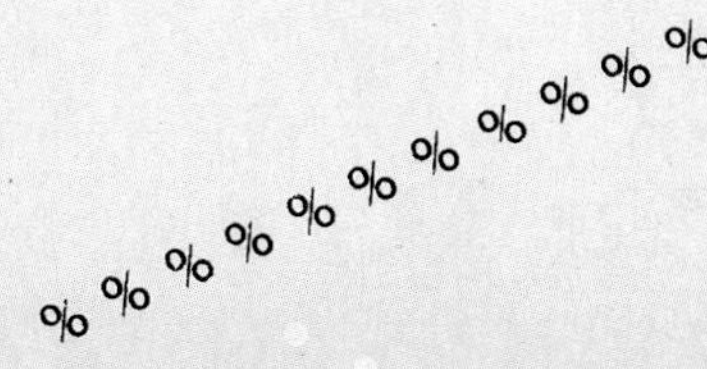

My real life was simply too dull to be worth recording.

I began stealing ideas from a book we had at home called *Boyhood Stories of Famous Men.* In the book one boy saved the day by carving a lion out of butter to be used as a decoration for the King's table. Another made his own paints by crushing berries and boiling roots, and little Wolfgang Mozart and his big sister went to perform on the harpsichord before the child Marie Antoinette. The book went on to explain how each boy later became famous.

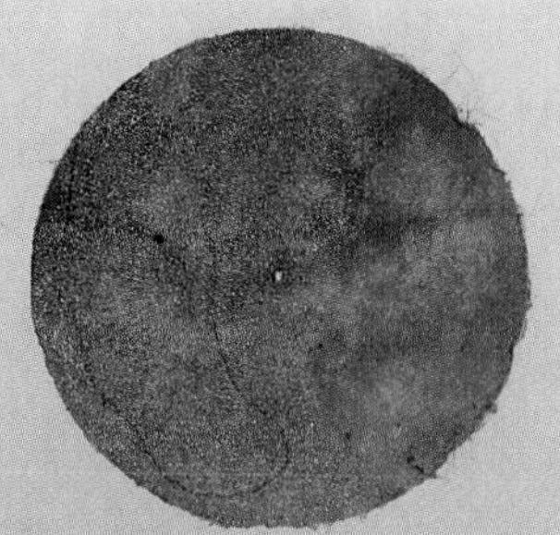

I liked the story about the young Mozart best. What drew me to it was his older sister. She was shown in the illustration, standing behind Wolfgang and the pretty little princess. I knew exactly how she must be feeling. She, too, was a gifted musician, but her little brother was the hero of the story. It never said what happened to her.

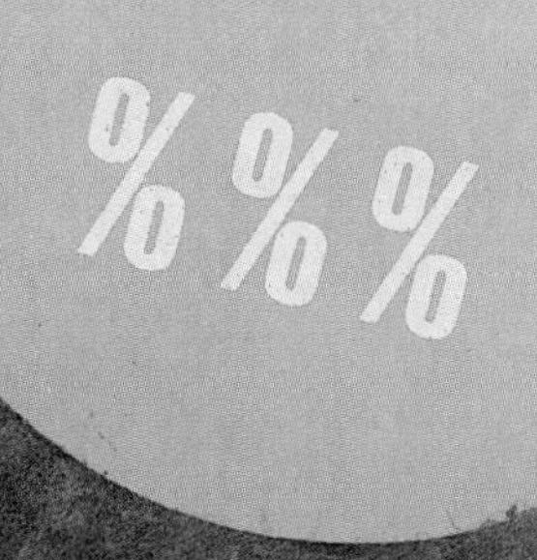

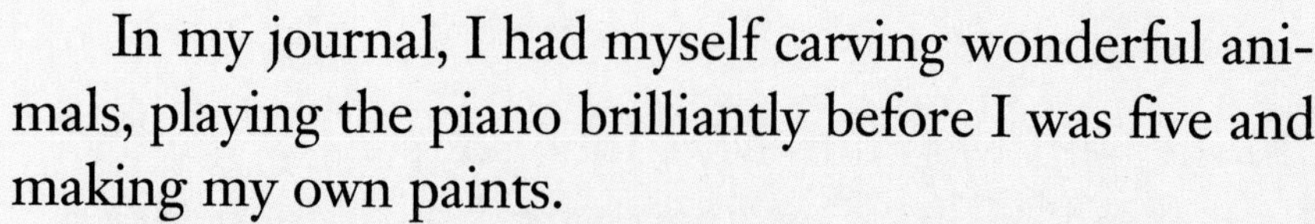

In my journal, I had myself carving wonderful animals, playing the piano brilliantly before I was five and making my own paints.

One day's entry read like this:

> Last night, a famous artist came to have supper at our house. Mother took him down to the cellar. The great painter stopped dead in his tracks and pointed to our cellar walls.
>
> "Madam," he cried, "whoever painted these magnificent murals on your walls?"
>
> Mother stared at the wondrous paintings.
>
> "I have no idea," she said in a bewildered voice. She turned to her children.
>
> "Children," she said, "have you any idea who painted these magnificent murals?"
>
> The other children shook their heads.
>
> "As a matter of fact," I said, "I painted them."

"But you had no paints!" Mother cried.

"I know," I said modestly, "but I so longed to paint that I boiled roots and squeezed berries and made my own paints."

The great artist patted my head.

"Madam," he said, with tears in his eyes, "someday this little girl of yours will be world famous as an artist."

Each afternoon when the bell rang and Miss Ibbotson told us to put the books away, I emerged from my fantasy life reluctantly. All day I looked forward to three-fifteen. Then one afternoon, instead of telling us to put our books away, Miss Ibbotson told us to hand them in.

I was horrified. It had never crossed my mind that Miss Ibbotson planned to read our journals. I thought diaries were private.

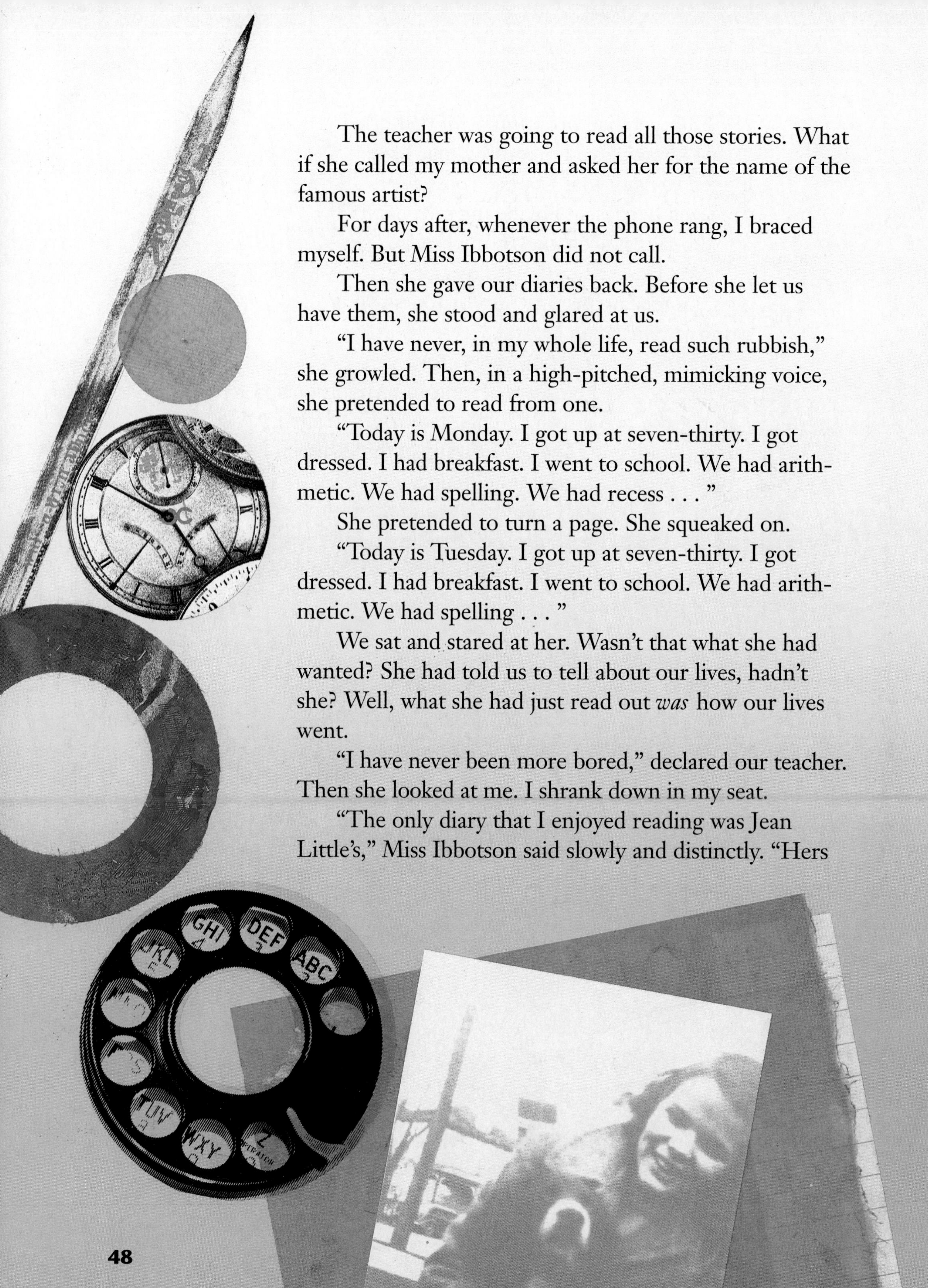

The teacher was going to read all those stories. What if she called my mother and asked her for the name of the famous artist?

For days after, whenever the phone rang, I braced myself. But Miss Ibbotson did not call.

Then she gave our diaries back. Before she let us have them, she stood and glared at us.

"I have never, in my whole life, read such rubbish," she growled. Then, in a high-pitched, mimicking voice, she pretended to read from one.

"Today is Monday. I got up at seven-thirty. I got dressed. I had breakfast. I went to school. We had arithmetic. We had spelling. We had recess . . . "

She pretended to turn a page. She squeaked on.

"Today is Tuesday. I got up at seven-thirty. I got dressed. I had breakfast. I went to school. We had arithmetic. We had spelling . . . "

We sat and stared at her. Wasn't that what she had wanted? She had told us to tell about our lives, hadn't she? Well, what she had just read out *was* how our lives went.

"I have never been more bored," declared our teacher. Then she looked at me. I shrank down in my seat.

"The only diary that I enjoyed reading was Jean Little's," Miss Ibbotson said slowly and distinctly. "Hers was at least entertaining. I shall never assign journal writing to a class again. Sylvia, pass out the books."

I sat there dazed. She had liked it. Not only that, she had liked it best. Yet mine had been a bunch of lies almost from start to finish.

As my journal smacked down on the lid of my desk and I caught the baleful look on Sylvia's face, I knew the teacher had not helped me in my search for friends. But I didn't care. I wanted to hug my blue book. I had entertained Miss Ibbotson. That was far more important than being good at decimals and percents.

Real writers kept diaries. I would become a writer.

As I walked home, I thought about books I might write. Perhaps I should write one called "Girlhood Stories of Famous Women." No. I wanted instead to tell about the big sisters who stood at the back of the picture and had to put up with famous little brothers. I knew how they felt.

In December, Dad came home on leave. At first we hung around him, all clamoring for attention.

Hugh got it when he said, "We got up one morning and there was a snowman in the yard. Guess who made it?"

"You?" Dad said, sitting down to listen.

"No," I interrupted, wanting to tell it properly.

"Let Hugh finish," my father said,

Me, age 10, with our dog Chummy. (Chummy didn't notice I was different.)

reaching out to pull me onto the arm of his chair but still watching Hugh.

"Mother made it!" Hugh said excitedly.

Dad looked confused. Mother laughed. She sounded a bit flustered.

"I came home from the hospital at three in the morning," she explained, straightening a pile of magazines.

"I wasn't a bit sleepy. And there was all this fresh snow and a full moon . . . "

I could not keep quiet another second.

"We went to bed," I burst out, "and there wasn't a snowman. And when we came down in the morning . . . "

"There *was* a snowman!" Hugh yelled.

"Have mercy on our eardrums," my mother said. I saw her glance at Dad. "I did wonder if any of our neighbors were looking out their windows," she added.

My father began to laugh. We were all pleased. But I knew I could have told it far better if they had let me.

A couple of days later, I came into the living room late in the afternoon and found my father sitting all by himself. He was reading the paper. I seldom had one of my parents to myself, because there were so many people in our house.

But now here he was.

"Dad, would you like me to sing for you?" I asked.

"Not just now, Jean," he said, without even looking up from the paper.

"Would you like me to dance for you?" I inquired. I did not know any dances, but I had just read *Ballet Shoes* and I thought I could improvise the way Posy Fossil did.

"No," he mumbled and continued reading.

I stared at the back of his paper. Eatons wanted you to do your Christmas shopping there.

Perhaps I should try poetry. I knew he liked poems. He had given me books of poetry for Christmas and my birthday. I liked poems, too. And I knew several by heart. But I did not feel hopeful as I asked if he wanted to hear me recite one.

"Uh-uh," he grunted and turned to the next section. I wandered disconsolately up to the room I shared with Pat. She was out with Mother, so I had it to myself. I went to the window and stood looking out at the sunset. It was a vivid one that lifted my drooping spirits with its glorious banners of orange and yellow, its streak of purple.

If they put it in a book, I thought, it would sound unreal.

Then, turning away from the window, I saw blank paper and a pencil lying on the table I used as a desk.

I could write about it myself, I thought, sitting down and picking up the pencil. There were only three sheets of paper. Whatever I wrote must not be too long.

A poem, I thought. I could maybe write a poem.

The first line was easy.

"Orange flags are flying," I wrote. Then the next line wrote itself, and the next and the next.

Orange flags are flying,
No overhanging grey
Dims the rosy sunset
At the close of day.

I stared down at the page in incredulous delight. I could do it. I was a poet. It wasn't hard. And it satisfied something in me, something that would not have felt the same if I had written, "The clouds at sunset look like orange flags. There is no grey cloud to dim their brightness."

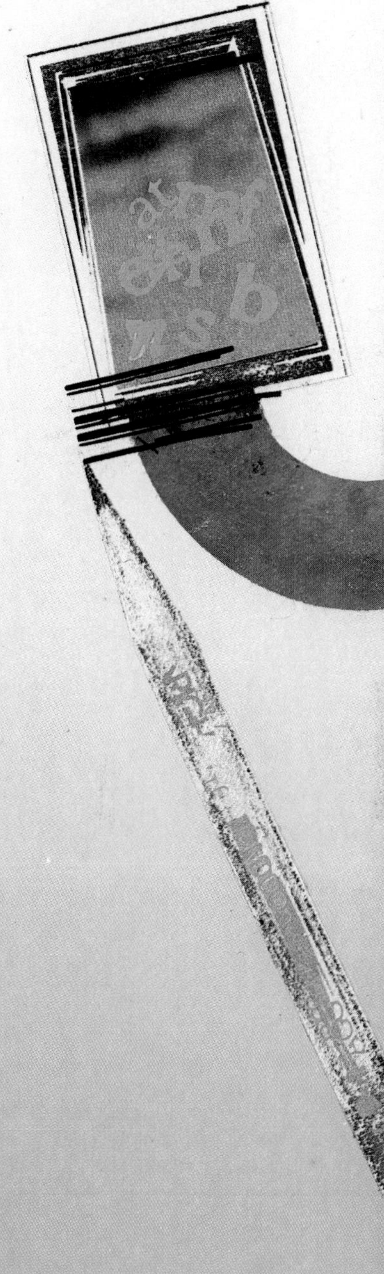

I went on eagerly, excited by what I was creating.

Royal purple nestles
'Round the golden clouds.

I paused to find a rhyme for "clouds." I could not think of a single one. Louds. Souds. They weren't even words. If I'd written "cloud," there were lots. Plowed. Loud. Bowed.

I could change it to "cloud."

Royal purple nestles
'Round the golden cloud.
And the windblown poplars
Before their Maker bowed.

There was something wrong with it. Part of it sounded as though it was happening now and part of it as though it happened yesterday. Never mind. I liked those poplars. I knew poplar trees by their shape. They were the only trees I could recognize that way. They lifted up their branches instead of bowing them, really, but never mind that, either.

O'er the snowy landscape,
Christmas bells ring out,
While, in nearby doorways,
Happy children shout.

I could hardly wait to show it to somebody. I had written three verses. But it did not sound finished. I had to put an end on it.

I chewed my pencil and stared into space. Then I had it.

Many busy people
Their tiresome work take leave

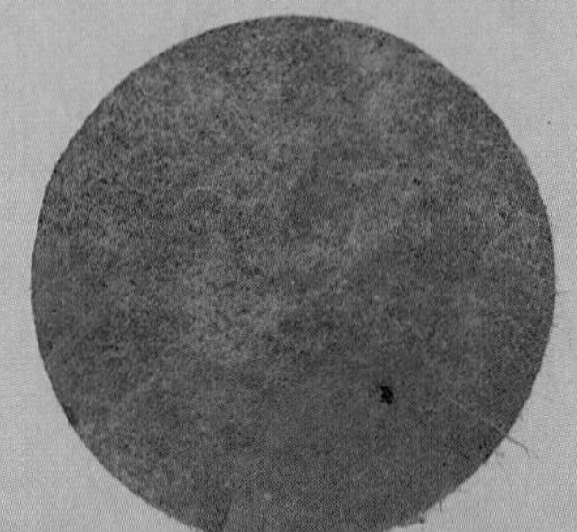

To hurry home and welcome
This year's Christmas Eve.

I read it over. I'd have to fix it. But first I wanted Dad to see it. Holding it up so that I could read it over while I walked along, I started to go back to where my father was sitting.

No. It looked too messy. He didn't like messy things. Besides, my poem deserved better than that.

I sat down again, took a fresh sheet of paper and copied it out. I changed "nestle" to "nestled" so the whole verse was in the past. I changed "nearby" to "neighboring." It sounded fancier. I made "overhanging" into "o'erhanging." That was poetic. I smiled at " 'Round." There were lots of words like those in the poems we read at school.

Then I took the poem down to the living room. Dad was still reading the paper. I drew a deep breath.

"Dad," I announced, my voice shaking, "I've written a poem."

My father dropped the newspaper. His head jerked up. The sheets of newspaper floated to the floor all askew. He paid absolutely no attention to them.

"A poem!" he exclaimed. "Let me see it."

He looked as excited as I felt. He thought writing a poem was important. Wonderful, even. Shyly, I placed the sheet of paper in his hand.

Slowly, carefully, respectfully, he read to himself each word I had written. Then, just as slowly, carefully and respectfully, he read it out loud.

I basked in his pride in me, but I heard, too, that it was not quite right.

"I have to fix it a bit," I said.

On the front porch of our house in Taipei. Standing are Aunt Gretta, Dad and Mother. Grandma is holding Pat and Hugh. Jamie and I are sitting on the steps.

IN RESPONSE

Moments to Remember

Skim through the story and find moments when Jean Little experiences strong feelings, such as sadness or joy. Draw a picture to illustrate each moment. Explain in a caption why Jean Little feels as she does.

Write About Writing

Write a letter to Jean Little. Compare your feelings about writing to the way she felt about writing as a young girl.

A Little Advice

In "Copycat," the main character has trouble writing in his diary. Jean Little, however, finds plenty of interesting things to write about. Look back at both stories. What advice do you think Jean Little could give the boy in "Copycat" to improve his writing? Write your ideas.

On Christmas Day, the year I turned 16

Students enjoy listening to Jean tell her stories.

Jean Little wrote her first book about a girl with cerebral palsy. She was a teacher at the time, working with students who had physical disabilities.

When she discovered there were few stories about children like her students, she decided to write some.

Since then, Ms. Little has written more than fifteen books. Most are about physically challenged children. One of her books, *Mama's Going to Buy You a Mockingbird*, was made into a movie.

As a child, Ms. Little had trouble with her vision. Today, she is blind. She has a guide dog named Zephyr and a talking computer that helps her continue writing.

Library Link This story was taken from *Little by Little* by Jean Little. You might enjoy reading the entire book to find out more about this writer.

★ Award-winning Author

Other Books by . . .

Jean Little

Hey World, Here I Am! by Jean Little, illustrated by Sue Truesdell, HarperTrophy, 1990

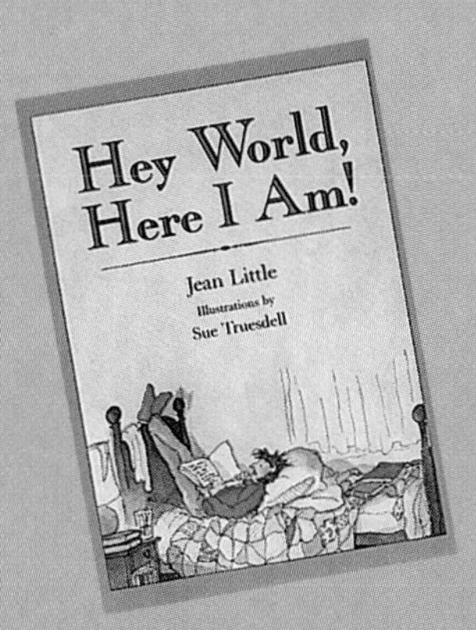

Mama's Going to Buy You a Mockingbird by Jean Little, Viking Penguin, 1984

You can use a diary any way you want to. Some of the young people whose diaries appear on these pages kept diaries to share their thoughts with others. Some just wanted a place to express their ideas. Two of these diarists grew up to become famous writers of children's books.

This entry is from a book called *The Diary of Latoya Hunter.* A publisher heard about Latoya's writing talent and asked her to keep a diary of her first year in junior high school. Like many authors, Latoya gave her diary a name.

September 30, 1990

Dear Diary,

I think I need a name for you. You've become like a best friend to me, you're someone I can talk to without being argued with. I think I know just the name for you. I'll call you Janice after my best friend from Jamaica. We were like sisters before I left. Over the years we've grown apart though, the letters have stopped but that friendship is still going on within me!

So today I christen you diary, Janice Page.

Do you remember the stories about Peter Rabbit? Beatrix Potter was the author of these tales. While she was growing up, Beatrix kept a diary, using a secret code she made up. The diary was found and decoded after her death.

This entry was written in 1881. In code, Beatrix describes a trip she made with her grandmother. They visited a place where beautiful cups, dishes, and jewelry were designed and made from silver. The building was also a warehouse and showroom. The diary includes details that make the old building and the skilled workers seem real.

Beatrix Potter's entry for November 4 is on the right in the code she used. The entry is decoded below.

Friday, November 4

We entered a dark lobby with four or five doors, a passage and a staircase leading out of it. The house sounded singularly silent and deserted except for the faint click of hammers from an upper room. While waiting for my grandmother, Mr. Saunders took us into a small room on the right.

Wanda Gág grew up to write and illustrate children's books, including *Millions of Cats.* As a girl, Wanda kept notebooks and diaries filled with pencil drawings. She drew these sketches in 1905, when she was twelve. In a diary entry Wanda wrote in 1908, she talks about the painting and drawing she did for other people.

September 5, Sunday

How do you do? Fine day to-day. Drew 12 pictures in my birthday book. The birthday book is going to be one in which people write their names and birthdays.

Have asked mama to wake me early to-morrow morning so that I can paint Miss Dillon's place cards before school. I have noticed that Miss Dillon doesn't only smile with her eyes and mouth but with her whole face, even her eyebrows.

Dirk van der Heide lived in Holland. He kept a diary at the start of World War II. When the German Nazis invaded The Netherlands in 1940, Dirk and his sister left for the United States. On the long voyage, Dirk made a copy of his diary so that others could read about life in a country at war.

Wednesday

July 10, 1940

I do not remember everything that happened when the Nazis came so it will be hard for me to go back over my diary. Some things I remember very well, especially the bombs. There were many fires and much smoke and noise. Sometimes I hardly remember anything else. Keetje remembers things too. She is my sister and is nine years old while I am twelve and two months. We are going to America because of the war and this is our eighth day on the ocean.

There are many children on this boat going to America. There is an English boy named Jack who is my age. He has very good manners. Most of the children are English and they cannot understand Keetje and me so very well. We studied English in school but it sounds different when the English talk.

AWARD
WINNER

1942
True Vine Baptist Church

It seemed like the hottest day ever in Navasota, Texas, the small, dusty town where Alvin Ailey and his mother, Lula, lived. Blue-black flies buzzed their songs while the church bell rang.

Alvin and Lula worshiped at True Vine Baptist Church every Sunday. When they arrived for services, Alvin slid into his usual seat in the first-row pew. There he could watch his mother sing in the gospel choir. And Lula sure could sing. Her voice rose clear and strong as she sang the morning hymn.

The men at True Vine dressed in dignified suits. The women showed off wide-brimmed hats and fanned away the Texas heat. Some cuddled powdered babies; others hugged their Bibles.

True Vine's Reverend Lewis delivered a thundering sermon. The organ rang out, followed by a bellow of tenors singing "Rocka My Soul in the Bosom of Abraham."

Sweet sopranos and tambourines joined the rousing refrain:

Rocka-my-soul in the bosom of Abraham
Rocka-my-soul in the bosom of Abraham
Rocka-my-soul in the bosom of Abraham
Ohhh, rocka-my-soul. . . .

The congregation made a joyful noise. They stepped and swayed with the warmth of the spirit and raised their palms in revelation. Alvin stomped his feet and clapped his hands so hard, they hurt. "Ohhh . . . rocka-my-soul . . . ," he sang along.

Alvin was going to miss the music and rejoicing at True Vine Baptist Church.

Days later, Alvin rode a creaky locomotive headed west. He and Lula were going to try life in Los Angeles, California. Times had been hard in Texas; there weren't many jobs. Lula wanted a better life for Alvin. She told him there were more opportunities in the city, more ways to make a decent living.

Alvin stared out his window while the train rocked and lurched its way through the dry Texas land. Life in the city would be so different.

1945–1947
Los Angeles

Los Angeles was a flashy town. Lula found plenty of work. Most mornings she left their apartment on East 43rd Place before sunrise, and she didn't return home until the sun was long past setting.

Alvin didn't mind, though. On Saturdays and after school he liked spending time alone, exploring the city streets. He strolled Central Avenue, where nightclubs such as the Club Alabam boomed with the sounds of big-band jazz—swinging music that spilled out into the street—while the musicians inside rehearsed for the evening show.

Alvin especially liked downtown Los Angeles, where the lights on the theater houses reflected off the pavement. There was the Orpheum Theater, the Biltmore, the Rosebud, and the Lincoln.

Outside each theater a blinking marquee announced the latest show:

Pearl Bailey Performing Live
Billie Holiday—A Night of Blues
Duke Ellington and His Band

The men who owned the theaters stacked handbills on their stoops. Each handbill announced coming attractions. Alvin collected them all.

He dawdled along the sidewalk and spotted a handbill showing a black dancer, something Alvin had never seen advertised before. The paper said

Coming Soon to the Biltmore Theater
Katherine Dunham and Her Dancers
in
Tropical Revue

Alvin looked carefully at the picture of Katherine Dunham, a beautiful dancer fluttering exotic ruffles. Katherine Dunham and her dance troupe were one of the few traveling shows in the world with black dancers performing dances from Africa, Haiti, and Latin America.

Alvin was curious. As he tucked the announcement into his pocket, he noticed Ted Crumb, a skinny boy with spindly legs, hanging out at a stage door nearby.

Ted knew all kinds of things about dance; he hoped to dance onstage someday. Ted told Alvin that Katherine Dunham's afternoon show was about to start and that they could see dancing like they'd never seen before.

Alvin and Ted crept down the alley that led to the Biltmore's stage entrance. They kept quiet and out of sight. With the stage door opened just so, they watched the splendor of *Tropical Revue*.

Katherine Dunham and her dancers swirled and lunged to the rhythms of West Indian drums. They were famous for *Bahiana,* a spicy Brazilian routine, and for a sizzling number called *Rumba with a Little Jive Mixed In*. Alvin's soul danced along when he saw Katherine Dunham's style.

Alvin nudged Ted. "What is that they're doing? What *is* that?" he asked.

"That's modern dancing," Ted said. "Watch this!"

Ted tried Katherine Dunham's *Bahiana*. Alvin slapped out a beat on his knees and followed Ted's lead.

Slowly, Alvin began to move. He curled his shoulders from back to front and rippled his hands like an ocean wave. He rolled his hips in an easy, steady swivel, dancing with an expression all his own.

Alvin moved like a cat, *smooth* like quicksilver. When he danced, happiness glowed warm inside him.

Dusk crept over the city. The streetlights of Central Avenue winked on, one by one. Alvin made his way back to East 43rd Place.

That night, Alvin told his mother he'd seen black people performing their own special dances. It was a show Alvin would never forget.

1949–1953
Lester Horton's Dance School

More than anything, Alvin wanted to study dance. But when Alvin arrived in Los Angeles not everyone could take dance lessons. In 1949 not many dance schools accepted black students. And almost none taught the fluid moves that Alvin liked so much—almost none but the Lester Horton Dance Theater School, a modern dance school that welcomed students of all races.

Lester's door was open to anyone serious about learning to dance. And, at age eighteen, Alvin Ailey was serious, especially when he saw how Lester's dancers moved. One student, Carmen de Lavallade, danced with a butterfly's grace. Another, James Truitte, made modern dance look easy. But Lester worked his students hard. Sometimes they danced all day.

After hours in the studio, droplets of sweat dotted Alvin's forehead. He tingled inside, ready to try Lester's steps once more. At first, Alvin kept time to Lester's beat and followed Lester's moves. Then Alvin's own rhythm took over, and he started creating his own steps. Alvin's tempo worked from his belly to his elbows, then oozed through his thighs and feet.

"What is Alvin *doing*?" one student asked.

"Whatever he's doing, he's sure doing it fine," two dancers agreed.

Some tried to follow Alvin's moves, but even Alvin didn't know which way his body would reel him next.

Alvin's steps flowed from one to another. His loops and spins just came to him, the way daydreams do.

Alvin danced at Lester Horton's school almost every day. He taught the other students his special moves.

In 1950, Alvin joined Lester Horton's dance company. Soon Alvin performed his own choreography for small audiences who gathered at Lester's studio. Alvin's dances told stories. He flung his arms and shim-shammed his middle to express jubilation. His dips and slides could even show anger and pain. Modern dance let Alvin's imagination whirl.

All the while, Lester watched Alvin grow into a strong dancer and choreographer. Lester told Alvin to study and learn as much as he could about dance. He encouraged Alvin to use his memories and his African-American heritage to make dances that were unforgettable.

1958–1960
Blues Suite–Revelations

Alvin's satchel hung heavy on his shoulder. His shoes rapped a beat on the sidewalk while taxicabs honked their horns. He was glad to be in New York City, where he came to learn ballet from Karel Shook and modern dance techniques from Martha Graham, two of the best teachers in the world.

Alvin took dance classes all over town, and he met dancers who showed him moves he'd never seen before. So many dancers were black. Like Alvin, their dreams soared higher than New York's tallest skyscrapers.

Alvin gathered some of the dancers he'd seen in classes around the city. He chose the men and women who had just the right moves to dance his choreography. Alvin told them he wanted to start a modern dance company that would dance to blues and gospel music—the heritage of African-American people. Nine dancers believed in Alvin's idea. This was the beginning of the Alvin Ailey American Dance Theater.

On March 30, 1958, on an old wooden stage at the 92nd Street Y, Alvin and his friends premiered with *Blues Suite,* dances set in a honky-tonk dance hall. Stage lights cast moody shadows against the glimmer of each dancer's skin. The women flaunted red-hot dresses with shoes and stockings to match; the men wore black hats slouched low on their heads. They danced to the swanky-swank of a jazz rhapsody.

Alvin's choreography depicted the blues, that weepy sadness all folks feel now and then. *Blues Suite* stirred every soul in the room.

Alvin was on his way to making it big. Word spread quickly about him and his dancers. Newspapers hailed Alvin. Radio stations announced his debut.

An even bigger thrill came when the 92nd Street Y asked Alvin to perform again. He knew they hardly ever invited dance companies to come back. Alvin was eager to show off his next work.

On January 31, 1960, gospel harmonies filled the concert hall at the 92nd Street Y.

Rock-rock-rock
Rocka-my-soul
Ohhh, rocka-my-soul

Alvin clapped in time to the music, the same way he did when he was a boy. But now, Alvin rejoiced onstage in

Revelations, a suite of dances he created to celebrate the traditions of True Vine Baptist Church in Navasota, Texas.

The audience swayed in their seats as Alvin and his company gloried in their dance. High-stepping ladies appeared onstage sweeping their skirts. They danced with grace and haughty attitudes. Alvin and the other men jumped lively to the rhythm, strutting and dipping in sassy revelry.

Revelations honored the heart and the dignity of black people while showing that hope and joy are for everyone. With his sleek moves, Alvin shared his experiences and his dreams in a way no dancer had ever done.

When *Revelations* ended, the audience went wild with applause. They stomped and shouted. "More!" they yelled. *"More!"*

Taking a bow, Alvin let out a breath. He raised his eyes toward heaven, satisfied and proud.

When I Grow Up

Why do you think Alvin Ailey became a successful dancer? Look back at the story and find at least three reasons for his success. What is something at which you would like to be successful someday? List three things you would need to do to reach your goal.

Influences on Alvin

What people and places influenced Alvin Ailey's dancing? Find examples in the story. Then think of something you enjoy doing. Have people and places influenced you as they did Alvin Ailey? How so?

It's Showtime!

Design a poster for one of Alvin Ailey's performances. Include information about the time, date, and location. Also add some interesting details that will get people excited about the show.

Andrea Davis Pinkney and Brian Pinkney

Alvin Ailey is the first book that Andrea Davis Pinkney and her husband, Brian Pinkney, worked on together. Before writing the book, Ms. Pinkney interviewed Mr. Ailey's mother and some of his friends.

Mr. and Ms. Pinkney say they work well together because they accept each other's advice. Sometimes Ms. Pinkney feels her husband can make his pictures better with some small changes. Other times, Mr. Pinkney suggests ways his wife can improve her writing. They usually talk about changes on Saturday mornings at their dining room table.

★ Award-winning Illustrator

The Pinkneys filled notebooks, drew mock-ups of pages, and took photographs of models as they worked on *Alvin Ailey*.

Ms. Pinkney has loved to write and tell stories since she was a child. In her family, suppertime was "storytelling" time. She has a special secret to share with fifth graders who want to become writers: "Write as much and as often as you can about everything!" Good writing, Ms. Pinkney says, can take any form. "A letter to a friend, the words to a song, and a diary are all great forms of writing," she adds.

For his illustrations, Mr. Pinkney uses a special style called "scratchboard." He takes paper coated in black ink and scratches it with a sharp tool to create pictures. Mr. Pinkney says he likes this technique because it makes him feel like he is drawing and sculpting at the same time.

Brian Pinkney watches as students experiment with the scratchboard technique on small squares.

Other Books by . . .

Andrea Davis Pinkney and Brian Pinkney

Dear Benjamin Banneker by Andrea Davis Pinkney, illustrated by Brian Pinkney, Harcourt Brace, 1994

Seven Candles for Kwanzaa by Andrea Davis Pinkney, illustrated by Brian Pinkney, Harcourt Brace, 1993

Katherine Dunham's MAGIC

Katherine Dunham in a dance based on rhythms and movements she learned in the West Indies

Alvin Ailey was fourteen in 1945 when he watched Katherine Dunham's dancers for the first time. The dances from Africa, the West Indies, and South America had an energy and rhythm that thrilled him. The fast drum beats made him want to dance, too.

"I was completely hooked," he said later, "from the moment I saw those beautiful black dancers doing dances from all over the world."

Like Alvin Ailey, many audiences familiar with ballet found the Dunham Dance Company fresh and exciting. Ballerinas danced on their toes. They kept their backs straight. Dunham's dancers rolled their backs. They

The Dunham dancers, about 1935

pounded their feet. They moved their shoulders back and forth in time to bongo drum beats.

Katherine Dunham was born in Glen Ellyn, Illinois, in 1909. She became not only a famous dancer and choreographer but also an anthropologist. Anthropologists are people who study other cultures. Ms. Dunham loved to study African culture almost as much as she loved to dance. As a student at the University of Chicago, she learned that some West Indians still performed dances their ancestors brought from Africa.

In 1935, Ms. Dunham traveled to the West Indies to study African dancing. She learned war and funeral dances. She learned dances that honored African gods.

Back in the United States, Ms. Dunham taught people of all races new ways to dance. She insisted that her dancers study anthropology, too.

Alvin Ailey used movements learned from Ms. Dunham in his own choreography. Two years before he died, Mr. Ailey produced one of his dance company's most spectacular works. He called it *The Magic of Katherine Dunham*.

Katherine Dunham in *Tropical Revue,* the first Dunham dance Alvin Ailey ever saw

Solidarity

Lark, let's sing!
Waterfall, jump!
Brook, let's run!
Diamond, shine!
Eagle, let's fly!
Dawn, be born!
Singing!
Jumping!
Running!
Shining!
Flying!
We are born!

Solidaridad

Alondra, ¡vamos a cantar!
Cascada, ¡vamos a saltar!
Riachuelo, ¡vamos a correr!
Diamante, ¡vamos a brillar!
Águila, ¡vamos a volar!
Aurora, ¡vamos a nacer!
¡A cantar!
¡A saltar!
¡A correr!
¡A brillar!
¡A volar!
¡A nacer!

—Amado Nervo
translated from the Spanish by Lori M. Carlson

This Day Is Over

When the day is over,
I think of all I did.
Did I goof off,
Or did I accomplish something?
Did I make a new friend,
Or did I make an enemy?
Was I mad at everybody,
Or was I nice?
Anyway, what I did today is over.
While I sleep,
The world will be shining up
A new day for me to use,
Or goof up,
Or whatever I decide
To do with it.
Tonight, I pick out
"Nice," and
"Friendly," and
"Accomplish something."

—Calvin O'John

Slower Than the Rest

AWARD WINNER

from *Every Living Thing*
by Cynthia Rylant

Leo was the first one to spot the turtle, so he was the one who got to keep it. They had all been in the car, driving up Tyler Mountain to church, when Leo shouted, "There's a turtle!" and everyone's head jerked with the stop.

Leo's father grumbled something about turtle soup, but Leo's mother was sympathetic toward turtles, so Leo was allowed to pick it up off the highway and bring it home. Both his little sisters squealed when the animal stuck its ugly head out to look at them, and they thought its claws horrifying, but Leo loved it from the start. He named it Charlie.

The dogs at Leo's house had always belonged more to Leo's father than to anyone else, and the cat thought she belonged to no one but herself, so Leo was grateful for a pet of his own. He settled Charlie in a cardboard box, threw in some lettuce and radishes, and declared himself a happy boy.

Leo adored Charlie, and the turtle was hugged and kissed as if he were a baby. Leo liked to fit Charlie's shell on his shoulder under his left ear, just as one might carry a cat, and Charlie would poke his head into Leo's neck now and then to keep them both entertained.

Leo was ten years old the year he found Charlie. He hadn't many friends because he was slower than the rest. That was the way his father said it: "Slower than the rest." Leo was slow in reading, slow in numbers, slow in

understanding nearly everything that passed before him in a classroom. As a result, in fourth grade Leo had been separated from the rest of his classmates and placed in a room with other children who were as slow as he. Leo thought he would never get over it. He saw no way to be happy after that.

But Charlie took care of Leo's happiness, and he did it by being congenial. Charlie was the friendliest turtle anyone had ever seen. The turtle's head was always stretched out, moving left to right, trying to see what was in the world. His front and back legs moved as though he were swimming frantically in a deep sea to save himself, when all that was happening was that someone was holding him in midair. Put Charlie down and he would sniff at the air a moment, then take off as if no one had ever told him how slow he was supposed to be.

Every day, Leo came home from school, took Charlie to the backyard to let him explore and told him about the things that had happened in fifth grade. Leo wasn't sure how old Charlie was, and, though he guessed Charlie was probably a young turtle, the lines around Charlie's forehead and eyes and the clamp of his mouth made Leo think Charlie was wise the way old people are wise. So Leo talked to him privately every day.

Then one day Leo decided to take Charlie to school.

It was Prevent Forest Fires week and the whole school was making posters, watching nature films, imitating Smokey the Bear. Each member of Leo's class was assigned to give a report on Friday dealing with forests. So Leo brought Charlie.

Leo was quiet about it on the bus to school. He held the covered box tightly on his lap, secretly relieved that turtles are quiet except for an occasional hiss. Charlie rarely hissed in the morning; he was a turtle who liked to sleep in.

Leo carried the box to his classroom and placed it on the wide windowsill near the radiator and beside the geraniums. His teacher called attendance and the day began.

In the middle of the morning, the forest reports began. One girl held up a poster board pasted with pictures of raccoons and squirrels, rabbits and deer, and she explained that animals died in forest fires. The pictures were too small for anyone to see from his desk. Leo was bored.

One boy stood up and mumbled something about burnt-up trees. Then another got up and said if there were no forests, then his dad couldn't go hunting, and Leo couldn't see the connection in that at all.

Finally it was his turn. He quietly walked over to the windowsill and picked up the box. He set it on the teacher's desk.

"When somebody throws a match into a forest," Leo began, "he is a murderer. He kills trees and birds and animals. Some animals, like deer, are fast runners and they might escape. But other animals"—he lifted the cover off the box—"have no hope. They are too slow. They will die." He lifted Charlie out of the box. "It isn't fair," he said, as the class gasped and giggled at what they saw. "It isn't fair for the slow ones."

Leo said much more. Mostly he talked about Charlie, explained what turtles were like, the things they enjoyed, what talents they possessed. He talked about Charlie the turtle and Charlie the friend, and what he said and how he said it made everyone in the class love turtles and hate forest fires. Leo's teacher had tears in her eyes.

That afternoon, the whole school assembled in the gymnasium to bring the special week to a close. A ranger in uniform made a speech, then someone dressed up like Smokey the Bear danced with two others dressed up like squirrels. Leo sat with his box and wondered if he should laugh at the dancers with everyone else. He didn't feel like it.

Finally, the school principal stood up and began a long talk. Leo's thoughts drifted off. He thought about being home, lying in his bed and drawing pictures, while Charlie hobbled all about the room.

He did not hear when someone whispered his name. Then he jumped when he heard, "Leo! It's you!" in his ear. The boy next to him was pushing him, making him get up.

"What?" Leo asked, looking around in confusion.

"You won!" they were all saying. "Go on!"

Leo was pushed onto the floor. He saw the principal smiling at him, beckoning to him across the room. Leo's legs moved like Charlie's—quickly and forward.

Leo carried the box tightly against his chest. He shook the principal's hand. He put down the box to accept the award plaque being handed to him. It was for his presentation with Charlie. Leo had won an award for the first time in his life, and as he shook the principal's hand and blushed and said his thank-you's, he thought his heart would explode with happiness.

That night, alone in his room, holding Charlie on his shoulder, Leo felt proud. And for the first time in a long time, Leo felt *fast.*

An Eye for Reality

from *Dorothea Lange*

text by Milton Meltzer

photographs by Dorothea Lange

Dorothea Lange, 1934
(photograph by Rondal Partridge)

When she was seven, Dorothea Lange came down with polio. The disease left her with a limp for the rest of her life. Her own suffering made her sensitive to the suffering of others. During the Great Depression of the 1930's, Lange put that sensitivity and her love for photography to good use. Her work revealed the pain of many people in the United States who were out of work and homeless.

One day Dorothea was standing at her studio window, staring down at the street below. She saw an unemployed young man drift by, stop, turn, look this way, then that. She wondered, Where can he go? What can he do? There was no planned welfare then. No program to put people back to work. Dorothea's portraits of the rich and comfortable were no longer real to her. It was on the street that real life was going on. She left the studio and went down into the streets to photograph.

White Angel Bread Line, San Francisco, 1933

"Life for people begins to crumble on the edges; they don't realize it. But this particular section was not far from the place where my studio was, and I observed some things that were happening."
—Dorothea Lange

Almost at once she saw how photography in a studio was very different from photography outside. Upstairs she could arrange her subjects. Now she had to train herself to select them, and to shoot at the decisive moment. It was scary, going up to strangers with a camera. Down the street she saw jobless men standing in a line, waiting for free food. A rich woman known as "The White Angel" had set up a place to feed the hungry. Dorothea turned her camera on the line, and made three shots. Why this subject? She didn't know. All she knew was that she wanted to be useful, to help them somehow.

It turned out to be a natural thing for her to do. On the first day she took what has become one of her best-known photographs, "White Angel Bread Line." It is one of the most moving images of what happened to Americans in the 1930s. It was art for life's sake.

She pinned the print to her wall. A customer looked at it, and said, "Yes, but what will you do with it?"

Dorothea had no idea. She simply had to respond with her camera to the life that beat in upon her. She made more and more pictures out on the streets. Seamen and longshoremen on the waterfront went on strike for better wages and working conditions. Dorothea's camera captured the bloody clash with the police. Her lens caught pictures of homeless families trudging the highways, of people evicted from their homes, of picket lines and protest meetings and hunger marches.

She had found her commitment—to people. At this moment in American life, it was to the people tossed on the garbage dump by a wrecked economic system. She remembered her childhood walks on New York's Bowery. Here, too, she herself was not one of the homeless and hungry. But she had to move with her camera among angry and bitter men and women. She was afraid at first, but she taught herself how to do it. She still had to make studio portraits to help support her family. More and more, however, she wanted to give her whole self to this new work.

An opening came when a new president, Franklin D. Roosevelt, took office in March 1933. He knew that after years of hunger the people wanted action. He had shown courage in overcoming the polio that had crippled him in both legs. He could understand human suffering and he was not afraid to experiment. First came federal funds to relieve the suffering. Then huge public works projects to provide jobs for the unemployed. The fog of hopelessness began to lift.

Migrant Mother, Nipomo, California, 1936

"I saw and approached the hungry and desperate mother, as if drawn by a magnet. I do not remember how I explained my presence or my camera to her, but I do remember she asked me no questions. . . . There she sat in that lean-to tent with her children huddled around her, and seemed to know that my pictures might help her, and so she helped me. There was a sort of equality about it."

—Dorothea Lange

Dorothea soon got her chance. It happened when a photography gallery asked to exhibit her new work. "Documentary," they called these photographs. The Latin root of that word is *docere,* to teach. Documentary photographs are important because of their power not only to inform us but to move us. Dorothea wanted her photographs to touch the viewer, to open heart and mind to the world we live in. Paul Taylor, a college professor in nearby Berkeley, saw her show and liked it. He borrowed her pictures for an article he wrote about the waterfront strike.

Soon he took Dorothea with him to visit a commune near San Francisco. It was one of the many self-help groups that sprang up as a way of meeting the problems

Mexican Migrant Fieldworker, Imperial Valley, California, 1937

"I had to get my camera to register the things about those people that were more important than how poor they were—their pride, their strength, their spirit."
—Dorothea Lange

Woman of the High Plains, Texas Panhandle, 1938

"Woman of the high plains: 'If you die, you're dead—that's all.'"
—Dorothea Lange

of the unemployed. These people banded together to get through the Depression by doing work in exchange for the fruits and vegetables the local farmers could not sell. Dorothea watched Professor Taylor interview them. He drew facts and feelings from them so gently they did not realize how much they told him. She saw how eager most

Rural Rehabilitation Client, Tulare County, California, 1938

people are to talk, even to strangers. The more so when they talk about their own lives. Taylor in turn watched her make pictures of the same people. He liked how quietly she did it, and the meaningful details her camera caught.

Paul Taylor was an economist raised in Iowa. He had the prairie farmer's pride in his own land and labor. He wanted to use his knowledge to make people's lives better. He believed you could bring about change if you took the trouble to find out what was wrong and to think through what to do about it. His fine mind could get to the heart of a question, and organize the facts to win public support for making a change.

In Dorothea, Taylor saw a photographer with deep feeling for people in trouble. Her eye looked for the heart of a situation and the details that revealed it. Her pictures recorded both the life in front of her lens and her feelings about it. She always made pictures of people with respect for their dignity.

In the mean, cold winter of 1934–35 she saw strangers streaming into California. They came by the tens of thousands. They were farmers from the Midwest and Southwest, hit hard by the Depression. Great dust storms following a terrible drought had ruined vast tracts of farmland. The desperate farmers took to the roads, fleeing what was called the Dust Bowl. They joined the harvest hands and migrant workers. They followed the seasonal crops as pickers and laborers. If they earned a hundred dollars a year they were lucky.

The hungry men, women, and children wandered over California's rural counties. The state had few or no means to shelter and feed them. The government turned to Professor Taylor for help. Find out, they said, what the trouble is. Why so many migrants? When will they stop coming? What can we do about it right now?

Taylor knew the Depression was only partly to blame. Another cause was the increasing use of new machines—tractors, mechanical pickers—to replace human labor. And a third force was such natural disasters as drought and dust storms. He agreed to find out how the state could help the migrant families.

Waterboy, Mississippi Delta, 1938

Homeless Family, Oklahoma, 1938

Paul Taylor knew that the bare facts alone would not get politicians to act. Give them a mountain of statistics and they would yawn. They needed to *feel* what was wrong. So he hired Dorothea to make pictures of the terrible conditions the migrants lived in. "My words in reports won't be enough," he said. "The people who make decisions need to *see* what these lives are like."

They both knew that photographs of a social problem were quite rare. They had seen the pictures Jacob Riis had made in the 1890s of the New York slums, and Lewis Hine's heartbreaking images of children working in coal mines and cotton mills. But most scientists paid no attention to pictures. Research had to be "objective," they thought. Keep it cool. Leave out the feelings. Not Taylor, he didn't think that way.

Dorothea went on field trips with Taylor. She was the first to photograph the migrants. She and Taylor worked together, preparing reports strongly illustrated with dozens of her photographs. The soft-voiced, bright-eyed woman with the weather-beaten face and short-cut hair would walk up to the migrants and look around quietly. She wore slacks, and a beret cocked over one ear. Perhaps when they noticed her limp they knew she, too, had been hit by the unfairness of life. She would wait till they got used to her. Then she'd talk with them. When they seemed to accept her, she would start taking pictures. What made her good at it was her natural feeling for people. She could put them at ease, make them feel she cared. She never shoved her camera into anyone's privacy. If people did not want to be photographed, she would not find some sneaky way to do it. If she saw they were shy, or suspicious of a stranger, she would just sit in a corner and let them look her over. Then she would speak to them about who she was, what her family was like, why she was here. Always the truth. It took more time that way. But it was the human way to meet other humans.

Dorothea Lange and Paul Taylor on field trip, 1935 (photograph by Helen Dixon)

IN RESPONSE

Photo Exhibit

Choose any four of the Dorothea Lange photos for a photo exhibit about life in the 1930's. Write a caption for each picture.

Dear Diary

Choose one of the people Dorothea Lange photographed. Imagine you are that person. Write a diary entry in which you describe your day and express your feelings.

Discuss a Character

You've read about many characters in this theme. Which ones might Dorothea Lange have wanted to photograph? Choose one real or fictional person. Explain your choice as you talk it over with a group.

AUTHOR AT WORK

Milton Meltzer never met Dorothea Lange, but he has admired her pictures. He remembers that both Ms. Lange and he worked for the government during the 1930's Depression.

Mr. Meltzer has written for radio and for movies. He also is the author of dozens of books, including several biographies of famous people in the United States. The biographer's job, he says, "is to try to get as close as possible to the complicated truth of another human being."

★ Award-winning Author

Other Books by . . .

Milton Meltzer

The Amazing Potato: A Story in Which the Incas, Conquistadors, Marie Antoinette, Thomas Jefferson, Wars, Famines, Immigrants, and French Fries All Play a Part by Milton Meltzer, HarperCollins Children's Books, 1992

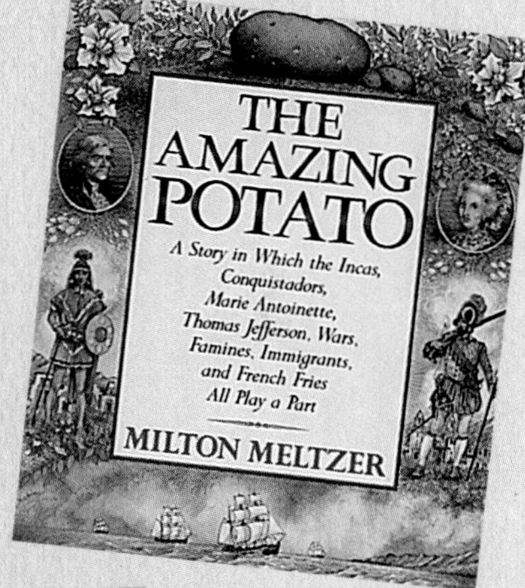

Mary McLeod Bethune: Voice of Black Hope by Milton Meltzer, illustrated by Stephen Marchesi, Puffin Books, 1987

Library Link This story was taken from *Dorothea Lange: Life Through the Camera* by Milton Meltzer. You might enjoy reading the entire book to find out more about Dorothea Lange.

Express **Yourself**

In Who Am I? you've seen how some fictional characters and real people have tried to answer that question. Some kept a diary as a way of learning about themselves and exploring their feelings. Others expressed themselves through dance, photography, poetry, and other means of communicating.

Life Stories

"Alvin Ailey" and "An Eye for Reality" are biographies. "It Started With Miss Ibbotson" is an autobiography. How is a biography different from an autobiography? Using examples from the three selections, show at least three differences. Would you like your life story to be written as an autobiography or a biography? Write a paragraph to explain your choice.

Tell Your Diary

Some characters in this theme answered the question Who Am I? by comparing themselves to other people. Which character would you compare yourself to? Write the comparison as a diary entry. Include details from the story and your own experience. How might the character help you learn more about yourself?

A Person to Remember

"Alvin's soul danced along when he saw Katherine Dunham's style," writes Andrea Pinkney ("Alvin Ailey"). Like Alvin Ailey, Jean Little ("It Started With Miss Ibbotson") received inspiration from others. Find one example from the selection of someone who inspired Jean Little.

Two of a Kind

The main characters in "Copycat" and "Slower Than the Rest" think they are poor students. Yet both feel successful at the end of the stories. What advice could you give the two characters early in the stories to help them feel better about who they are? Write your ideas. Can you relate to their experiences? Why?

Finding Themselves

Jean Little, Alvin Ailey, and Dorothea Lange ("An Eye for Reality") all made discoveries about themselves. What did they discover? How did they do it? With a partner, write a short paragraph for each of them. What do their experiences tell you about the importance of expressing yourself?

More Books for You to Enjoy

Brooklyn Doesn't Rhyme

by Joan W. Blos, illustrated by Paul Birling, Charles Scribner's Sons, 1994

When Rosie's teacher asks her students to write in a journal about their lives, Rosie is convinced that her life is too ordinary to be exciting. But her stories about living in a Jewish family in the years before World War I are funny and loving and full of wonderful characters you won't soon forget.

Zeely

by Virginia Hamilton, illustrated by Symeon Shimin, Macmillan, 1967

While riding the train to her uncle's farm, Elizabeth hopes this will be a special summer. When she meets tall and graceful Zeely, she is sure her dreams have come true. Zeely looks just like the Watusi queen whose picture Elizabeth found in a magazine.

From the Mixed-Up Files of Mrs. Basil E. Frankweiler

by E. L. Konigsburg, Atheneum, 1967

Feeling unappreciated at home, Claudia goes to New York and moves into the Metropolitan Museum of Art. Life at the museum is an adventure, especially when she discovers a mysterious statue and meets its strange former owner.

The Dancing Cats of Applesap

by Janet Taylor Lisle, illustrated by Joelle Shefts, Bradbury Press, 1984

Mr. Jiggs surprises shy Melba when he decides to sell his drugstore. Melba must come up with a plan to save the store and the one hundred stray cats who live there.

Master of Mahogany: Tom Day, Free Black Cabinetmaker

by Mary E. Lyons, Charles Scribner's Sons, 1994

Tom Day was an African American cabinetmaker in North Carolina before and after the Civil War. He created masterpieces in wood. As this story shows, his legacy lives on in the beautiful works he created.

Moving On

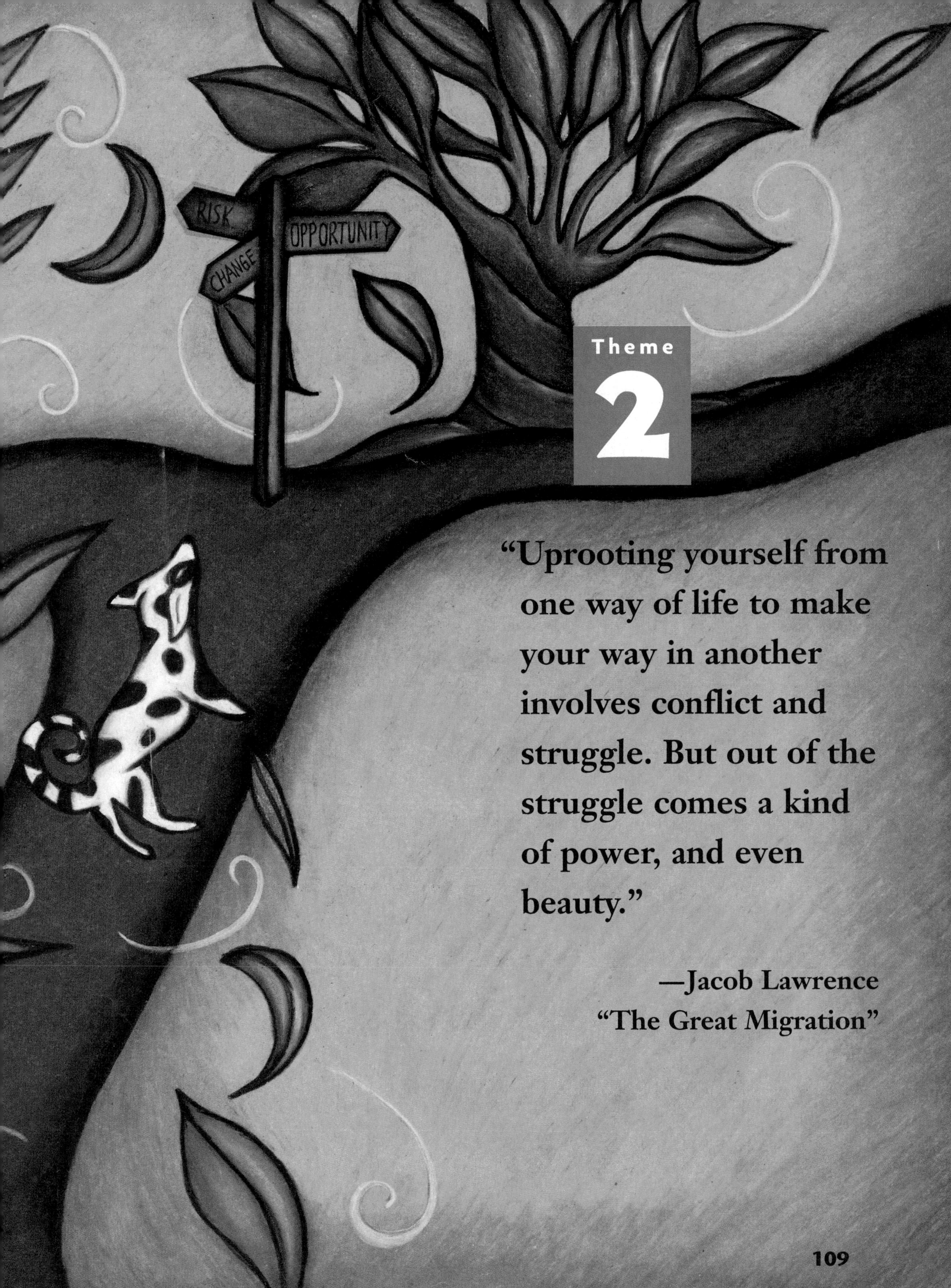

Theme 2

"Uprooting yourself from one way of life to make your way in another involves conflict and struggle. But out of the struggle comes a kind of power, and even beauty."

—Jacob Lawrence
"The Great Migration"

Theme 2

Moving On

CONTENTS

Theme Trade Books

Misery Guts

by Morris Gleitzman

Keith Shipley hopes moving to Australia will make his parents happy. They cheer up, but will the move turn Keith into a worrier—a real misery guts?

Children of Flight Pedro Pan

by Maria Armengol Acierno

Maria and Jose Aleman fly to Miami to visit their cousin. When their visit turns out to be permanent, the children fear they will never see their parents again.

Theme Magazine

Where do Americans go when they move? How well do you deal with change? Read Theme Magazine *On the Go Zone* to find out.

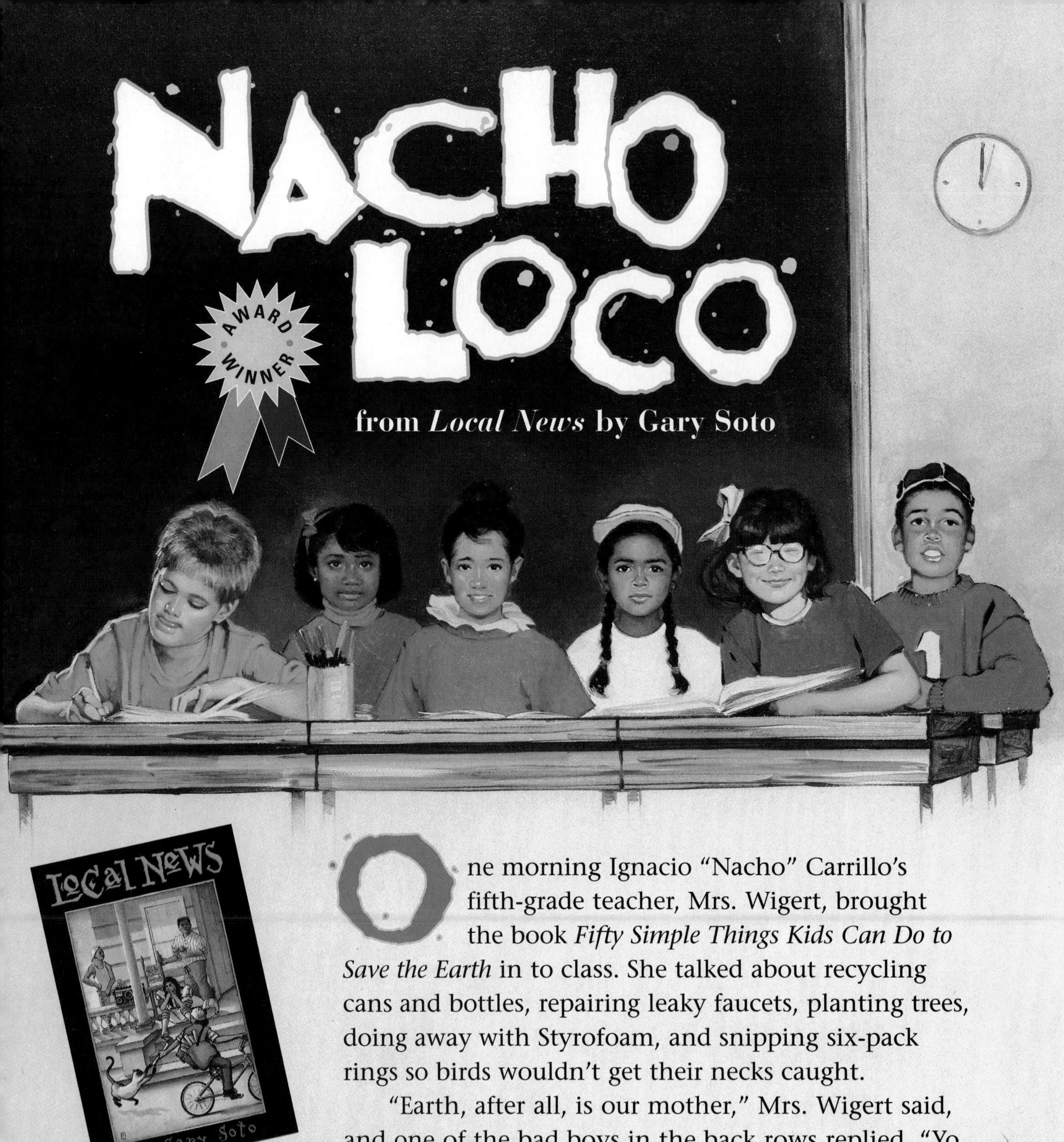

Nacho Loco

from *Local News* by Gary Soto

One morning Ignacio "Nacho" Carrillo's fifth-grade teacher, Mrs. Wigert, brought the book *Fifty Simple Things Kids Can Do to Save the Earth* in to class. She talked about recycling cans and bottles, repairing leaky faucets, planting trees, doing away with Styrofoam, and snipping six-pack rings so birds wouldn't get their necks caught.

"Earth, after all, is our mother," Mrs. Wigert said, and one of the bad boys in the back rows replied, "Yo momma!"

Mrs. Wigert shushed the boy, a finger to her lips. She scanned the class, asking for quiet. Then she announced, "I'm a vegetarian. Do you know what a vegetarian is?"

"It's when you don't like meat," said Desi, a fat boy whose *chones*[1] could be seen when he ran.

"It's when you just eat grass," Leticia said.

"Not grass, Leticia—noodles," Robert corrected.

Mrs. Wigert smiled at these definitions. She said, "It's when you decide not to eat meat for the welfare of your body and the planet."

"I ain't on welfare!" Robert snickered.

The class laughed, and Mrs. Wigert frowned. She clapped the book closed and said that they would go on to math. As she stood up behind her desk, her stomach rumbled, making her sound very, very hungry.

---

1 chones (*CHOH nehs*) underpants

But Nacho had listened to what she said. He knew what a vegetarian was because his brother, Felipe, had gone to college and come back with ideas that would solve the world's problems. His brother had decided not to buy anything at department stores and dressed in clothes from the Salvation Army thrift store on Tulare Street.

"You're supposed to be educated," his father grumbled at his oldest son. *"¿Por qué te vistes en garras?* Why are you dressed in rags?"

"Mi'jo,[2] what will your *abuelita*[3] think?" his mother pleaded.

His father and mother had worked hard to send their son to college, and now, to their minds, he looked like a bum.

And Felipe was a vegetarian.

Yes, Nacho knew what a vegetarian was, and at that moment, as he opened his math book and licked his pencil preparing to do division, he decided to become one. Mrs. Wigert was right, he thought. We must save the planet in small ways.

Nacho left the classroom a committed vegetarian—or at least determined to become one after he ate his lunch, which was weighed down with a thick bologna sandwich. He liked bologna, especially when his mom also packed corn chips in his lunch. He would open his sandwich and methodically place nine corn chips to form a square, as if he were playing tick-tack-toe. Then he'd put it together, close his eyes, and take a big bite, the corn chips crunching in his ears.

And that's what his mother had packed in a paper bag today: a bologna sandwich and corn chips, along with a box of juice and a plastic bag of carrot sticks.

---

2 **Mi'jo** (*MEE hoh*) my son

3 **abuelita** (*ah bway LEE tah*) grandma

Nacho looked at the carrot sticks and put them aside. Then he went to town on the sandwich.

Nacho ate with his friend, Juan, on a bench outside the cafeteria. Juan was one of the best baseball players at school and he could shoot hoop, fight, and keep up with the smartest girls in a spelling bee. He was everything Nacho was not. Nacho was a dreamer, quick to pick up on the most recent scientific fad. Once he read in the "Grab Bag" section of the newspaper that if you place a dull razor blade under a pyramid structure and point it south, the pyramid's energy will restore the sharpness of the blade. He tried it with his father's old blades and wrapped them up as a Christmas present. Unfortunately, the blades remained dull, and his poor father had ended up with nicks from his throat to his upper lip.

"I'm not eating meat after this," Nacho said. "It's bad for the world."

"What are you talking about?" Juan said. His cheeks were fat with bites from a tuna sandwich.

"I'm a vegetarian."

"A what?"

"A vegetarian. I'm a person who thinks of mankind. I won't eat meat anymore." Nacho bit into his juicy bologna sandwich, savoring the taste, eyes closed.

"But you're eating meat now, ain't you?" Juan asked.

"This is the last time," Nacho said, wiping his mouth on the paper bag. His mother had forgotten to pack him a napkin.

"That's weird," Juan said. "Won't you get sick if you don't eat meat?"

"Mrs. Wigert is a vegetarian," Nacho commented.

"She's already grown," Juan said. "Anyways, I like hamburgers."

Nacho saw in his mind's eye a hamburger wrapped in a greasy wrapper and finger-sized french fries steaming on a white plate. He shook the images off and eyed his carrot sticks. He took one out from the sandwich bag and held it in his lips like a cigarette.

"And I don't smoke either," he said, laughing.

After lunch they played baseball, but their game ended when Juan hit the ball onto the roof of a building. Nacho had batted only once, hitting a feeble grounder back to the pitcher.

After school Nacho and Juan walked home together. Both of them were hungry so they stopped at the corner grocery store. Juan scraped up enough money in the corners of his pockets to buy a Hostess cupcake. Nacho bought a package of beef jerky, using the money he got from recycling aluminum cans on Saturday.

"I thought you were a vegetarian," Juan said as they left the store. He tore off the Hostess cupcake wrapper and threw it absentmindedly on the ground.

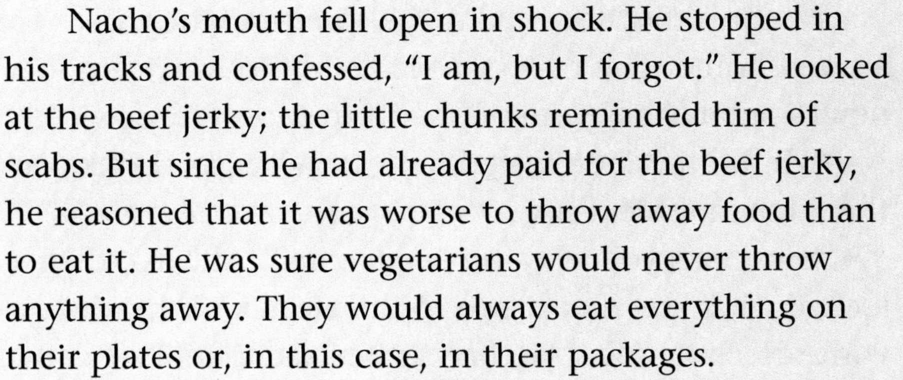

Nacho's mouth fell open in shock. He stopped in his tracks and confessed, "I am, but I forgot." He looked at the beef jerky; the little chunks reminded him of scabs. But since he had already paid for the beef jerky, he reasoned that it was worse to throw away food than to eat it. He was sure vegetarians would never throw anything away. They would always eat everything on their plates or, in this case, in their packages.

Juan's cellophane scuttled in a light breeze, and Nacho picked it up.

"I'll trade you then," Juan said.

Nacho bit his lip because at the moment he preferred salt to sugar. Reluctantly he handed over his beef jerky. He took Juan's cupcake and stuffed it in his mouth; its chewy sweetness dissolved in three bites. For the rest of the walk home he had to watch Juan tear off pieces of jerky and chew slowly, the smoky juice dripping from his mouth.

out to celebrate with their *compa*[9] and brought back spicy pepperoni pizza for the kids.

Nacho played slapball until his father came home, and then the two of them shot hoop. They played a quick game to twelve, one point per basket. His father was big around the middle but a sweet outside shooter.

"You're just a little *piojo,*[10] but you'll grow," his father said, wiping his face with the sleeve of his work shirt. He sat on the back steps. His chest was heaving, and the lines on his throat glistened with sweat.

"Dad," Nacho said, "I think I might be a vegetarian."

"Qué dices?"[11] his father asked, his face still.

"Today we had a talk about the world. Mrs. Wigert said eating meat is bad for you."

"So?"

"So, I'm a vegetarian. I don't eat meat anymore."

"¿Qué hacen a mi familia?[12] First your brother and now you?" His father got up and turned on the garden hose. He drank long and hard from it. He patted his belly and then agreed, "OK, you be a vegetaran . . ."

"Vegetarian," Nacho said.

"Yes, but you'll be such a *flaco*[13] we won't know where you are," he said playfully. "Not like this." He smacked his belly and laughed.

His father went inside, leaving Nacho on the back steps staring at the empty pizza box. When he finally went inside, his older brother, Felipe, was in the kitchen, lowering a piece of *carne asada*—marinated round steak—into his mouth.

---

9 **compa** (*KOHM pah*) pal

10 **piojo** (*pee OH hoh*) louse, flea

11 **¿Qué dices?** (*KAY DEE sehs*) What are you saying?

12 **¿Qué hacen a mi familia?** (*KAY AH sehn ah MEE fah MEE lee ah*) What's happening to my family?

13 **flaco** (*FLAH koh*) skinny guy

"Hey, Felipe," Nacho said, his stomach suddenly grumbling from emptiness.

"Hey, you little Nacho-head," Felipe said to his brother. "Give me five."

They slapped each other's hands. Then Nacho said, "I thought you were a vegetarian."

"Not anymore. My girlfriend left me."

"What?"

"Yeah, she moved on to greener pastures. A lawyer. I guess she doesn't like accountants."

"You mean you were a vegetarian because of your girlfriend?" Nacho was shocked. He turned on the faucet in the kitchen and washed his hands.

"Sort of. But I have a new girlfriend. She likes good food and bad movies."

"But I thought you had principles!"

"I do. But I got a new girlfriend."

Nacho felt cheated. He wanted to tell Felipe that he had become a vegetarian, but he kept quiet.

From the dining room their father called, *"Hombres,*[14] let's eat."

"Chow time," Felipe said.

---

14 Hombres (*OHM brays*) men

Felipe sat down, a napkin crushed in one hand and a fork shining in the other. After a prayer of thanks, during which he kept his eyes open looking at the meat, Felipe dove into the *carne asada.* He ate like a barbarian, ripping a tortilla and pinching up smudges of *frijoles.*[15]

"See, if you were living at home you would be eating good," his mother said as she passed him another tortilla from the basket.

"Claro,"[16] he said.

Nacho sat in front of his plate of rice and beans. He took a forkful of beans, eyeing his brother's plate, which was loaded with steaming meat. He looked at his little brother's face, his mother's face, and his father's dark and stubbled face: they were all enjoying meat. They were barbarian meat-eaters.

---

15 frijoles (*free HOH lays*) beans

16 Claro (*KLAH roh*) Of course

Later Nacho helped do the dishes. He rinsed while his mother washed, and he kept turning around and looking at the stove; the pan of meat still rested on one of the burners. His mouth watered.

After the dishes were done, the family sat and watched a sitcom on television. Nacho didn't care about the program, except when one of the actors lifted a fork or wiped his mouth on a cloth napkin. But he zeroed in on the Denny's commercial and its parade of fried chicken, burgers, club sandwiches, bacon and eggs, and milk shakes. While they watched television, Nacho's father told his son Felipe that he was proud of him.

"You went all the way," he said. "In a few years it will be Nacho's turn. Already he has big ideas, like being a . . . *cómo?*"[17]

"A vegetarian," Nacho's mother said. She had changed the channel to *las noticias,*[18] the evening news.

"Yes, a human who doesn't eat meat," his father said. "How he will grow, *no sé.*"[19]

"That's cool," Felipe said to Nacho. "Start young. What grade are you in?"

"Fifth," Nacho said, staring at a commercial for Pioneer Chicken.

"Yeah, go to State. I'll tell you about financial aid."

"Yes, ask about money. This ol' burro won't last," his father said, pointing to himself and braying like a donkey. "Ask your teacher *también.*"[20]

Nacho heard some of their chatter, but his eyes were locked on the screen. A bucket of chicken was being devoured by a family of five, just like their family. Nacho's mouth flooded with the waters of hunger, and he had to leave the living room to eat a cracker.

---

17 cómo? (*KOH moh*) what?

18 las noticias (*LAHS noh TEE see ahs*)

19 no sé (*NOH SAY*) I don't know

20 también (*tahm BYEHN*) also

Nacho went to bed hungry but determined not to ruin the planet. He lay awake, thinking about food, and when he closed his eyes, he saw a floating chicken drumstick.

But as he moved toward sleep he told himself that he should get serious. The next day he was going to ask Mrs. Wigert about college—financial aid, majors, and easy courses. And in privacy, away from Juan and the others, he was going to ask point-blank: how can you live without meat?

IN RESPONSE

Change of Appetite

Nacho decides to become a vegetarian even though it sets him apart from his family. How does Nacho's choice show that he wants to move on in his life? Do you think he will be able to stick with it? Why? Write your thoughts in a paragraph.

A Meaty Debate

Should Nacho be a vegetarian? Yes or no—you decide! Use information from the story and your own knowledge to make a choice. Then debate the issue with a partner who takes the other side. Use examples from the story to support your argument.

AUTHOR AT WORK

Gary Soto is a poet, children's book author, and essayist. He also teaches Chicano studies and English at the University of California, Berkeley.

Much of Mr. Soto's work reflects his Mexican American background. He was born and raised in Fresno, California.

His writing focuses on story elements such as characterization and dialogue. Mr. Soto says that his goal is to help students "understand how a writer puts things together."

Mr. Soto writes fiction and poetry from his home in Berkeley, California.

★ Award-winning Author

Other Books by . . .

Gary Soto

Baseball in April and Other Stories
by Gary Soto, Harcourt Brace Jovanovich, 1990

Crazy Weekend
by Gary Soto, Scholastic, 1994

Library Link "Nacho Loco" was taken from *Local News,* a collection of short stories by Gary Soto. You might enjoy reading some of the other stories about young Mexican Americans in this book.

A Challenge for Celinda

from *Kinaaldá*
text and photographs by Monty Roessel

It was a Friday night in December and 13-year-old Celinda McKelvey lay awake worrying about the weekend. She knew it would be hard work. But this was a time she had dreamed about since she was a little girl. Nothing was going to stop her.

As she tried to go to sleep, all the stories she had heard swirled in her head. She was excited and a little scared. The last thing she remembered before finally falling asleep was an image of herself running. It wasn't

Celinda McKelvey gets ready to run for the Kinaaldá ceremony. She has to run four miles in the direction of the sun.

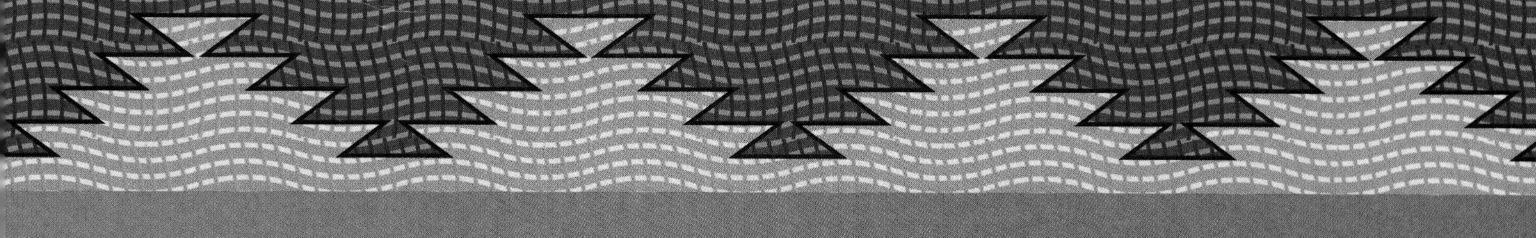

a normal run, like when she went for a jog near her home in Bloomfield, New Mexico. This was her Kinaaldá race. It's a race that Celinda begins as a child. When she crosses the finish line, from that moment forward she is an adult.

The Kinaaldá is a coming-of-age ceremony for Navajo girls. . . . The ceremony lasts two to four days.

Navajo people believe that the Kinaaldá is a way for young girls to understand what life will be like when they grow up. As she participates in the Kinaaldá, a girl learns about her culture, and, for the first time, she feels the responsibility of her family. Even as she works side by side with her elders, she knows it is up to her to see that the Kinaaldá is a success.

The Navajo Legend of Kinaaldá

This legend, which appeared in Monty Roessel's Kinaaldá, *describes the first Kinaaldá ceremony.*

The first Kinaaldá was performed for Changing Woman, the most honored of all Navajo Holy People.

One morning at dawn, First Man and First Woman saw a dark cloud over Gobernador Knob. (Gobernador Knob is what it sounds like—a bump on a flat mesa.) When they went to see the cloud, they heard a baby crying within it. First Man found the baby girl who was born of darkness; the dawn was her father. First Man and First Woman raised the child under the direction of the Holy People.

The Holy People wanted to make a ceremony for [the child] so she could have children. First Woman told the girl, who was called Changing Woman, that she must run four times in the direction of the rising sun. "As you come back you must make the turn sunwise," First Woman said.

Celinda's Kinaaldá

1

Just like Changing Woman in the Navajo legend above, Celinda McKelvey takes part in the traditions of the Kinaaldá ceremony. Here we see Celinda (**1**) touching the eyes of a woman who complains of bad eyesight, (**2**) mixing corn batter, (**3**) sewing corn husks together to make a crust-cover for the cake, and (**4**) sharing the cake with honored guests.

To begin the ceremony, Changing Woman's hair was washed with suds made from the root of the yucca plant. Then her hair was tied back.

Next, First Woman decorated a dress for Changing Woman. First she spread out an unwounded buckskin—one without an arrow hole. On it she placed a piece of turquoise, a bit of white abalone shell, a piece of black obsidian, and a white bead. Then she put white beaded moccasins on the girl's feet. She gave her a skirt and leggings that were also made of white beads. She designed white-bead sleeve fringes and wristlets.

Then First Woman placed her hand on Changing Woman's forehead and moved her hand from Changing Woman's shoulders up over her head. She did this to mold the girl into a woman like herself.

The Holy People said that Changing Woman must make a large cake for the Sun. She was to grind and mix the corn for the batter. When the Sun rose in the east, and after all the prayers were finished, the cake would be given to the Sun. The Sun was given the first piece of cake because he was one of the most powerful of the Holy People. He controlled night and day.

Later, when Changing Woman grew up, the Sun married her. He took her to his home in the western ocean.

Celinda used a basket of cornmeal to sprinkle on top of the cake batter as a blessing.

Missing Maizon

from *Last Summer with Maizon*
by Jacqueline Woodson

Over the summer, Margaret's father has died and her best friend, Maizon, has moved away to attend a boarding school outside the city. As Margaret begins another year of school, she struggles to cope with grief and loneliness. Her sadness isolates her from her fellow students and makes it difficult for her to concentrate in class.

Margaret pressed her pencil to her lips and stared out the classroom window. The school yard was desolate and gray. But everything seemed that way since Maizon left. Especially since a whole week had passed now without even a letter from her. Margaret sighed and chewed her eraser.

"Margaret, are you working on this assignment?"

Margaret jumped and turned toward Ms. Peazle. Maizon had been right—Ms. Peazle was the crabbiest teacher in the school. Margaret wondered why she had been picked to teach the smartest class. If students were so smart, she thought, the least the school could do was reward them with a nice teacher.

"I'm trying to think about what to write, Ms. Peazle."

"Well, you won't find an essay on your summer vacation outside that window, I'm sure. Or is that where you spent it?"

The class snickered and Margaret looked down, embarrassed. "No, ma'am."

"I'm glad to hear that," Ms. Peazle continued, looking at Margaret over granny glasses. "And I'm sure in the next ten minutes you'll be able to read your essay to the class and prove to us all that you weren't just daydreaming. Am I right?"

"I hope so, ma'am," Margaret mumbled. She looked around the room. It seemed everyone in 6–1 knew each other from the previous year. On the first day, a lot of kids asked her about Maizon, but after that no one said much to her. Things had changed since Maizon left. Without her, a lot of the fun had gone out of sitting on the stoop with Ms. Dell, Hattie, and Li'l Jay. Maybe she could write about that. No, Margaret thought, looking down at the blank piece of paper in front of her. It was too much to tell. She'd never get finished and Ms. Peazle would scold her—making her feel too dumb to be in 6–1. Margaret chewed her eraser and stared out the window again. There had to be something she could write about quickly.

"Margaret Tory!" Ms. Peazle warned. "Am I going to have to change your seat?"

"Ma'am? I was just . . ."

"I think I'm going to have to move you away from that window unless you can prove to me that you can sit there without being distracted."

"I can, Ms. Peazle. It helps me write," she lied.

"Then I take it you should be ready to read your essay in"—Ms. Peazle looked at her watch—"the next seven minutes."

Margaret started writing frantically. When Ms. Peazle called her to the front of the room, her sheet of notebook paper shook in her hand. She pulled nervously at the hem of the maroon dress she and Maizon had picked out for school and tried not to look out at the twenty-six pairs of eyes she knew were on her.

"Last summer was the worst summer of my life. First my father died and then my best friend went away to a private boarding school. I didn't go anywhere except Manhattan. But that wasn't any fun because I was taking Maizon to the train. I hope next summer is a lot better."

She finished reading and walked silently back to her desk and tried to concentrate on not looking out the window. Instead, she rested her eyes on the half-written page. Margaret knew she could write better than that, but Ms. Peazle had rushed her. Anyway, she thought, that *is* what happened last summer.

"I'd like to see you after class, Margaret."

"Yes, ma'am," Margaret said softly. *This is the end,* she thought. One week in the smartest class and it's over. Maizon was smart enough to go to a better *school* and I can't even keep up in this class. Margaret sighed and tried not to stare out the window for the rest of the day.

When the three o'clock bell rang, she waited uneasily in her seat while Ms. Peazle led the rest of the class out to the school yard. Margaret heard the excited screams and laughter as everyone poured outside.

The empty classroom was quiet. She looked around at the desks. Many had words carved into them. They reminded her of the names she and Maizon had carved into the tar last summer. They were faded and illegible now.

Ms. Peazle came in and sat at the desk next to Margaret's. "Margaret," she said slowly, pausing for a moment to remove her glasses and rub her eyes tiredly. "I'm sorry to hear about your father . . ."

"That's okay." Margaret fidgeted.

"No, Margaret, it's not okay," Ms. Peazle continued, "not if it's going to affect your schoolwork."

"I can do better, Ms. Peazle, I really can!" Margaret looked up pleadingly. She was surprised at herself for wanting so badly to stay in Ms. Peazle's class.

"I know you can, Margaret. That's why I'm going to ask you to do this. For homework tonight . . ."

Margaret started to say that none of the other students had been assigned homework. She decided not to, though.

"I want you to write about your summer," Ms. Peazle continued. "I want it to express all of your feelings about your friend Maizon going away. Or it could be about your father's death and how you felt then. It doesn't matter what you write, a poem, an essay, a short story. Just so long as it expresses how you felt this summer. Is that understood?"

"Yes, ma'am." Margaret looked up at Ms. Peazle. "It's understood."

Ms. Peazle smiled. Without her glasses, Margaret thought, she wasn't that mean-looking.

"Good, then I'll see you bright and early tomorrow with something wonderful to read to the class."

Margaret slid out of the chair and walked toward the door.

"That's a very pretty dress, Margaret," Ms. Peazle said.

Margaret turned and started to tell her that Maizon was wearing the same one in Connecticut, but changed her mind. What did Ms. Peazle know about best friends who were almost cousins, anyway?

"Thanks, ma'am," she said instead, and ducked out of the classroom. All of a sudden, she had a wonderful idea!

The next morning Ms. Peazle tapped her ruler against the desk to quiet the class. "Margaret," she asked when the room was silent. "Do you have something you want to share with us today?"

Margaret nodded and Ms. Peazle beckoned her to the front of the room.

"This," Margaret said, handing Ms. Peazle the sheet of looseleaf paper. It had taken her most of the evening to finish the assignment.

Ms. Peazle looked it over and handed it back to her.

"We're ready to listen," she said, smiling.

Margaret looked out over the class and felt her stomach slide up to her throat. She swallowed and counted to ten. Though the day was cool, she found herself sweating.

Margaret couldn't remember when she had been this afraid.

"My pen doesn't write anymore," she began reading.

"I can't hear," someone called out.

"My pen doesn't write anymore," Margaret repeated. In the back of the room, someone exaggerated a sigh. The class chuckled. Margaret ignored them and continued to read.

"It stumbles and trembles in my hand.
If my dad were here—he would understand.
Best of all—It'd be last summer again.

But they've turned off the fire hydrants
Locked green leaves away.
Sprinkled ashes on you
and sent you on your way.

I wouldn't mind the early autumn
if you came home today
I'd tell you how much I miss you
and know I'd be okay.

Mama isn't laughing now
She works hard and she cries

she wonders when true laughter
will relieve her of her sighs
And even when she's smiling
Her eyes don't smile along
her face is growing older
She doesn't seem as strong.
I worry cause I love her
Ms. Dell says, 'where there is love,
there is a way.'

It's funny how we never know
exactly how our life will go
It's funny how a dream can fade
With the break of day.

I'm not sure where you are now
though I see you in my dreams
Ms. Dell says the things we see
are not always as they seem.

So often I'm uncertain
if you have found a new home
and when I am uncertain
I usually write a poem.

Time can't erase the memory
and time can't bring you home
Last summer was a part of me
and now a part is gone."

The class stared at her blankly, silent. Margaret lowered her head and made her way back to her seat.

"Could you leave that assignment on my desk, Margaret?" Ms. Peazle asked. There was a small smile playing at the corners of her mouth.

"Yes, ma'am," Margaret said. Why didn't anyone say anything?

"Now, if everyone will open their history books to page two seventy-five, we'll continue with our lesson on the Civil War."

Margaret wondered what she had expected the class to do. Applaud? She missed Maizon more than she had in a long time. *She would know what I'm feeling,* Margaret thought. And if she didn't, she'd make believe she did.

Margaret snuck a look out the window. The day looked cold and still. *She'd tell me it's only a feeling poets get and that Nikki Giovanni feels this way all of the time.* When she turned back, there was a small piece of paper on her desk.

"I liked your poem, Margaret," the note read. There was no name.

Margaret looked around but no one looked as though they had slipped a note on her desk. She smiled to herself and tucked the piece of paper into her notebook.

The final bell rang. As the class rushed out, Margaret was bumped against Ms. Peazle's desk.

"Did you get my note?" Ms. Peazle whispered. Margaret nodded and floated home.

Ms. Dell, Hattie, and Li'l Jay were sitting on the stoop when she got home.

"If it weren't so cold," she said, squeezing in beside Hattie's spreading hips, "it would be like old times."

"Except for Maizon," Hattie said, cutting her eyes toward her mother.

"Hush, Hattie," Ms. Dell said. She shivered and pulled Li'l Jay closer to her. For a moment, Margaret thought she looked old.

"It's just this cold spell we're having," Ms. Dell said. "Ages a person. Makes them look older than they are."

Margaret smiled. "Reading minds is worse than eavesdropping, Ms. Dell."

"Try being her daughter for nineteen years," Hattie said.

"Hattie," Margaret said, moving closer to her for warmth. "How come you never liked Maizon?"

"No one said I never liked her."

"No one had to," Ms. Dell butted in.

"She was just too much ahead of everyone. At least she thought she was."

"But she was, Hattie. She was the smartest person at P.S. 102. Imagine being the smartest person."

"But she didn't have any common sense, Margaret. And when God gives a person that much brain, he's bound to leave out something else."

"Like what?"

Ms. Dell leaned over Li'l Jay's head and whispered loudly, "Like the truth."

She and Hattie laughed but Margaret couldn't see the humor. It wasn't like either of them to say something wrong about a person.

"She told the truth . . ." Margaret said weakly.

Ms. Dell and Hattie exchanged looks.

"How was school?" Hattie asked too brightly.

"Boring," Margaret said. She would tuck what they said away until she could figure it out.

"That's the only word you know since Maizon left. Seems there's gotta be somethin' else going on that's not so *boring* all the time," Ms. Dell said.

"Well, it's sure not school. I read a poem to that stupid class and no one but Ms. Peazle liked it." She sighed and rested her chin on her hand.

"That's the chance you gotta take with poetry," Ms. Dell said. "Either everybody likes it or everybody hates it, but you hardly ever know 'cause nobody says a word. Too afraid to offend you or, worse yet, make you feel good."

Margaret looked from Ms. Dell to Hattie then back to Ms. Dell again.

"How come you know so much about poetry?"

"You're not the first li'l black girl who wanted to be a poet."

"And you can bet your dress you won't be the last," Hattie concluded.

"You wanted to be a poet, Hattie??!!"

"Still do. Still make up poems in my head. Never write them down, though. The paper just yellows and clutters useful places. So this is where I keep it all now," she said, pointing to her head.

"A poem can't exist inside your head. You forget it," Margaret said doubtfully.

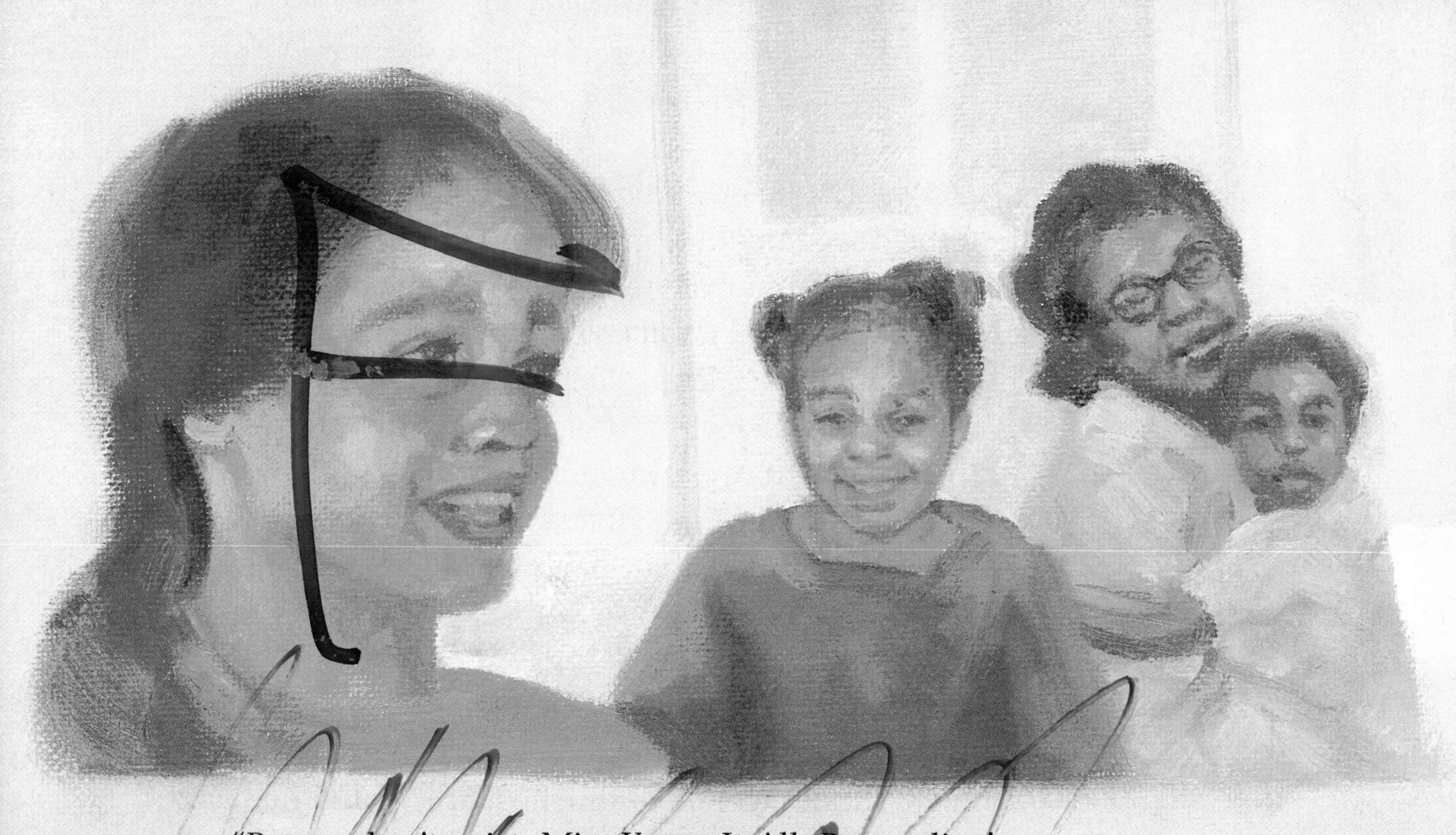

"Poems don't exist, Miss Know-It-All. Poems live! In your head is where a poem is born, isn't it?"

Margaret nodded and Hattie continued. "Well, my poetry chooses to live there."

"Then recite one for me, please." Margaret folded her arms across her chest the way she had seen Ms. Dell do so many times.

"Some poems aren't meant to be heard, smarty-pants."

"Aw, Hattie," Ms. Dell interrupted, "let Margaret be the judge of that."

"All right. All right." Hattie's voice dropped to a whisper. "Brooklyn-bound robin redbreast followed me from down home / Brooklyn-bound robin, you're a long way from your own / So fly among the pigeons and circle the sky with your song."

They were quiet. Ms. Dell rocked Li'l Jay to sleep in her arms. Hattie looked somberly over the block in silence and Margaret thought of how much Hattie's poem made her think of Maizon. What was she doing now that the sun was almost down? she wondered. Had she found a new best friend?

"Maybe," she said after a long time. "Maybe it wasn't that the class didn't like my poem. Maybe it was like your poem, Hattie. You just have to sit quietly and think about all the things it makes you think about after you hear it. You have to let . . . let it sink in!"

"You have to feel it, Margaret," Hattie said softly, draping her arm over Margaret's shoulder.

"Yeah. Just like I felt when I wrote my poem, or you felt when you found a place for that one in your head!"

"Margaret," Ms. Dell said, "you gettin' too smart for us ol' ladies."

Margaret leaned against Hattie and listened to the fading sounds of construction. Soon the building on Palmetto Street would be finished. She closed her eyes and visions of last summer came into her head. She saw herself running down Madison Street arm in arm with Maizon. They were laughing. Then the picture faded into a new one. She and Maizon were sitting by the tree watching Li'l Jay take his first steps. He stumbled and fell into Maizon's arms. Now it all seemed like such a long time ago.

When she opened her eyes again, the moon was inching out from behind a cloud. It was barely visible in the late afternoon. The sky had turned a wintry blue and the streetlights flickered on. Margaret yawned, her head heavy all of a sudden from the long day.

"Looks like your mother's workin' late again. Bless that woman's heart. Seems she's workin' nonstop since your daddy passed."

"She's taking drawing classes. She wants to be an architect. Maybe she'll make a lot of money."

"Architects don't make a lot of money," Hattie said. "And anyway, you shouldn't be worrying your head over money."

"She has a gift," Ms. Dell said. "All of you Torys have gifts. You with your writing, your mama with her drawings, and remember the things your daddy did with wood. Oh, that man was something else!"

"What's Li'l Jay's going to be?"

Ms. Dell stood up and pressed Li'l Jay's face to her cheek.

"Time's gonna tell us, Margaret. Now, come inside and do your homework while I fix you something to eat. No use sitting out in the cold."

Margaret rose and followed them inside.

"You hear anything from Maizon yet?" Hattie asked.

Margaret shook her head. If only Maizon were running up the block!

"I wrote her two letters and she hasn't written me one. Maybe she knows we're not really best friends anymore." Margaret sighed. She had been right in thinking she and Maizon were only old friends now, not the friends they used to be. "Still, I wish I knew how she was doing," she said, turning away so Hattie wouldn't see the tears in her eyes.

"We all do, honey," Hattie said, taking Margaret's hand. "We all do."

Two weeks later, Margaret sat at the kitchen table, scribbling furiously into her diary. When she looked up, the clock on the kitchen wall said ten thirty. She couldn't believe she had spent three hours writing. She flipped back to where she had begun and counted. Fifteen pages! Margaret heard her mother's key in the lock and quickly stuffed the diary back into her bookbag.

"Margaret," her mother said, coming into the kitchen, "what are you doing up? It's after ten o'clock."

"I wanted to stay up to tell you the news," Margaret said. Her mother sat across from her. "Ms. Peazle entered my poem in a contest! If I win, I get scholarship money and I get to read it in front of the mayor!"

Ms. Tory smiled and Margaret almost laughed with pleasure at the pride in her mother's eyes. "That's wonderful, Margaret," she said, rising to give Margaret a hug.

Margaret shivered a little. They had never sat like this before, just the two of them in the soft quiet light of the kitchen. The feeling was new and strange. She felt closer to her mother all of a sudden. And the closeness felt grown-up and good.

"That would have made your daddy proud," her mother said softly.

Margaret swallowed. She hadn't thought about her father all day and now, looking away from the sadness in her mother's eyes, she saw her father clearly, smiling proudly down at her.

"He is proud, Mama," Margaret whispered. "From his place in heaven, he's real proud."

Her mother shook her head and dabbed at her eyes quickly, then rose. "Want to have some tea with me to celebrate?" she asked, going over to the stove. Not waiting for an answer, she put the teabags in cups and turned on the fire beneath the kettle. "You hear anything from Maizon?"

Margaret looked down at the table. The cloth blurred a little. Maizon had left a month ago. She shook her head.

Her mother turned back to the stove and poured the water into the cups. "I guess Blue Hill must be pretty hard. It's not like Maizon not to let anyone know how she's doing." She brought the cups over to the table. Margaret blew at the cloud of steam above her cup. "Have you spoken to her grandmother? Maybe she's heard something."

Margaret shook her head again. "I haven't been by there since Maizon left." All of a sudden she felt guilty. "It would just make me miss her more."

"She must be pretty lonely in that big house by herself," her mother said, reading her thoughts.

Margaret took a small sip of tea. It was minty and almost bitter. "I'll go see her after school tomorrow."

The kitchen fell silent. "You think Maizon forgot about Madison Street, Mama?"

Her mother laughed a little uncertainly. "It would take a lot to forget Madison Street."

"I was talking to some girls in school and they said they like me better since Maizon left. They said she was bossy and snotty."

Her mother looked up. "What did you say to them?"

Margaret picked nervously at the vinyl checkered tablecloth. The small hole wore away to a bigger one.

"Don't, Margaret," her mother said gently.

"I didn't say anything," she admitted.

"Don't let them say bad things about her when she's not here to defend herself. That's not what a real friend would do."

Margaret swallowed and took a quick sip of tea. The hot liquid washed the sadness back down for a moment.

"I wanted to tell them that Maizon's not like that, that they didn't know her like I did," she said quietly.

Her mother laid her hand on top of Margaret's. "Why didn't you? It's not like you not to."

Margaret shrugged. "The words got stuck. Those girls never paid any attention to me. I wanted them to keep liking me. I don't hardly have any friends in school." She looked up at her mother helplessly. "I felt real bad when I walked away, though."

Her mother shook her head. "It's hard to know what to do," she said, almost to herself. "I miss your father and I want to talk about him with a friend sometimes, but then I don't want anyone to remind me how empty I feel." She sniffed and gave Margaret a weak smile. "You better get to bed. School tomorrow."

"You okay, Mama?" She felt as though a strong wind had blown in between them, pulling them further and further apart. The closeness she had felt a moment ago was gone.

"It's going to take time, Margaret. Everything will fall into place. But it's going to take time."

Margaret hugged her. "We have a lot of time, Mama."

IN RESPONSE

Picture the Poem

Reread Margaret's poem. How does it make you feel? Draw a picture using some of the images from the poem or write a paragraph explaining why the poem makes you feel the way it does.

Pros and Cons of Change

Nacho ("Nacho Loco") makes a change when he decides to become a vegetarian. Margaret must deal with change after Maizon moves away. With a partner, list the pros and cons of each character's change. Based on your lists, who do you think is moving on more in life—Nacho or Margaret? Why?

AUTHOR AT WORK

The setting and the characters in "Missing Maizon" come from Jacqueline

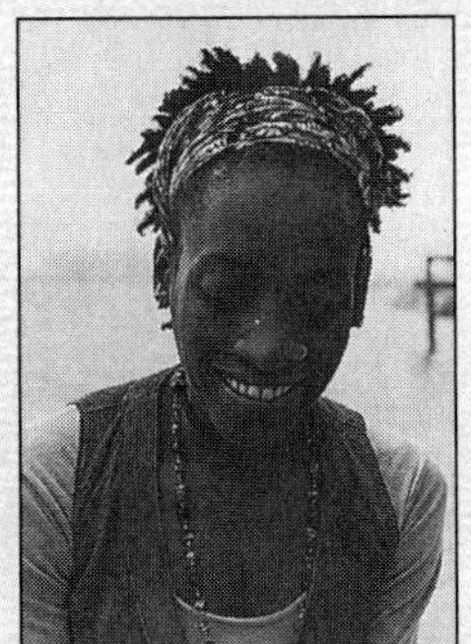

Woodson's own experience. In fact, the author based the story on a childhood friendship. Ms. Woodson believes in putting herself into her writing. "That's how you create fiction," she says. "Well, that's how I create fiction." *Last Summer with Maizon* is Ms. Woodson's first novel.

Other Books by . . .

Jacqueline Woodson

Maizon at Blue Hill by Jacqueline Woodson, Delacorte Press, 1992

Between Madison and Palmetto by Jacqueline Woodson, Delacorte Press, 1993

Library Link This story was taken from *Last Summer with Maizon* by Jacqueline Woodson. You might enjoy reading the entire book to find out whether Margaret wins the poetry contest.

Since Hanna Moved Away

The tires on my bike are flat.
The sky is grouchy gray.
At least it sure feels like that
Since Hanna moved away.

Chocolate ice cream tastes like prunes.
December's come to stay.
They've taken back the Mays and Junes
Since Hanna moved away.

Flowers smell like halibut.
Velvet feels like hay.
Every handsome dog's a mutt
Since Hanna moved away.

Nothing's fun to laugh about.
Nothing's fun to play.
They call me, but I won't come out
Since Hanna moved away.

–Judith Viorst

Portraits of People on the Move

AWARD WINNER

from *Children of the Wild West* by Russell Freedman

On May 19, 1841, a dozen covered wagons and seventy men, women, and children left Missouri and headed for the Pacific Coast. They were the first pioneers to travel west by wagon train. It is doubtful that any of these people had ever seen a photograph.

Photography was a new invention. The earliest photographs had been displayed for the first time in France just two years before, in the summer of 1839.

The growth of photography and the opening of the American West took place at the same time. By the 1850s, frontier photographers were traveling throughout the West. Their cameras were big and bulky. Their equipment was often crude. Even so, they were able to picture the frontier as the pioneers actually saw it.

A wagon train drawn by teams of oxen

In those days, simple rolls of film were unknown. Instead, photographers used large glass plate negatives that were messy and hard to handle. Just before a picture was taken, the glass plate was coated with sticky chemicals. It had to be placed in the camera and exposed right away, while it was still moist. Then the plate had to be removed from the camera and developed on the spot, before the chemicals dried. A photographer's covered wagon served as his darkroom. Wherever he went, he had to haul with him hundreds of pounds of photographic equipment.

Below, **a frontier school;**
right, **two Kiowa girls with a baby in a cradle board**

The first cameras could not capture motion. Because of the long exposure time needed, the camera had to be placed securely on a tripod. The people being photographed had to stand or sit absolutely still. If anyone moved, the picture would be blurred.

A frontier photographer might take more than an hour to assemble a group for a portrait, prepare the glass negative, take the picture, and then develop the negative. Yet people were eager to pose in front of the camera. Some of them would have their picture taken only once in their lives.

By the 1880s, many advances in photography had been made. Cameras were becoming smaller and easier to handle. Faster shutters and shorter exposure times made action shots possible. Photographers no longer had to carry their darkrooms with them. They now used improved glass negatives that could be developed long after the picture was taken.

Resting along the trail

Hundreds of thousands of photographs were taken while the West was being settled. Over the years, a large number of these pictures were lost or accidentally destroyed. Others remained hidden away in forgotten family albums, in attics and storerooms. But as time passed, the old photographs were discovered and placed in the archives of libraries, museums, and historical societies. Many of the photos that survive today are faded, scratched, or torn. But others, printed from undamaged glass negatives, are as clear and luminous as any photographs ever taken.

Left, **a Kiowa boy on horseback;** ***below,*** **posing for a frontier photographer**

Coming Over

from Immigrant Kids

by Russell Freedman

AWARD WINNER

In the years around the turn of the century, immigration to America reached an all-time high. Between 1880 and 1920, 23 million immigrants arrived in the United States. They came mainly from the countries of Europe, especially from impoverished towns and villages in southern and eastern Europe. The one thing they had in common was a fervent belief that in America, life would be better.

Most of these immigrants were poor. Somehow they managed to scrape together enough money to pay for their passage to America. Many immigrant families arrived penniless. Others had to make the journey in stages. Often the father came first, found work, and sent for his family later.

Immigrants usually crossed the Atlantic as steerage passengers. Reached by steep, slippery stairways, the steerage lay deep down in the hold of the ship. It was occupied by passengers paying the lowest fare.

Men, women, and children were packed into dark, foul-smelling compartments. They slept in narrow bunks stacked three high. They had no showers, no lounges, and no dining rooms. Food served from huge kettles was dished into dinner pails provided by the steam ship company. Because steerage conditions were crowded and uncomfortable, passengers spent as much time as possible up on deck.

The voyage was an ordeal, but it was worth it. They were on their way to America.

The great majority of immigrants landed in New York City, at America's busiest port. They never forgot their first glimpse of the Statue of Liberty.

Immigrants crowd the deck as the S.S. *Patricia* sails into New York harbor on December 10, 1906.

Edward Corsi, who later became United States Commissioner of Immigration, was a ten-year-old Italian immigrant when he sailed into New York harbor in 1907:

"My first impressions of the New World will always remain etched in my memory, particularly that hazy October morning when I first saw Ellis Island. The steamer *Florida*, fourteen days out of Naples, filled to capacity with 1600 natives of Italy, had weathered one of the worst storms in our captain's memory; and glad we were, both children and grown-ups, to leave the open sea and come at last through the Narrows into the Bay.

"My mother, my stepfather, my brother Giuseppe, and my two sisters, Liberta and Helvetia, all of us together, happy that we had come through the storm safely, clustered on the foredeck for fear of separation and looked with wonder on this miraculous land of our dreams.

"Giuseppe and I held tightly to Stepfather's hands, while Liberta and Helvetia clung to Mother. Passengers all about us were crowding against the rail. Jabbered conversation, sharp cries, laughs and cheers—a steadily rising din filled the air. Mothers and fathers lifted up babies so that they too could see, off to the left, the Statue of Liberty. . . .

"Finally the *Florida* veered to the left, turning northward into the Hudson River, and now the incredible buildings of lower Manhattan came very close to us.

"The officers of the ship . . . went striding up and down the decks, shouting orders and directions and driving the immigrants before them. Scowling and gesturing, they pushed and pulled the passengers, herding us into separate groups as though we were animals. A few moments later we came to our dock, and the long journey was over."

An aerial view of Ellis Island

But the journey was not yet over. Before they could be admitted to the United States, immigrants had to pass through Ellis Island, which became the nation's chief immigrant processing center in 1892. There they would be questioned and examined. Those who could not pass all the exams would be detained; some would be sent back to Europe. And so their arrival in America was filled with great anxiety. Among the immigrants, Ellis Island was known as "Heartbreak Island."

When their ship docked at a Hudson River pier, the immigrants had numbered identity tags pinned to their clothing. Then they were herded onto special ferryboats that carried them to Ellis Island. Officials hurried them along, shouting "Quick! Run! Hurry!" in half a dozen languages.

Filing into an enormous inspection hall, the immigrants formed long lines separated by iron railings that made the hall look like a great maze.

Now the examinations began. First the immigrants were examined by two doctors of the United States Health Service. One doctor looked for physical and mental abnormalities. When a case aroused suspicion, the immigrant received a chalk mark on the right shoulder for further inspection: *L* for lameness, *H* for heart, *X* for mental defects, and so on.

The second doctor watched for contagious and infectious diseases. He looked especially for infections of the scalp and at the eyelids for symptoms of trachoma, a blinding disease. Since trachoma caused more than half of all medical detentions, this doctor was greatly feared. He stood directly in the immigrant's path. With a swift movement, he would grab the immigrant's eyelid, pull it up, and peer beneath it. If all was well, the immigrant was passed on.

Those who failed to get past both doctors had to undergo a more thorough medical exam. The others moved on to the registration clerk, who questioned them with the aid of an inter-

The great inspection hall at Ellis Island

preter: What is your name? Your nationality? Your occupation? Can you read and write? Have you ever been in prison? How much money do you have with you? Where are you going?

Some immigrants were so flustered that they could not answer. They were allowed to sit and rest and try again.

About one immigrant out of every five or six was detained for additional examinations or questioning.

The writer Angelo Pellegrini has recalled his own family's detention at Ellis Island:

"We lived there for three days—Mother and we five children, the youngest of whom was three years old. Because of the rigorous physical examination that we had to submit to, particularly of the eyes, there was this terrible anxiety that one of us might be rejected. And if one of us was, what would the rest of

Waiting for the ferry in Manhattan, 1912

the family do? My sister was indeed momentarily rejected; she had been so ill and had cried so much that her eyes were absolutely bloodshot, and Mother was told, 'Well, we can't let her in.' But fortunately, Mother was an indomitable spirit and finally made them understand that if her child had a few hours' rest and a little bite to eat she would be all right. In the end we did get through."

Most immigrants passed through Ellis Island in about one day. Carrying all their worldly possessions, they left the examination hall and waited on the dock for the ferry that would take them to Manhattan, a mile away. Some of them still faced long journeys overland before they reached their final destination. Others would head directly for the teeming immigrant neighborhoods of New York City.

AUTHOR AT WORK

When Russell Freedman was a boy, he loved to pretend that he was a cowboy on the frontier. He grew up to be a writer instead of a cowboy. However, his interest in stories about the Old West, and history in general, still shines through.

Mr. Freedman is the author of more than forty nonfiction books. Among them is *Children of the Wild West*, which describes the rugged life of frontier children during the 1800's.

Mr. Freedman likes to use old photographs in his books. Pictures, he says, "bring the past to life in a way that nothing else can." For the book *Immigrant Kids,* he examined thousands of photographs at museums and libraries. This research reminded Mr. Freedman of his own family history. His grandparents moved to the United States from Russia around the same time as the people in this selection came to Ellis Island.

★ Award-winning Author

Library Link This excerpt was taken from *Immigrant Kids* by Russell Freedman. You might enjoy reading the entire book to find out how immigrant children adjusted to life in the United States.

Other Books by . . .

Russell Freedman

Lincoln: A Photobiography by Russell Freedman, Clarion Books, 1987

Kids at Work by Russell Freedman, photographs by Lewis Hine, Clarion Books, 1994

AWARD WINNER
THE GREAT MIGRATION
AN AMERICAN STORY • PAINTINGS BY JACOB LAWRENCE
SOUTHERN RAILWAY SYSTEM
RAIL ROAD CROSSING

Beginning about 1916, many African Americans left their homes in the southern part of the United States. They traveled to Chicago, New York, and other northern cities in search of better jobs and better lives. Their movement came to be known as the great migration, one of the biggest population shifts this country has ever known.

Around the time I was born, many African-Americans from the South left home and traveled to cities in the North in search of a better life. My family was part of this great migration.

There was a shortage of workers in northern factories because many had left their jobs to fight in the First World War. The factory owners had to find new workers to replace those who were marching off to war.

Northern industries offered southern blacks jobs as workers and lent them money, to be repaid later, for their railroad tickets. The northbound trains were packed with recruits.

Nature had ravaged the South. Floods ruined farms. The boll weevil destroyed cotton crops. The war had doubled the cost of food, making life even harder for the poor. Railroad stations were so crowded with migrants that guards were called in to keep order. The flood of migrants northward left crops back home to dry and spoil.

For African-Americans the South was barren in many ways. There was no justice for them in the courts, and their lives were often in danger. Although slavery had long been abolished, white landowners treated the black tenant farmers harshly and unfairly.

And so the migration grew.

Segregation divided the South. The black newspapers told of better housing and jobs in the North.

Families would arrive very early at railroad stations to make sure they could get on the northbound trains. Early arrival was not easy, because African-Americans found on the streets could be arrested for no reason.

And the migrants kept coming.

In the South there was little opportunity for education, and children labored in the fields. These were more reasons for people to move north, leaving some communities deserted. There was much excitement and discussion about the great migration.

Agents from northern factories flocked into southern counties and towns, looking for laborers.

Families often gathered to discuss whether to go north or to stay south. The promise of better housing in the North could not be ignored.

The railroad stations were crowded with migrants.

Letters from relatives in the North and articles in the black press portrayed a better life outside the South.

Many migrants arrived in Chicago.

In Chicago and other cities they labored in the steel mills . . . and on the railroads.

And the migrants kept coming.

Southern landowners, stripped of cheap labor, tried to stop the migration by jailing the labor agents and the migrants. Sometimes the agents disguised themselves to avoid arrest, but the migrants were often taken from railroad stations and jailed until the trains departed.

Black and white southern leaders met to discuss ways to improve conditions to stop the flow of workers north.

Although life in the North was better, it was not ideal.

Many migrants moved to Pittsburgh, which was a great industrial center at the time.

Although they were promised better housing in the North, some families were forced to live in overcrowded and unhealthy quarters.

The migrants soon learned that segregation was not confined to the South.

Many northern workers were angry because they had to compete with the migrants for housing and jobs. There were riots.

Longtime African-American residents living in the North did not welcome the newcomers from the South and often treated them with disdain.

The migrants had to rely on each other. The storefront church was a welcoming place and the center of their lives, in joy and in sorrow.

Black professionals, such as doctors and lawyers, soon followed their patients and clients north. Female workers were among the last to leave.

Life in the North brought many challenges, but the migrants' lives had changed for the better. The children were able to go to school, and their parents gained the freedom to vote.

And the migrants kept coming.

Theirs is a story of African-American strength and courage. I share it now as my parents told it to me, because their struggles and triumphs ring true today. People all over the world are still on the move, trying to build better lives for themselves and for their families.

AUTHOR AND ILLUSTRATOR AT WORK

Jacob Lawrence

Jacob Lawrence continues to paint from his home in Seattle, Washington.

Jacob Lawrence's parents were part of the great migration. They moved from the South to New Jersey, where Mr. Lawrence was born in 1917. When Mr. Lawrence was thirteen, his family moved to New York City's Harlem neighborhood. He studied painting in an after-school program.

Mr. Lawrence was twenty-two years old in 1940 when he began the Migration series. For him, the series was an opportunity to find out how his own life fit into the history of African Americans in the United States. He spent many hours at the library reading books and taking notes before he started painting.

"Soon my research gave me the images I needed to tell the story of the great migration," he says. It took sixty panels to tell the story. Mr. Lawrence painted them all in one year.

Jacob Lawrence mixes thick paint with water to give his paintings a textured look.

★ Award-winning Author and Illustrator

Jacob Lawrence (United States), *Self-Portrait*, 1977

"While I was painting," he says," I thought about trains and people walking to the stations. I thought about field hands leaving their farms to become factory workers, and about the families that sometimes got left behind. The choices made were hard ones, so I wanted to show what made the people get on those northbound trains."

Mr. Lawrence also drew on his parents' memories to help him paint. "My family and others left the South on a quest for freedom, justice, and dignity," he says. "If our story rings true for you today, then it must still strike a chord in our American experience."

Other Books with Art by . . .

Jacob Lawrence

Harriet and the Promised Land written and illustrated by Jacob Lawrence, Simon & Schuster, 1993

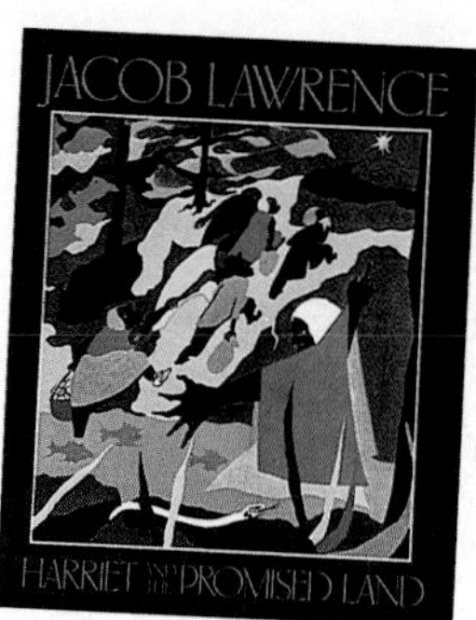

John Brown: One Man Against Slavery by Gwen Everett, illustrated by Jacob Lawrence, Rizzoli, 1993

IN RESPONSE

A Moving Picture

Jacob Lawrence's paintings show many details of the African American movement to the North. Draw a picture that shows details of a European immigrant's arrival on Ellis Island.

Bon Voyage!

Jacob Lawrence's parents were part of the great migration. Think about what it might have been like if you and your family made the journey. Write a poem or short story describing the trip. Include your own information and details from Mr. Lawrence's work.

New Arrivals

Compare the experiences of African Americans who moved to the North ("The Great Migration") with those of European immigrants who moved to the United States ("Coming Over"). How were their experiences similar? different? What do these stories tell you about life for some newcomers in this country?

Migration

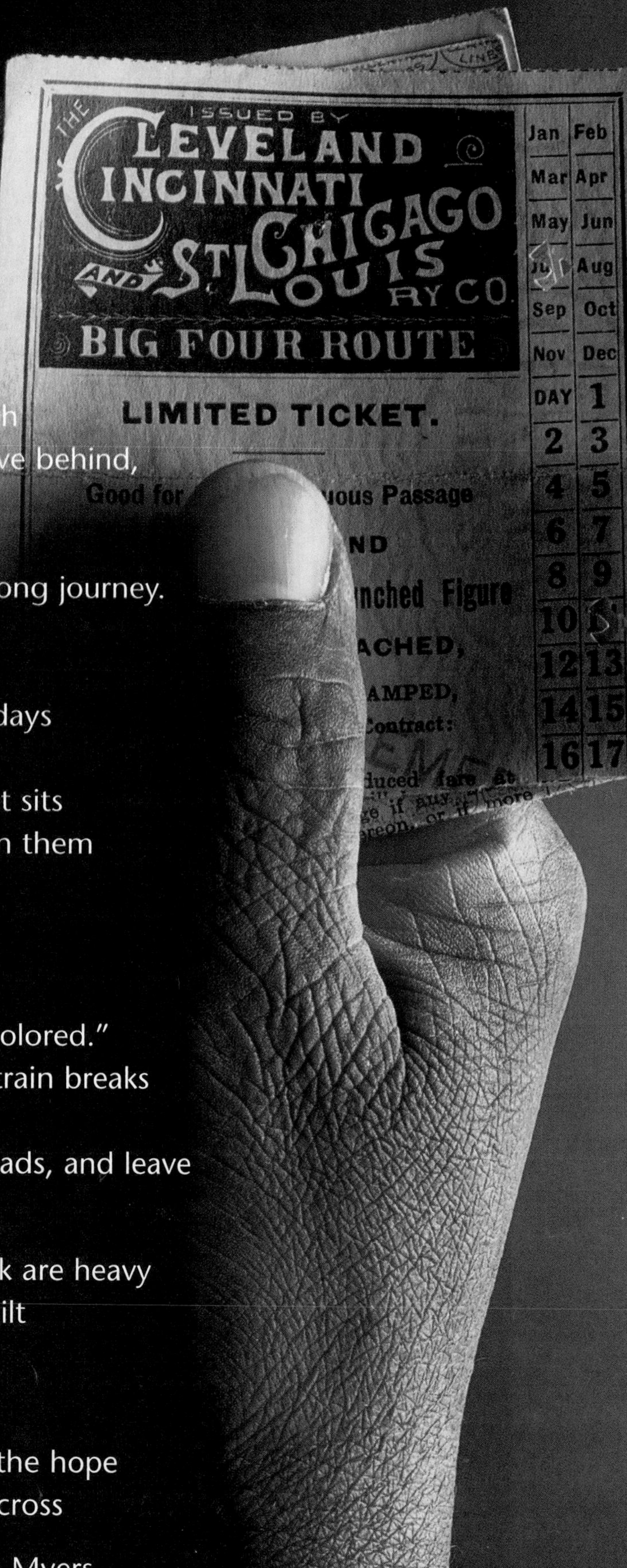

In the waiting room, "Colored,"
Hands, calloused and as black as the rich
Georgia/Carolina/Alabama dirt they leave behind,
Clasp and unclasp silently,
Some hold Bibles older than freedom,
Others hold food that will not last the long journey.
There is no need to speak, to explain
How so many nights of love and terror
So many back cracking, heartbreaking days
So many humbled dreams
Can fit into the small rope-tied case that sits
On the ancient hardwood floor between them

A stirring at the ticket counter
Stiffens backs, tightens stomachs
Hard-eyed men with guns in their belts
Stare daggers into the waiting room,"Colored."
In the distance the *whoo! whoo!* of the train breaks
The stillness of a forever moment
The men with guns look, shake their heads, and leave
Life goes on

The tickets to Chicago/Detroit/New York are heavy
As heavy as the memory of a church built
With sweat and faith and knotted pine
On the edge of the old burying ground

But there are the children, and there is the hope
Of a people with yet one more river to cross

—Walter Dean Myers

Faces of a Nation

In painting and sculpture, these artists show the ideas, dreams, and experiences of the immigrants.

This unusual flag is on display at Ellis Island's Museum of Immigration. Where might the people on the flag have come from? What does *Flag of Faces* tell you about the United States?

Mosaic of photographs by Pablo Delano (Puerto Rican) and Thomas Geismar (United States), *Flag of Faces,* 1990

Arshile Gorky based *The Artist and His Mother* on an old photograph taken before he came to the United States. What are the picture's main colors? What mood do the colors create for you? What other details add to the mood of the painting?

Arshile Gorky, The Artist and His Mother, c. 1926–1936, oil on canvas, 60 x 50 in. (152.4 x 127 cm), collection of Whitney Museum of American Art, New York, gift of Julian Levy for Maro and Natasha Gorky in memory of their father, 50.17, photo by Geoffrey Clements, New York/c 1955 Estate of Arshile Gorky/Artists Rights Society (ARS), New York

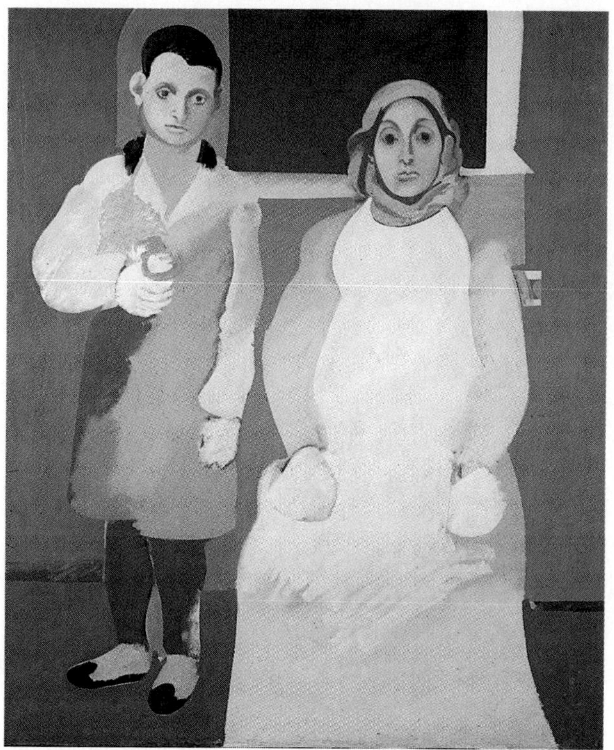

Painting by Arshile Gorky (Armenian), *The Artist and His Mother*, 1926–1929

For many immigrants, the Statue of Liberty means freedom and the promise of a better life. What details in the statue might make the sculpture seem welcoming to people?

Sculpture by Auguste Bertholdi (French), *Statue of Liberty*, 1886

Old Traditions New Beginnings

from Hoang Anh: A Vietnamese-American Boy
by Diane Hoyt-Goldsmith
photographs by Lawrence Migdale

My name is Hoang Anh Chau (WONG ON CHOH). I live in the town of San Rafael, California. In our home, we speak two languages: Vietnamese and English. I came to this country with my family when I was just a baby. We are all refugees from Vietnam, here to begin a new life. My parents, my older brothers, my sister, and I are new citizens of the United States. We are Vietnamese-Americans.

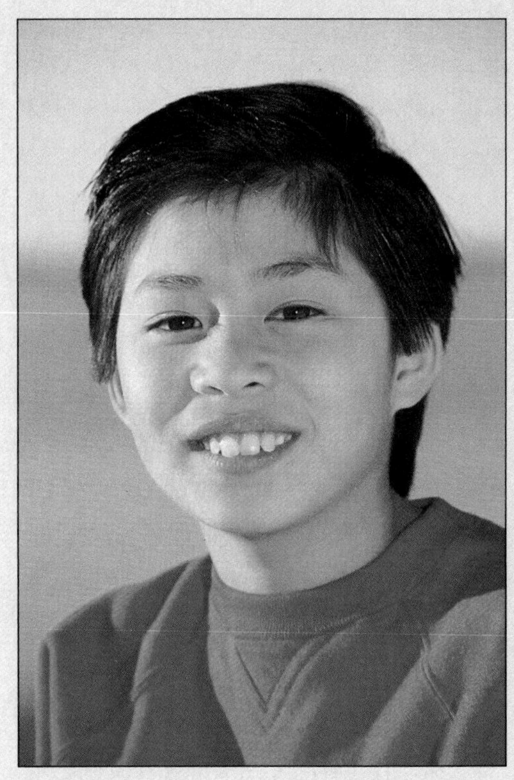

HOW WE CAME

My father, Thao Chau (TAU CHOH) is a fisherman. On days when the weather is good, he gets up at three o'clock in the morning. He goes to his boat and heads out to the ocean. Working hard all day, my father visits the places where he has set traps to catch crabs and eels. Usually, he doesn't get home until long after dark. My father learned to be a fisherman in Vietnam.

My parents came from a small town called Kieng Giang (KEENG JANG) on the Mekong (MAY-KONG) Delta in the southern part of Vietnam. In that region, there are many rice farms. My father, like his father before him, owned a tractor and earned a living by plowing the fields for farmers.

But in 1977, my parents made a decision that changed their lives. They decided to leave Vietnam.

My father had been a soldier in the South Vietnamese army since 1971. For years, he had fought alongside the Americans against the Communist forces led by North Vietnam. During the war, many of my father's friends and relatives were killed. He watched as the war destroyed homes, farms, and towns. He saw that his way of life was changing forever.

Unable to defeat the Communists, the United States sent its soldiers home in 1973. Two years later, the Communists of North Vietnam took control of the entire country. The new government acted harshly toward people like my father who had fought against them. My parents were frightened for their own safety. They worried about the future. They wanted to raise their children in a better place.

The Communist government of Vietnam, however, would not allow people to leave the country. So my parents planned secretly to escape from Vietnam and seek a new life of safety and freedom in the United States. In doing so, they would become refugees.

To carry out his plan, my father sold his tractor and bought a small fishing boat. He learned to fish, working in the waters of the Gulf of Thailand. He had a plan to escape, but he did not want the Vietnamese government to become suspicious. He watched and waited for the right time.

Then one day in 1978, my parents gathered together some food and clothing for a long journey. They said goodbye to their parents and their friends. In the dark of the night, my parents brought their four young children on board the small fishing boat. With his family and twenty-four other refugees hidden below the deck, my father sailed away from the shores of Vietnam.

He pretended it was just another day of fishing. But when the little boat reached the open water, he did not stop to put out the crab traps. Sailing west and south, he kept on going toward the island nation of Malaysia.

My brothers and sister were much too young to realize what was happening. They had no idea of the danger they were in. The small, overcrowded boat faced many hardships on the journey. It could have been lost at sea. It could have been swamped in a terrible storm. The passengers could have run out of food and water before reaching land again. Worst of all, sea pirates could have discovered the boat and taken everybody's belongings and even their lives.

A news clipping shows the Chau family shortly after their arrival in the United States. Hoang Anh, on his mother's lap, is still a small baby. His father and a brother sit on the couch and his aunt stands in the doorway behind.

But my family was lucky. After two days and two nights on the ocean, they reached Malaysia safely. For more than a year, they lived in a camp for refugees. It was filled with many other people who had fled from Vietnam. Conditions in the camp were very poor. There was little food to eat and nothing for people to do.

It was in this refugee camp in Malaysia that I was born. In spite of the poor conditions there, I was a very healthy baby. When I was a few months old, a church in Oregon sponsored my family, and we emigrated to the United States.

Happy that the morning's catch was good, Hoang Anh helps his father put the crabs into a tall barrel. His father will take the crabs to a fish market in San Francisco, where they will be sold.

I have read in books that over a million people fled from Vietnam after the war because they were frightened about what the country would be like under a Communist government. Many of these "boat people" made it to safety, as my family did. But many more were shipwrecked and had to be rescued by passing boats. Some were discovered by the Communist government and sent back to Vietnam. The most unfortunate people were those who met pirate ships. They were robbed, beaten, kidnapped, sold as slaves, or even tossed overboard. As a result many refugees have just disappeared completely.

Sometimes, when I help my father at the docks, I look at his fishing boat and think about his daring escape. The boat that carried my family away from Vietnam was ten feet shorter in length, yet it brought thirty people to a new life. My parents were very brave to have taken such risks to bring us all to the United States.

Sometimes Hoang Anh helps his father with his fishing gear. These floats will mark the places where the crab traps are put in the ocean.

LIFE AT HOME

Often, my father brings home some fresh crab or Cua (KOO-AH) for us to eat. An ordinary evening meal at our home in California is like an ordinary evening meal anywhere in Vietnam. We eat many of the same foods here.

At our table, we use deep rice bowls instead of plates, and chopsticks instead of forks, knives, and spoons. First, we might have a soup called Canh bi Dao (CAN BEE DOW) made from sliced squash, pork, and onions. With that, we have Suon Ram (SOON RAM), which is pork ribs prepared with fish sauce. Usually, we eat some type of fish or seafood as a main course, and there is always lots of rice or Com (KOLM).

Hoang Anh and his family eat some of the same foods in the United States as they did in Vietnam. They often enjoy fish and seafood as a main course for the evening meal.

My favorite American food is pizza, but I like to make a Vietnamese snack for myself after school. I cut up a fresh cucumber and dip the slices in nuoc mam (NOOK MAM), a spicy, brown fish sauce. Vietnamese people use this sauce with lots of different foods, the same way Americans use catsup.

In Vietnam, only women work in the kitchen. But here, my family has adopted an American life-style. Everyone in our household knows how to cook.

My mother, Phuong Lam (FONG LAM), has a full-time job outside our home. She works six and occasionally seven days a week at a beauty shop doing manicures for people. Because she doesn't get home until quite late in the evening, we all help out. Sometimes my father makes dinner. He has learned to be a good cook.

There are five children in our family, and I am the youngest. My older brothers are named Tung (TUNG), Binh (BIN), and Tuan (TWAN). My sister's name is Tu Anh (TOO ON).

As in all of Southeast Asia, rice is a staple food for the Vietnamese people.

All of us are busy with school. I go to junior high school, Tu Anh and Tuan are in high school, and Tung and Binh attend college. My brothers and sister each have a part-time job as well.

In my school, there are many children who come from other parts of the world and speak English as a second language. There are kids from Mexico, Central America, China, and the Middle East. Two of my best friends are from Kampuchea (Cambodia), a country in Southeast Asia near Vietnam.

Our life in the United States is good, but like most families, we have problems too. My parents, my brothers, and my sister work hard to earn enough money to buy the things we need and want. But when the crab season is over, my father is out of a job for several months. That puts more pressure on the rest of us.

In Hoang Anh's classroom, the students are making maps of the countries in Southeast Asia.

Although my father understands English well, he still has trouble speaking it. This makes it hard for him to find another job. I know how frustrated he feels because it is hard for me to switch from speaking Vietnamese at home to speaking English at school.

The Vietnamese language is quite different from English. In the Vietnamese alphabet, there is no *f, j, w* or *z*. Most of our letters are pronounced differently from how they sound in English. And some English sounds do not exist at all in Vietnamese.

Ours is a tonal language. This means that the pitch of the word is important to its meaning. In Vietnamese, most words have but one syllable. Each word has a distinct pitch, high or low, like a note on a musical scale. For example, the word *ma* can have six different meanings depending upon the pitch. It can mean *rice seedling, that* or *but, tomb* or *grave, ghost, horse,* or *mommy.*

I'm still too young to get a regular job, so I help out around the house as much as I can. Sometimes I get my father's fishing gear ready. I try to keep my room neat. And I help to water the trees and shrubs in the yard.

For several years, California has suffered from a drought. Not enough rain has fallen and the reservoirs are low. Water has become very scarce. This was never a problem for my parents in Vietnam, where it always rains a lot.

One of Hoang Anh's favorite pastimes is playing football with his brothers.

My father thought of a good way to save water during the rainy season to use later in the year. He made a storage area along the north side of our house. Stacking up empty plastic buckets to catch the rain, he made his own small reservoir. By carefully watering our shrubs with what we collect from the rains, I help to keep our water bills low.

Most of the time, I'm like any American kid. I like to ride my bike and listen to rap music with my friends. I go roller skating and play video games with my cousins on weekends. I dream about becoming a professional football player when I grow up, so I throw the football every chance I get. I would also like to be an artist.

IN RESPONSE

What a Day!

Pretend you are Hoang Anh Chau. Write a letter to your grandparents in Vietnam telling about a typical day in your life. Explain some of the similarities and differences between life in the United States and Vietnam.

A Fantastic Journey

You are a television news announcer. Give a report on an immigrant's move from Vietnam to this country. Tell the audience about the dangers or the hardships that person endured during the journey.

AUTHOR AT WORK

Diane Hoyt-Goldsmith's curiosity about the world has led her in many different directions. For instance, her interest in totem poles first brought her into contact with photographer Lawrence Migdale. Their shared interest in the subject resulted in *Totem Pole*, Ms. Hoyt-Goldsmith's first children's book. Since then, Mr. Migdale has taken the photographs for all of the author's books. These works describe everyday experiences of American children from different cultures. Like Hoang Anh Chau, many of the children in Ms. Hoyt-Goldsmith's books unite the traditions of their home culture with their lives in the United States.

Other Books by . . .

Diane Hoyt-Goldsmith

Cherokee Summer by Diane Hoyt-Goldsmith, photographs by Lawrence Migdale, Holiday House, 1993

Celebrating Kwanzaa by Diane Hoyt-Goldsmith, photographs by Lawrence Migdale, Holiday House, 1993

Library Link This story was taken from *Hoang Anh: A Vietnamese-American Boy* by Diane Hoyt-Goldsmith. You might enjoy reading the entire book to find out about the celebration of Tet, the Vietnamese New Year.

Express **Yourself**

In Moving On, you read about people who were left behind or went on to something new. Some coped with personal changes in their lives, while others faced the challenge of moving to a new home. Their experiences can help you recall how you have moved on in your life.

Words of Wisdom

Some characters in this theme made changes that affected other people. Felipe's decision ("Nacho Loco") to eat meat again affected Nacho. Maizon's departure ("Missing Maizon") changed Margaret's life. What did Nacho and Maizon think about the changes? What advice could you give both characters to help them cope? With a partner, list your ideas. Then think about changes you have coped with. Did you use your own advice?

Feelings About Change

Margaret ("Missing Maizon") feels different emotions during the story. How do her feelings compare with those of the girl in the poem ("Since Hannah Moved Away")? What change does Margaret make that the girl in the poem doesn't make? Discuss your answers in a small group.

Change for the Better

"In the South there was little opportunity for education, and children labored in the fields," writes Jacob Lawrence ("The Great Migration"). Compare this story with Hoang Anh's ("Old Traditions, New Beginnings"). What reasons for leaving home did both groups have in common? Which reason do you think is most important? Why?

Compare Two Voices

Hoang Anh ("Old Traditions, New Beginnings") gives a third-person account of his parents' journey to this country. European immigrants ("Coming Over") describe in first person their arrival at Ellis Island. Which story seems more vivid to you? What makes it so? Support your choice with examples from the selection.

Staying or Leaving

"The Great Migration" tells the story of African Americans moving to new cities. "Missing Maizon" tells about a character's reaction to a friend moving away. Who has a harder time—the people who leave home or the one who is left behind? Which story is closer to your own experience? Write a paragraph that includes details from one of the stories and your life.

More Books for You to Enjoy

Split Sisters

by C. S. Adler, Macmillan, 1990

It's bad enough that her parents are separating. But when Case learns that her beloved sister, Jen, is moving to New York to be with their mother, she tries to hold her family together by any means necessary.

Chevrolet Saturdays

by Candy Dawson Boyd, Macmillan, 1993

Joey Davis wants his old life back. Nothing has been the same since his dad left home and his new stepfather moved in. Even at school, things are bad. The class bully has it in for him. Can life get any worse for Joey?

Over Here It's Different: Carolina's Story

by Mildred Leinweber Dawson, photographs by George Ancona, Macmillan, 1993

Eleven-year-old Carolina Liranzo tells how her life changed when her family moved to the United States from the Dominican Republic. Like anyone new to this country, she had to adjust to the language, food, and a different way of life.

Next-Door Neighbors

by Sarah Ellis, Margaret K. McElderry Books, 1990

Peggy is dismayed when she and her family move to a new town. She dreads meeting new people her age but soon discovers that friends come in different ages and sizes.

The Cat Who Escaped from Steerage

by Evelyn Wilde Mayerson, Charles Scribner's Sons, 1990

What was it like to cross the ocean at the turn of the century? Chana's story tells of her family's arrival at Ellis Island and how her cat, Pitsel, survives the journey.

Looking Below the Surface

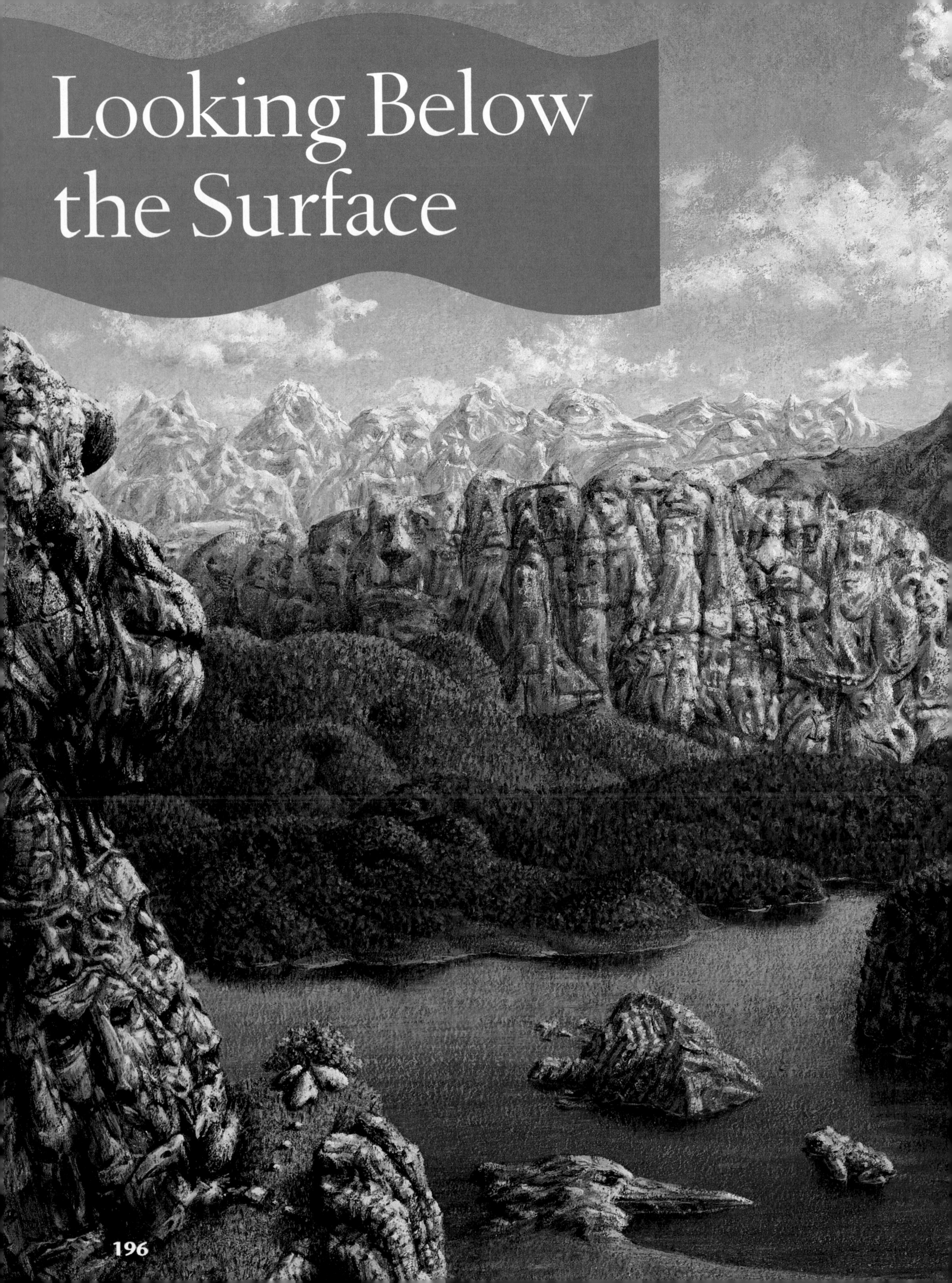

Theme

3

"There was a story there. . . ."

—Ardath Mayhar
"The Secret Among the Stones"

Theme 3

Looking Below the Surface

CONTENTS

Theme Trade Books

Home Place

by Crescent Dragonwagon

A family walking in the forest discovers the remains of an old house. They look around and find clues about the people who once lived there.

The Treasure Bird

by Peni R. Griffin

Ten-year-old Jessy hears rumors of buried treasure on the farm her family inherits. A talking parrot gives her clues as she hunts for the treasure.

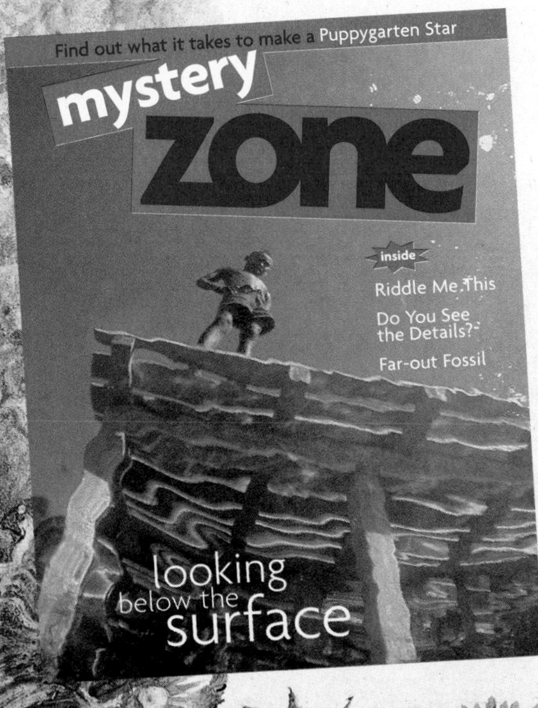

Theme Magazine

Who dug up a two-thousand-year-old egg? How good are you at noticing details? Theme Magazine *Mystery Zone* can help you figure it out.

AMSTERDAM AVE

Ali Baba *and the Missing Glass Slipper*

AWARD WINNER

from *Ali Baba Bernstein, Lost and Found*
by Johanna Hurwitz

David Bernstein was not like most of the other boys in his class at school. In the first place, back when he was only eight years, five months, and seventeen days old,he had given himself a new name. David Bernstein insisted that he wanted to be known as Ali Baba. That way he would not be confused with the three other boys named David in his class. And as Ali Baba, strange and mysterious things were sure to happen to him.

At home, he was the only David in his family. But even though they had no confusion about his identity, his parents, like his teachers, gradually found themselves calling him by his new name.

There was another way in which Ali Baba Bernstein differed from boys his age. Though he watched baseball, football, basketball, and hockey games on television, he was not crazy about sports. Though he accumulated stamps and baseball cards and superhero comic books, he was not a dedicated collector. By the time Ali Baba Bernstein was nine years, eleven months, and five days old, he was devoting most of his energy to developing his skills as a detective. He watched for suspicious people and occurrences. So far he hadn't found too many cases waiting to be solved. Still, he wanted to be ready when the time came.

AMSTERDAM
AVE

“Mom, have you seen Slipper?” he asked, walking into the kitchen.

“No,” said Mrs. Bernstein. “She was here when Mrs. Salmon came by to borrow some cinnamon. I remember because Mrs. Salmon commented on how surprised she was that we had a dog.” Mrs. Bernstein thought for a moment. “I don’t remember if she was here when the United Parcel delivery man brought me a package.”

“Slipper must be hiding,” said Ali Baba, grinning at the challenge. He set off to search for the dog.

It was fun at first. Ali Baba looked under his bed and under his parents’ bed, as well. He looked in the bathroom. He looked in all the closets and behind all the furniture. He looked in every corner, and still he couldn’t find Slipper.

When he played hide and seek with his friends, they could always call, “Come out, come out wherever you are.” But Slipper wouldn’t respond to that.

Although it wasn't time for Slipper's lone meal of the day, Ali Baba decided to fill her bowl with food. He hoped she would hear the sound and come out of her hiding place. Even after the bowl was filled and waiting, however, Slipper remained hidden.

Ali Baba began to worry. What if Slipper refused to come out of hiding all week long? Or worse. What if somehow she had really gotten lost?

"Slipper is missing," he told his mother.

"How could she be missing? That's impossible," Mrs. Bernstein said.

"Then you find her. I give up," said Ali Baba crossly. What was the fun of having a dog if she had hidden herself away?

"She's probably sleeping somewhere in the apartment," said Mrs. Bernstein. "You'll see. She'll come out and surprise us before you know it."

Ali Baba knew his mother was relieved that the dog wasn't making a mess in the apartment.

By midafternoon, Mrs. Bernstein was no longer so sure that the dog was asleep in the apartment. It was time for Slipper to go for another walk. "I don't want any accidents in the house," she said.

"Maybe she ran out of the house when you opened the door for the man with the parcel or for Mrs. Salmon," said Ali Baba.

"I suppose it's possible," said Mrs. Bernstein. "I'm not used to having a dog around, so I didn't shut the door quickly."

"If she got out, she may be out on the street."

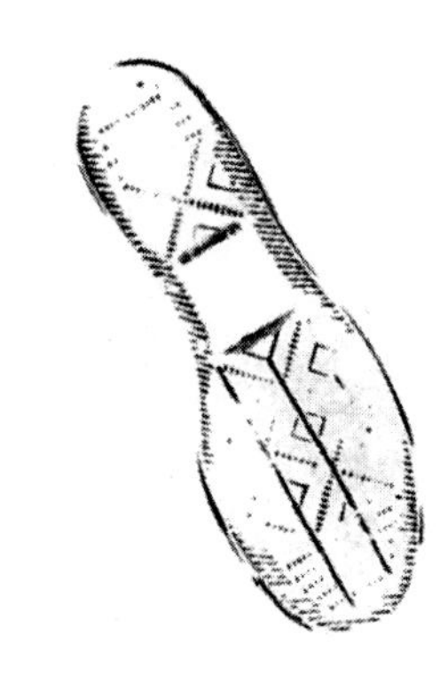

Mrs. Bernstein looked worried. "I don't know how we'll explain to Doris and Simon Glass that we lost their dog the very first day she was with us. They'll never forgive us."

"I'll go outside and look," said Ali Baba. Now that his mother agreed that Slipper wasn't in the apartment, this was becoming a real mystery.

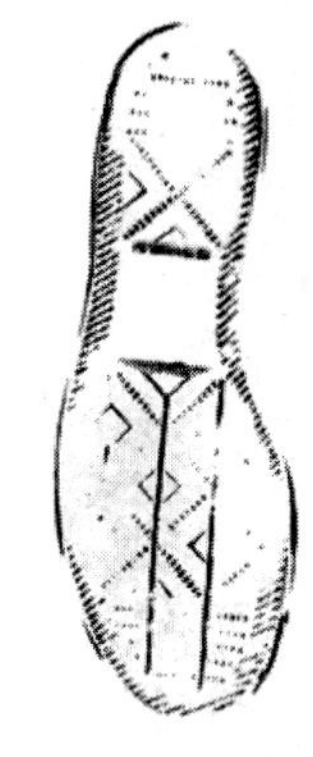

He grabbed the leash so that if he found Slipper, he could attach it to her collar. Ali Baba went out to the hallway and pressed the button for the elevator. Then it occurred to him that if he was to look for the dog, he should think and act like a dog. And no dog, especially no dog as small as Slipper, could reach the elevator button. If Slipper had gone outside, she would have had to walk down the stairs.

Ali Baba felt more and more excited by this mystery of the missing dog. He was convinced that he would find Slipper in the stairwell between two floors. He walked down the steps that connected the sixth floor with the fifth. Then he stopped at the fifth-floor landing and looked around for a sign of Slipper. There was no trace of her. He repeated his search down the steps and at each floor down to the ground floor.

In the lobby, he saw Charlie, the building janitor, and ran to him. "Did you see a dog? I'm looking for Slipper. She's the dachshund that belongs to the Glass family. She's staying in our apartment, but somehow she got lost," he explained.

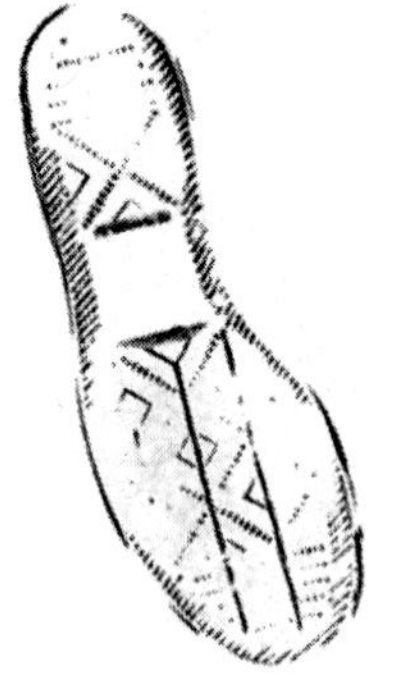

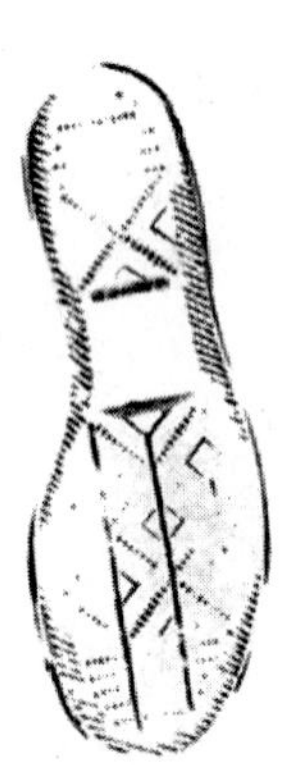

"I didn't see her," said Charlie. "But I'll keep a lookout. Do you think she's out on the street?"

Ali Baba didn't know, but he ran out hoping to find the dog. He ran toward Amsterdam Avenue, which was where Slipper had pulled him earlier in the day. Though he looked up and down the street, there was no Slipper in sight. Suppose some people had found her and taken her to their home?

Ali Baba remembered that from time to time he would see notices attached to the streetlights. Usually, they were about lost dogs or cats. Whenever he saw one of those signs, he wondered who had posted it. Now he thought he would be the person who was going to put a sign up.

Ali Baba ran back to his house. He would have to get out some paper and markers to make some signs. He took the elevator back to the sixth floor and was just about to go to his apartment when he realized something. In *The Incredible Journey*, the animals walked hundreds of miles to get home. Maybe Slipper was trying to get home, too. Before, when he had gone looking for Slipper, he had assumed that the dog had gone downstairs. Suppose she had walked up instead. But the floors of the apartment building all looked the same. Slipper could easily get lost.

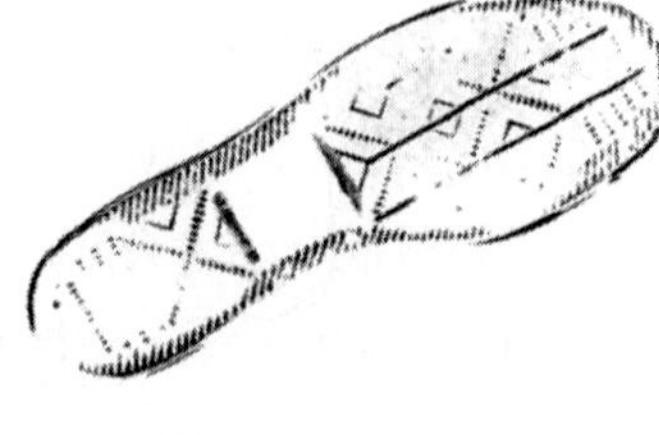

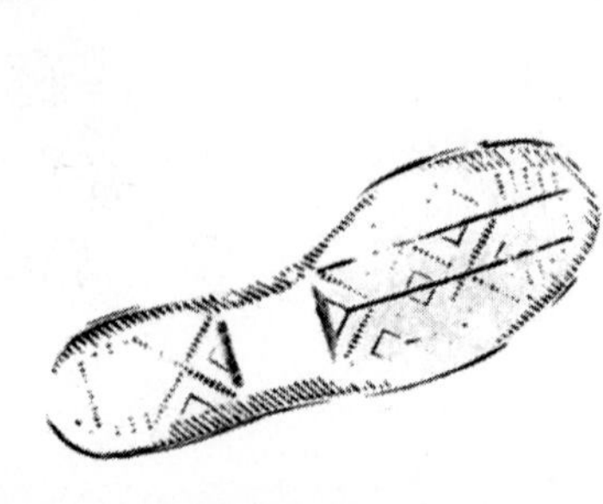

Immediately, Ali Baba ran to the stairwell and began to climb to the seventh floor. It would not be easy for Slipper to climb up or down with her tiny legs. On the landing of the seventh floor, Ali Baba looked around, but he saw nothing except a newspaper waiting to be picked up in front of apartment 7C. He continued his climb up to the next floor. Something dark was lying by the door of 8A, the Glass's apartment. Ali Baba raced down the hallway.

There, in front of apartment 8A, was the curled-up and sleeping body of Slipper.

"What are you doing here?" Ali Baba asked the dog as he snapped the leash onto her collar.

Of course, Slipper didn't give an answer. Ali Baba didn't expect one. Besides, he knew the answer. Slipper had found her way home. Ali Baba felt good about Slipper. And he felt good about himself, too. He had solved a mystery, just like a real detective. Ali Baba stopped on the sixth floor to tell his mother the good news.

"Thank goodness!" said Mrs. Bernstein. She was very relieved.

Then Ali Baba took the dog for her afternoon walk. As he passed the streetlights on the block, he was glad that he wouldn't have to post a message on one of them, after all.

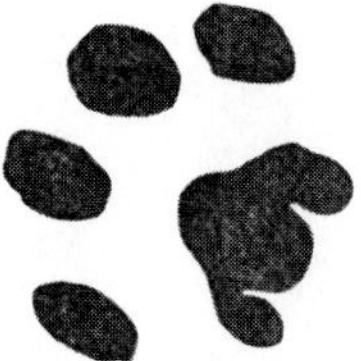

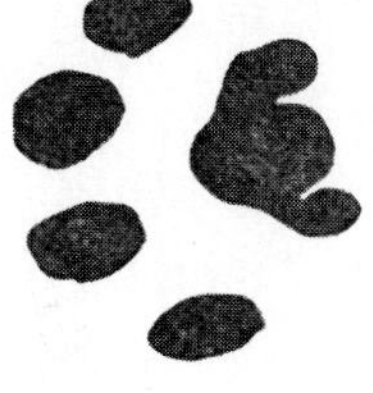

"Dogs have good instincts and good noses," said Mr. Bernstein that evening. "Slipper must have slipped out of our apartment when the door was opened for a minute, and then she smelled her way back upstairs."

Ali Baba sniffed hard. He could smell a faint whiff of the meat loaf his mother had cooked for the family's supper. He wondered if he could find his way home by sniffing and smelling if he was ever far away and lost. He doubted it.

"She's really very smart," he said to his father. "Maybe she could help me solve some mysteries." Ali Baba had only six days left before the Glass family returned home and claimed their dog. Still, who knew what mysterious events might happen tomorrow. Every day was a potential adventure for a boy like Ali Baba Bernstein.

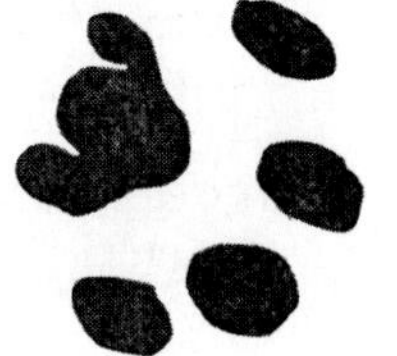

IN RESPONSE

Lost and Found

Help find the lost dog! Make a sign like the one Ali Baba thought about making to help him find Slipper. Include information or pictures to help people recognize the lost dog.

Slipper's "Incredible Journey"

How do you think Slipper found her way home? Write a description of the dog's escape from the Bernsteins' apartment. What problems might she have had getting home? Include the details of these problems in your story.

Dog Debate

Ali Baba wants a dog. Should his parents let him have one? Yes or no—it's up to you! Get a partner who agrees with you and debate the issue with partners who take the other side. Include arguments from the story and your own ideas too.

Johanna Hurwitz

★ Award-winning Author

In this interview, Johanna Hurwitz talks about writing stories, solving mysteries, and creating Ali Baba.

Q: Where did you get the idea to write about a child detective?

A: As a child, I was always looking for a mystery to solve. So I didn't do much research for Ali Baba. The ideas just came out of my head.

Q: How did you choose Ali Baba's real name, David Bernstein?

A: I had the idea to pick a name that was rather common, at least in the New York area. I opened the Manhattan phone book, and there were seventeen David Bernsteins! I thought that even if you share your name, you are still an individual with your own personality.

Ali Baba sniffed hard. He could smell a faint whiff of the meatloaf his mother had cooked for the family's supper. He wondered if he was ever far away and lost if he could find his way home by sniffing and smelling. He doubted it.

"You're pretty smart," he said to Slipper as he looked at the dog with new respect. "Maybe you could help me solve some mysteries." Dachhunds might not be as clever as bloodhounds, but Slipper had proven herself to be pretty savvy after all. Now Ali Baba only had six days left before the Glass family returned home and claimed their dog. Still, who knew what mysterious events tomorrow. Everyday was a potential adventure for a boy

Q: Have you written other books about Ali Baba?

A: Yes, there are three Ali Baba books. I only meant to write one, *The Adventures of Ali Baba Bernstein.* After the hard-cover book came out, they were going to print it in paperback. I got loads of letters from students, asking about my "new" book. I thought, "I can't leave all these children looking for a book that doesn't exist." So I wrote the second one, *Hurray for Ali Baba Bernstein.*

Q: When you write, how do you work?

A: I wrote my first book longhand. Now I have a computer. It's easier because I think and type much faster than I write!

Other Books by . . .

Johanna Hurwitz

Class President by Johanna Hurwitz, illustrated by Sheila Hamanaka, Morrow, 1990

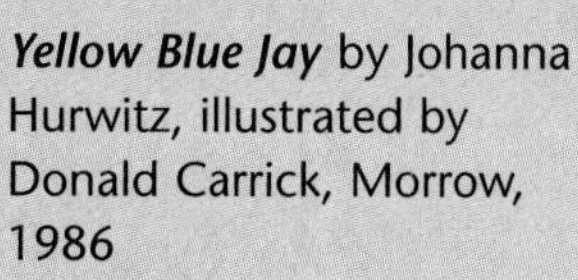

Teacher's Pet by Johanna Hurwitz, illustrated by Sheila Hamanaka, Morrow, 1988

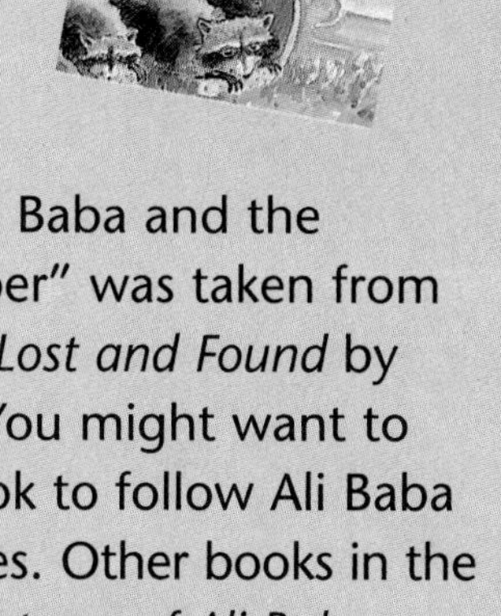

Yellow Blue Jay by Johanna Hurwitz, illustrated by Donald Carrick, Morrow, 1986

Library Link "Ali Baba and the Missing Glass Slipper" was taken from *Ali Baba Bernstein, Lost and Found* by Johanna Hurwitz. You might want to read the entire book to follow Ali Baba on more adventures. Other books in the series are *The Adventures of Ali Baba Bernstein* and *Hurray for Ali Baba Bernstein.*

What Do ANIMALS Know?

from *What Does the Crow Know?*

by Margery Facklam

"How much is four plus five?" a man in the audience shouted at the horse.

What a question to ask a horse! But his owner, Wilhelm von Osten, nodded to Hans, a signal to "go ahead." In the silent room, the only sound was the tapping of the horse's hoof—nine times.

Amazing, people said. What a smart horse!

The horse could also multiply, divide, and subtract. With a nod or a shake of his head, he could answer yes or no to questions about music, history, and other subjects. People began to call the horse Clever Hans. It wasn't long before scientists came to Germany from all over Europe to see him, and most of them agreed that this smart horse really knew the answers.

To prove that Hans was really clever, von Osten asked a horse trainer, a circus manager, two zoologists, and a psychologist to watch Hans at work. After the performance, these experts agreed that Hans was truly amazing.

But one scientist wasn't convinced. Oskar Pfungst, a young psychologist, decided to try a test of his own. He wanted to see what Hans would do if a question was asked by a person who didn't know the correct answer. Pfungst discovered that Hans didn't know math or music or other subjects at all. He didn't understand the questions. But in a way, the horse really *was* clever, because he had learned to pick up cues, or signals, that even his trainer didn't realize he was sending. If von Osten—or any other questioner—so much as raised an eyebrow, changed his or her breathing, shifted a foot, or moved a shoulder, it was message enough to tell Hans which way to move his head or when to stop tapping.

Ever since von Osten's horse fooled scientists more than a hundred years ago, anyone who tries to test an animal's intelligence worries about making the Clever Hans mistake. Scientists are careful to set up "blind" tests in which the animal cannot get any clues from the person

giving the test. It's not easy to find the right way to test an animal. It's hard enough to find the right way to test how smart a human is.

One test designed for people measures an individual's I.Q., or *intelligence quotient*. The score is a number that tells how well a person answers questions or figures out problems in comparison to other people of the same age who take the test. But people are smart in different ways. Some are good at math, while others have better language skills. Some are good mechanics, and others are all thumbs at figuring out how things work.

Background and culture, and where a person lives, can also affect test scores. A boy living in a big city might not be able to find edible plants or track an animal through a rain forest, any more than a boy raised in a rain forest would know how to program a VCR or use a computer. Even though both boys could be equally intelligent, it's unlikely that either one could pass a test based on skills learned in the other's environment. So it is with animals. Each animal is smart in a different way.

Two scientists made up a sixteen-part intelligence test that was supposed to measure a cat's ability to solve problems. It looked at how quickly a cat could perform various tasks, such as getting out from under a paper bag placed over its head, getting a piece of sticky tape off its nose, and getting at food wrapped in a napkin.

The test didn't work very well because the cats got bored with it. One cat loved hiding in the paper bag and didn't even try to get out. Another cat curled up and went to sleep during the test, and another hid under the couch. "If it feels as though you're pushing it, even the brightest cat will sit down and stare into space," said one trainer. "It's not stupid. It's just being a cat."

Dr. Penny Patterson is a scientist well known for her work with gorillas. After she taught a gorilla named Koko

how to communicate in sign language, she wrote, "Koko gets bored with tests, and she'll do anything to change the subject."

Koko seems to feel that if she does badly enough on a test, Dr. Patterson will stop giving it to her. One of her favorite ways to fail is to stare at the right answer while she points to the wrong one.

Answers that seem right to an animal are sometimes scored as errors on tests made for people. On one kind of intelligence test, a young child is asked to point to things that are good to eat. The choices are a block, an apple, a shoe, a flower, and an ice cream sundae. When Koko was given the test, she picked the apple and the flower, which are right answers for a gorilla. But the flower is a "wrong" answer for this test.

Another question asks children to point out where they would run for shelter from the rain. The choices are a hat, a spoon, a tree, and a house. As any sensible gorilla would, Koko chose the tree. But the test wasn't made for sensible gorillas.

Intelligence is a combination of many things—thinking, learning, planning, remembering, and making decisions. Some learning comes easily to animals, while other things are impossible for them to learn. That's true of us as well.

We could no more hunt like a pod of killer whales than killer whales could write. A dog can't read, but we can't follow a trail with our noses. Each animal uses different senses to learn what it must learn in order to survive in its habitat. Some animals have a sharp sense of hearing; others have eyes that see long distances or that adjust to darkness better than those of other creatures. Animals live in many different environments—underground, in the air, underwater, in deserts, in rain forests. All these differences make it almost impossible to compare intelligence among animals.

It's not easy to understand *thought* because we can't see it or feel it. We can't know what's going on in the mind of an animal any more than we can know what another human is thinking.

What does a lion think as it stalks a wary gazelle? What does a chimpanzee think as it pokes a stick into a termite's nest? Do these animals think about anything?

Dr. Donald Griffin is famous for his studies on animal intelligence. He wrote, "It makes sense that animals can think. If an animal thinks about what it might do, even in very simple terms, it can choose the action that will help it avoid dangerous mistakes. Thinking means survival."

But even if Dr. Griffin is right, and animals do think, can they remember things that happened in the past? Can they learn, and plan ahead, and teach others in their group? Are they creative? Do they have ideas? Are they aware of what they are doing? Or are they only programmed by the built-in patterns of behavior called instinct?

Some scientists look for answers in the laboratory. Others keep watch in the wild.

Tracking the Monarch Butterflies

from *Monarch Butterflies: Mysterious Travelers*
text and photographs by Bianca Lavies

Don't be fooled by the delicate appearance of the monarch butterfly. This tiny insect is stronger than it looks.

Each year monarch butterflies travel hundreds or even thousands of miles on their paper-thin wings. Many other butterflies also migrate south for the winter. Yet only the monarchs return north each spring.

During the summer, monarchs live in the continental United States and in some areas of southern Canada. In autumn monarchs that live west of the Rocky Mountains go to the California coast. Monarchs that live east of the Rockies also take to the sky. "But where do they go to avoid the killing frosts of winter?" Bianca Lavies asks in her book Monarch Butterflies: Mysterious Travelers. *For years the answer was a mystery.*

One scientist spent most of his life searching for the eastern monarchs' winter home. Here is the story of his long search and how it ended.

Since 1937, Dr. Fred Urquhart had been trying to discover where the eastern monarchs spent their winters. He and Norah, his wife and research assistant, tagged thousands of monarchs with labels that did not impede flight. Each tag carried a number and a request to mail it to the University of Toronto, where Dr. Urquhart worked.

Eventually children and adult volunteers all over North America helped with the tagging and also reported information about labeled monarchs they found. A picture began to emerge: Most monarchs that crossed the eastern United States seemed headed for Mexico.

Norah Urquhart wrote to newspapers in Mexico, asking people there to report sightings and help with tagging.

An American named Ken Brugger wrote back from Mexico City, offering to look for monarchs as he traveled the country with his dog, Kola, in his motor home. Shortly thereafter he married Cathy, a Mexican woman. She was a great help in the search because she could question local villagers in Spanish.

Ken, Cathy, and Kola—often with a guide—spent months following steep trails in the Sierra Madre Mountains. After about a year of searching, they were trekking up a two-mile-high peak in the early morning when they noticed a few monarchs circling downward. Local woodcutters had told them of swarms of butterflies nearby. Sure enough, a little higher, the ground proved littered with monarch wings—a sign that mice, birds, and other predators had been at work.

Near the summit, the trail of broken wings veered off into a dark forest of oyamels, local fir trees. At first glimpse, it seemed the trees were clothed in layers of dead brownish black leaves. But as sunlight pierced the dense evergreen forest, Cathy and Ken saw flashes of brilliant orange. They were looking at tens of millions of monarch butterflies hanging from tree trunks and branches, and covering the ground like a thick carpet, wings closed in the cool morning air. The first monarch overwintering site in central Mexico had finally been found by researchers.

The Bruggers hurried to share the good news with the Urquharts in Canada. While waiting for them to arrange a trip down, Cathy and Ken worked every day, tagging butterflies in order to learn more about the northward migration to come. They also found more than half of the dozen or so overwintering sites that were eventually documented within a three-hundred-square-mile radius.

Some of the butterflies, like the one that has settled on Kola (*below*), showed the wear and tear of their arduous journey. The spot on each hind wing—dark scales covering a scent pouch for attracting females—identifies this one as male.

At last the Urquharts arrived in Mexico City. Together with the Bruggers and photographer Bianca Lavies, they drove one

hundred and fifty miles west into the mountains. Their rented bus wheezed and sputtered as it climbed seven thousand feet over rough, twisting roads to a small hotel surrounded by hundreds of white and red geraniums.

The next morning they drove farther up the mountain, winding through villages of simple homes gaily decorated with flowering plants. In one village they picked up their guide, Juan Sanchez (*right*). After an hour and a half the road ended, and they drove on over a flat mountain plateau. Finally they parked the bus and continued on foot, Kola always by their side.

For the next two hours they climbed a steep path, until, at ninety-eight hundred feet, they came upon a forest of tall oyamel trees. The Urquharts stared up in amazement, tears in their eyes. Here before them was the reality—astonishing and beautiful to behold—that had been the hope of a lifetime's research and hard work.

Everywhere they looked, butterflies blanketed the ground and hung from branches and tree trunks, their wings held closely together. Each time a ray of sunlight reached the butterflies, they fluttered into the sky, rising above the trees like puffs of orange-and-black smoke.

Monarchs have no internal heating system. They rely on the sun to warm them. In order not to overheat, they spread their four-inch wings and fly. By alternately basking to gain heat and flying to shed it, they regulate their body temperature. The oyamel forest high in the mountains was generally cool enough for them to remain dormant—a resting state in which little nourishment is needed—but not so cold that they would freeze.

The monarchs hook their feet onto the needles and bark of the oyamels and rest securely, side by side. The thick forest growth offers shade on sunny days, keeps the temperature from falling too low at night, and provides shelter during storms.

Sometimes the clusters of monarchs get too heavy and an overloaded branch crashes to the ground. When Dr. Urquhart sat down to have his picture taken in

the middle of just such a fallen pile of monarchs, with great good fortune his eye came to rest upon a butterfly bearing a white tag.

The tag enabled him to trace the butterfly back to Chaska, Minnesota, where, four months earlier, a teacher and his students had marked it. Traveling two thousand miles over mountains and rivers, congested cities and wide-open spaces, this featherweight flier had journeyed to the very stand of oyamels where its great-grandparents had probably overwintered—and where its great-grandchildren would, in all likelihood, arrive next year.

While the Urquharts and Bruggers were busy tagging, crackling twigs more often than not announced the arrival of cows plodding through the brush. They trampled the thick carpet of butterflies, sucking them up by the dozens with large circular sweeps of their tongues. A local farmer told Cathy Brugger that his cows got fat during the winter from eating so many monarchs.

In the chill dawn air, when the butterflies were too cold to move, birds were also a menace. The birds picked them off the upper branches, stood on the monarchs' wings, and ate their

fleshy abdomens. Butterflies with torn wings, broken antennae, and missing legs were common findings.

Spring comes early to the Sierra Madre Mountains, bringing with it the development of the females' reproductive organs and the cue to migrate once again. On warm, sunny days in January, the monarchs cluster at streams and marshy areas to drink water, a sign that they are ready to mate and head north. The females store sperm from the males, then fly off, laying fertilized eggs on milkweed plants along their route north. In about three days these eggs hatch; the adult butterflies that finally emerge also head north.

In May or early June, hardy migrant females reach the very same areas where they first nibbled milkweed leaves as caterpillars. Here they lay their last eggs, bringing to a close the eight to ten months of their migrant lives. But soon they are followed by their offspring, busily dotting the landscape with their own eggs. This generation and its offspring live only a month, however. By the end of August and early September, three or four generations are in the more northern breeding regions. Then shorter days and cooler temperatures cue the last generation. It is time to migrate. The cycle begins again.

Discovery of the Mexican overwintering grounds is considered the most important development in the study of monarch butterflies in the twentieth century. It was hoped the sites could be kept secluded, but thousands of tourists flocked to visit them. Now sanctuaries are being created by cooperating governments and wildlife groups. Logging also threatens the forest havens, however.

Elsewhere, other conditions endanger the monarchs. Herbicides are killing milkweed plants in monarchs' summer habitats and along their migration routes. Real-estate development encroaches on many of their roosting sites. Only time will tell whether or not we care enough to help the monarch butterfly ensure the survival of its species.

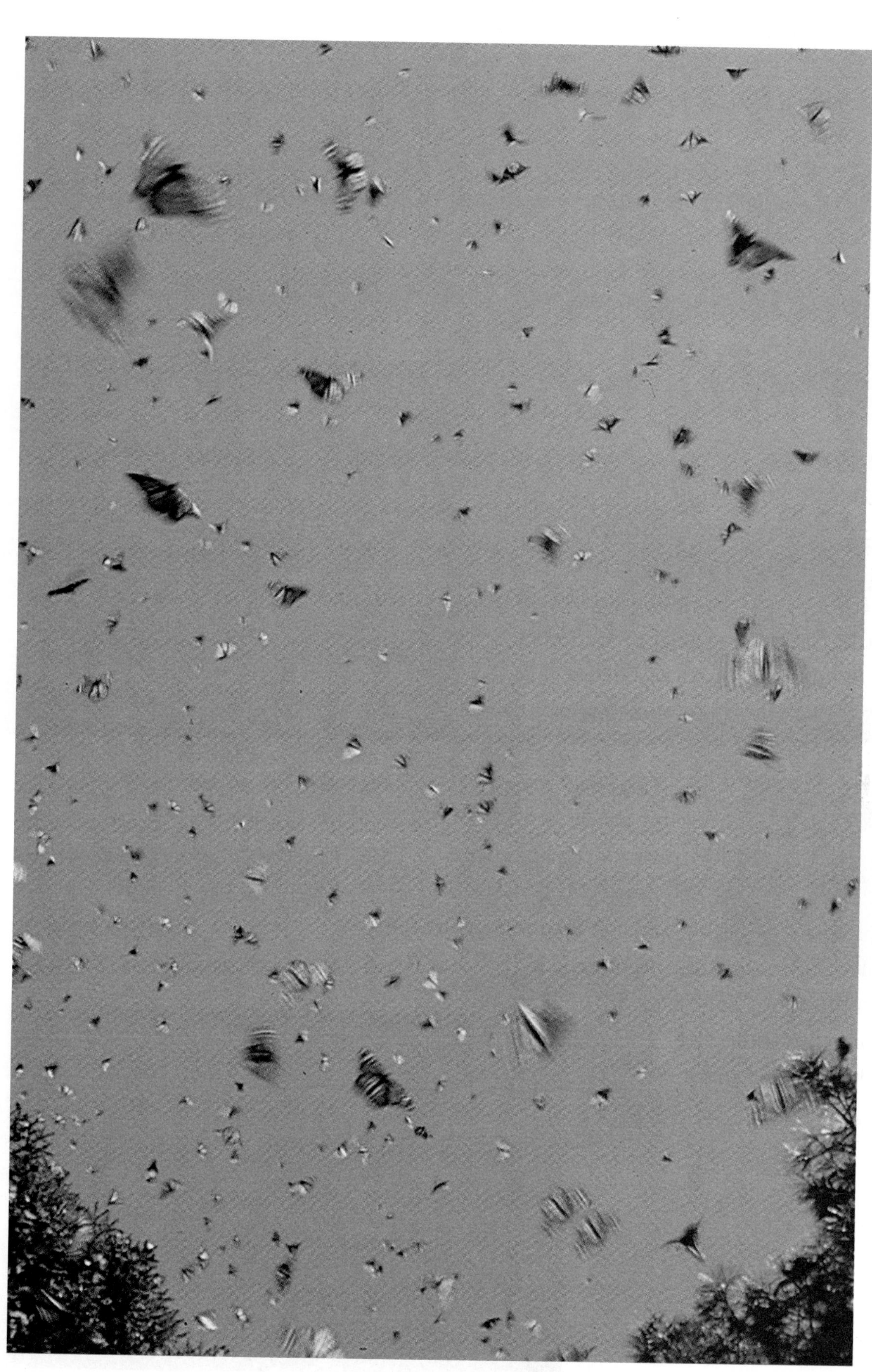

The Secret Among the Stones

by Ardath Mayhar

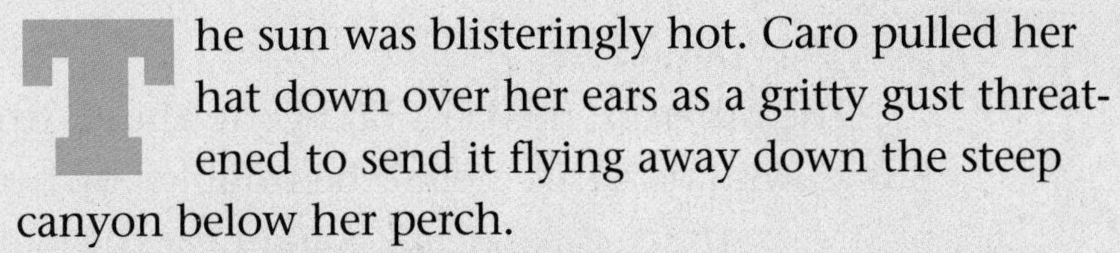

The sun was blisteringly hot. Caro pulled her hat down over her ears as a gritty gust threatened to send it flying away down the steep canyon below her perch.

The climb had been hard and dusty. She was exhausted, and she hated wearing a hat, but sitting on this gritty boulder in the desert sun without one would have been crazy.

She was almost at the top of the mesa now, the steep trail behind her leading down into shadow, for the sun was slanting toward the west already. All around was the vast expanse of broken land, flatlands shimmering with heat-haze, flat-topped mesas rising in the distance, scrub showing its dusty green wherever there was a trace or the hope of water.

The others in her class had gone ahead, led by Miss Burke, who never seemed to be troubled by heat or dust or stones in her shoes. Caro could hear the babble of their voices, but once she had the pebble out of her Nike she hated to move.

There was nothing she wanted to see up there on the tableland. Ruins, as far as she was concerned, were nothing but tumbles of rocks. She had no interest in the ancient people who had cut the stones and set them in place.

She took a sip from her canteen, thinking wryly how silly she'd thought it when Miss Burke insisted that every member of the class must have one, filled, before the bus left the motel.

The shadows beneath the height were inky in contrast to the bone-pale glare of the sun. She gazed into the depths, resting her eyes, and edges and curves came into focus.

That looked like a fascinating place down there, Caro thought. Instead of going up, which was going to be hot and tiring, she decided to go down again and cut back into the shade of the canyon. The last member of the class had already gone by, and nobody could make an objection.

Caro tied her scarf over her hat to help hold it on, made sure that her Nikes were free of pebbles, and started down. Miss Burke was entirely too far away now to notice one of her sheep going astray. The guide was leading the group. By the time anyone realized she was gone, the class would be back down on a level with her destination.

The way down was surprisingly difficult, because it was hard to see the footing. Miss Burke had cautioned everyone about walking carefully, and now Caro saw why. A misstep could send her tumbling down the steep path to splatter on the rocks below.

She felt her way cautiously, watching her feet, freezing when she heard a slithery sound that might be a snake. It turned out to be a dust-colored lizard, but she found her heart thudding hard and hot liquid rising in her throat. What if it *had* been a rattlesnake? She shivered and went even more slowly.

At the bottom of the slope the raw-edged cut, which her party had ignored before, led into a walled space opening out into a wider area. The sandy grit of the floor was swept into riffles by the wind pulled through the corridor in the rock; she had a strange feeling that no human being had ever set foot there.

Now that she was out of the sun, Caro's eyes adjusted to the dimness. Someone had been here after all. There were markings on the walls, random doodlings as if someone had occupied him- or herself by drawing circles and jagged lines of lightning and stick figures. She went close and stared up at the pictures, which must have been drawn by someone much taller than she.

There was a story there, she thought, running her gaze along the wall of the canyon. There had been a terrible rain—the slanting dashes couldn't be anything else. Then the sun had cooked everything, for she could see horned shapes that had to be the skulls of buffalo and crosshatched marks that might mean the ground had cracked with drought. There were sketchy shapes of buffalo and deer and men holding sticks and bows.

Interesting. Caro was glad she had stopped and let the others go on without her. She had seen many pictures of the ruins on top of the mesa, but she'd never seen anything about this slot of canyon with drawings on its walls.

She moved back and forth across the space, checking for further markings, but there were no more. Instead, she saw a cave cut back into the eastern wall, its

entrance so low that even she would have to stoop and crawl to get inside. A good place for snakes, Caro suspected, but even so she bent to stare into the dark recess.

There was something inside. A bundle of cloth? A stick? Something else, hard to see in the depths where it lay.

Score another for Miss Burke. She had dictated the contents of each hiker's pack, and there had to be a small flashlight and spare batteries. Caro had considered it silly, carrying all this stuff for miles up and down desert heights, but now she had a light.

She thumbed the button, and the narrow beam flicked into the little cave. She gave a stifled shriek and fell back to sit in the grit, staring at the thing that looked back at her from hollow eye sockets. She was almost eye to eye with a skull.

Feeling a chill of terror, Caro shivered, but she didn't retreat. Now she could see that the bundle was clothing of some kind. The stick was a leg bone, which she recognized only because they had studied bones in science last month.

The skull was small, not any larger than her own, she thought. Wisps of black hair straggled from its crown, and it lay on the dusty remnants of a long braid. Even a fragment of a feather still clung to the strands.

Caro had a sudden feeling that this had been a girl, just like herself. Had she been trapped here and starved to death? The entry into the canyon looked raw, as if it had recently been cracked open by some shifting of the rock. Could it have been another such shift that caught this one here?

But surely there was another end to the canyon. . . . She scrambled upright and ran to see.

The space ended after a dozen winding yards at a wall of rock that went up and up, as smoothly as if it had been sliced with a knife. There wasn't a handhold to be seen. Suddenly sure that she was right—the girl had been trapped—Caro returned to the cave and sat down on a flat stone to stare, fascinated and repelled, at her find.

This was a well-known area in a national park. Surely the archeologists had known about this place for years and had studied those markings and measured this pitiful remnant of humanity. Yet if that were so, why hadn't they removed it to a museum or something? It didn't make much sense.

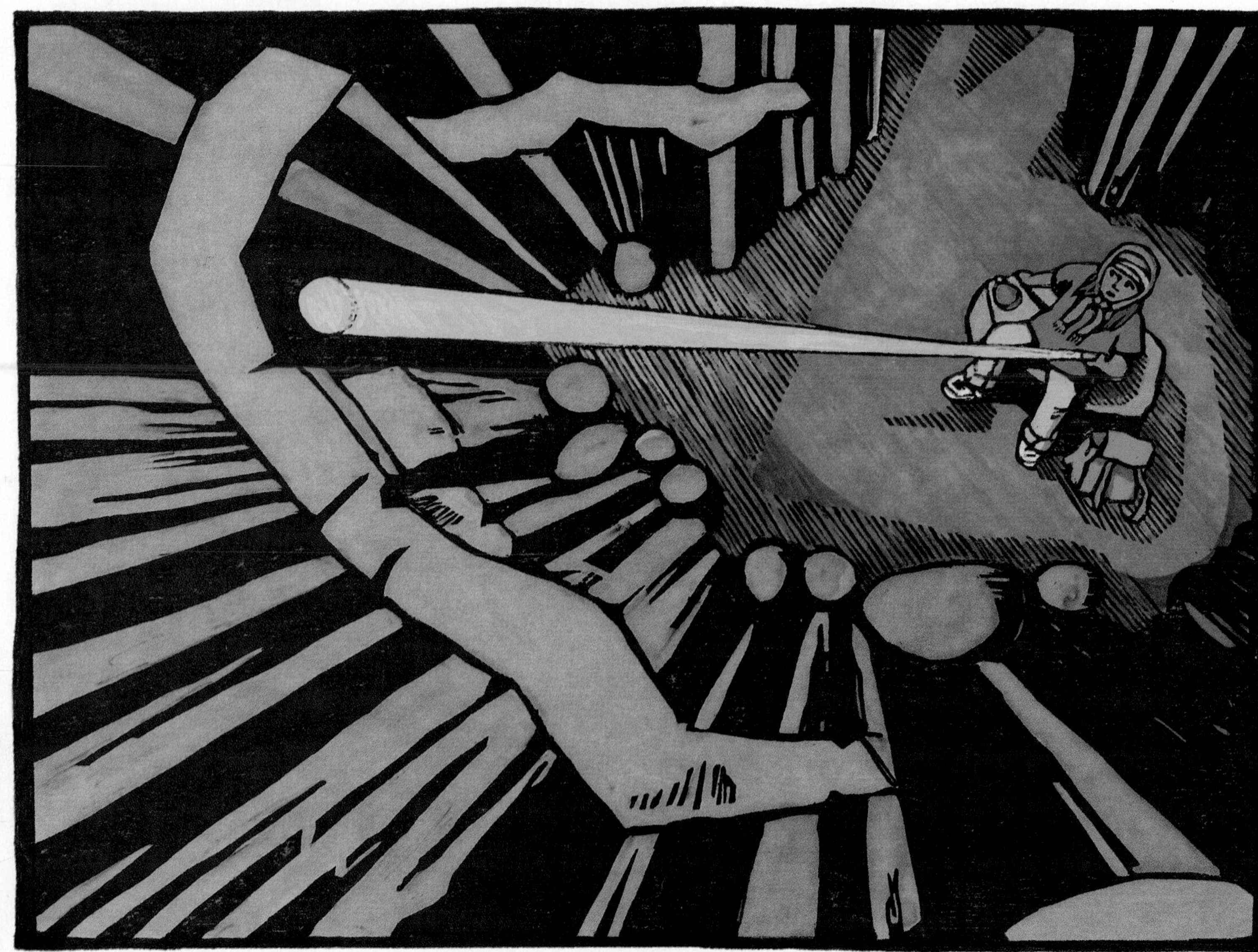

The canyon was warmer than she had expected, and Caro took off her hat and fanned herself as she sat in the shadow of the cliff, trying to decide what to do. The skull gazed with mournful intensity into the beam of her flash. The teeth were small, even, not jagged and stained like those of the museum skulls. This had to be a child about her own age, twelve or so.

Caro searched the interior of the space with her light, but she could see no movement that might be a snake. No scorpion sidled out of range. She felt compelled, though she had no idea why, to venture in and sort out this discovery.

"I am not brave," she said, marveling at the impulse. "I can't stand spiders or blood or anything my brothers like. But I have got to see what's in there. This is *mine!*"

Laying aside her hat, she went down on hands and knees, holding the flash in her teeth. She moved into the cramped space. It was low and dry, and smelled of dust and something very, very old. Not a dead smell, but a snuffy, acrid one.

When she was within a few feet of the pitiful little body, she stopped and looked at it, holding herself still with an effort. Behind the bundle of clothing was another leg bone, bent at the knee. A fall of finger bones extended from beneath a flap of leather sleeve, and something bright—beads?—decorated the upper part of the garment.

Caro knew better than to touch anything, but she felt it couldn't hurt to see it all, now that she had begun. She crawled forward and peered into the shadow behind the bundle of clothing. A small shape lay beside the other skeletal hand.

This was easily identified: a doll, made of a stick, with some sort of fur for hair and a leather dress. Two stick legs extended from beneath the dusty skirt.

Caro breathed a long sigh and settled onto the floor of the cave, knowing she had been right. She closed her eyes and saw, as if she were there, a little girl dressed in leather, playing in this shady place with her doll.

The vision seemed true and real, and she clicked off the flashlight, gazing into that distant past. The child was singing softly, a sort of chant, as she rocked the doll in her arms.

"Ai-hi-yee! Ai-hi-yee!" echoed in Caro's mind.

This was a secret place, Caro thought, forgotten by the child's elders, though the markings on the walls showed that others had known it. She came here, as Caro often went to her own secret place beyond the rock formation at home, to think, to dream, to sing to her doll.

As Caro watched that vision, the dream-sky darkened, making the canyon go black as night. Lightning scarred the upper air, its flash brightening the canyon in short bursts. There came a terrific blast of sound, followed by a rumble and a roar.

Terror filled her, and Caro opened her eyes and clicked on the flashlight again. The little shape lay still, its shadow harsh behind it, and Caro knew she had dreamed truly. This child had been trapped here by a rockslide caused, perhaps, by a lightning strike; no one among her people had known where to search for her.

"Did you starve to death?" She shivered. "Were you even more afraid than I was, just now?" Caro murmured, bending forward to lay a comforting hand on the leather sleeve.

Where she touched it, the ancient material powdered away to dust, leaving the slender arm bones exposed. Caro sighed. No, she mustn't touch anything else. She had to get Miss Burke, even if it meant climbing to the top of the mesa to report this discovery.

She felt sure the most recent storm, with the landslips and rockslides it had set off a few weeks back, must have opened the way that an ancient catastrophe had closed. There had been something on the news about an earth tremor caused by water going down into crevices in the mesas.

She backed out and retrieved her hat. Then Caro hurried to find her teacher, who knew what to do about everything. She met the group coming down the mesa, calling her name anxiously and searching every crevice into which she might have fallen.

"Oh, Miss Burke! I'm not lost, just out of pocket. I've found something awful and wonderful!" she panted.

"Carolyn, I cannot have my charges running off in country like this! It's dangerous. . . . *What* have you found?" Miss Burke was an amateur archeologist, and any hint of ancient finds caught her attention instantly.

By the time she saw the newly opened way into the canyon and the small bones in the cave, Miss Burke was as excited as she ever allowed herself to become. "I will inform the Rangers as soon as we get back to the motel," she said, her gaze fixed longingly on the half-visible bundle beneath the cliff.

She turned to José, who had been the guide for this field trip. "It will surprise me if this is not extremely unusual. Not because of the skeleton, of course, but because of the petroglyphs."

He stared into the cave, still looking astonished. "I think maybe you are right," he said. "We will call the University when we have the chance."

Caro felt sure this was something really important. She had a vision of returning in triumph to the scene of her discovery. The Carolyn Wheaton Canyon Area had a nice ring to it. She had a sudden vision of her triumph, lights, reporters, awed schoolmates and teachers.

Then she thought of that dark cave where the small skeleton still lay, heard again in her memory the devastating thunder, felt again the cold despair that had touched her as she crouched in that place.

There was tragedy here, not triumph. The fame that might come of it was not hers at all.

"Ai-hi-yee!" she whispered, as she bent to look through the dimness into those empty eyes once more. "Ai-hi-yee!"

The small, even teeth grinned at her silently.

Caro smiled back. She had done her best for this lost one. Maybe—who could say?—this girl knew at last that she was no longer alone.

IN RESPONSE

Plan a Field Trip

If you were Miss Burke, how would you plan next year's field trip? With a partner, look back at Caro's experiences for ideas. Present your plan to the class. Include any new rules you want students to follow. Also, tell students which items to bring and why they may need them.

Different Discoveries

Compare Caro's adventure to the discovery of the monarchs' winter home ("Tracking the Monarch Butterflies"). Who does a better job of looking below the surface to solve a mystery—Caro or the Urquharts? Write your answer. Include details from the selections.

AUTHOR AT WORK

Ardath Mayhar writes the kinds of books she loves to read: science fiction, fantasy, and Western novels. In addition, the author has published stories and novels for middle-grade readers.

Ms. Mayhar was researching the Anasazi cliff dwellers of Mesa Verde, Colorado, when she decided to write "The Secret Among the Stones." She says, "The deeper I dug, the greater my fascination became."

Other Books by . . .

Ardath Mayhar

Carrots and Miggle by Ardath Mayhar, Atheneum, 1986

Medicine Walk by Ardath Mayhar, Atheneum, 1985

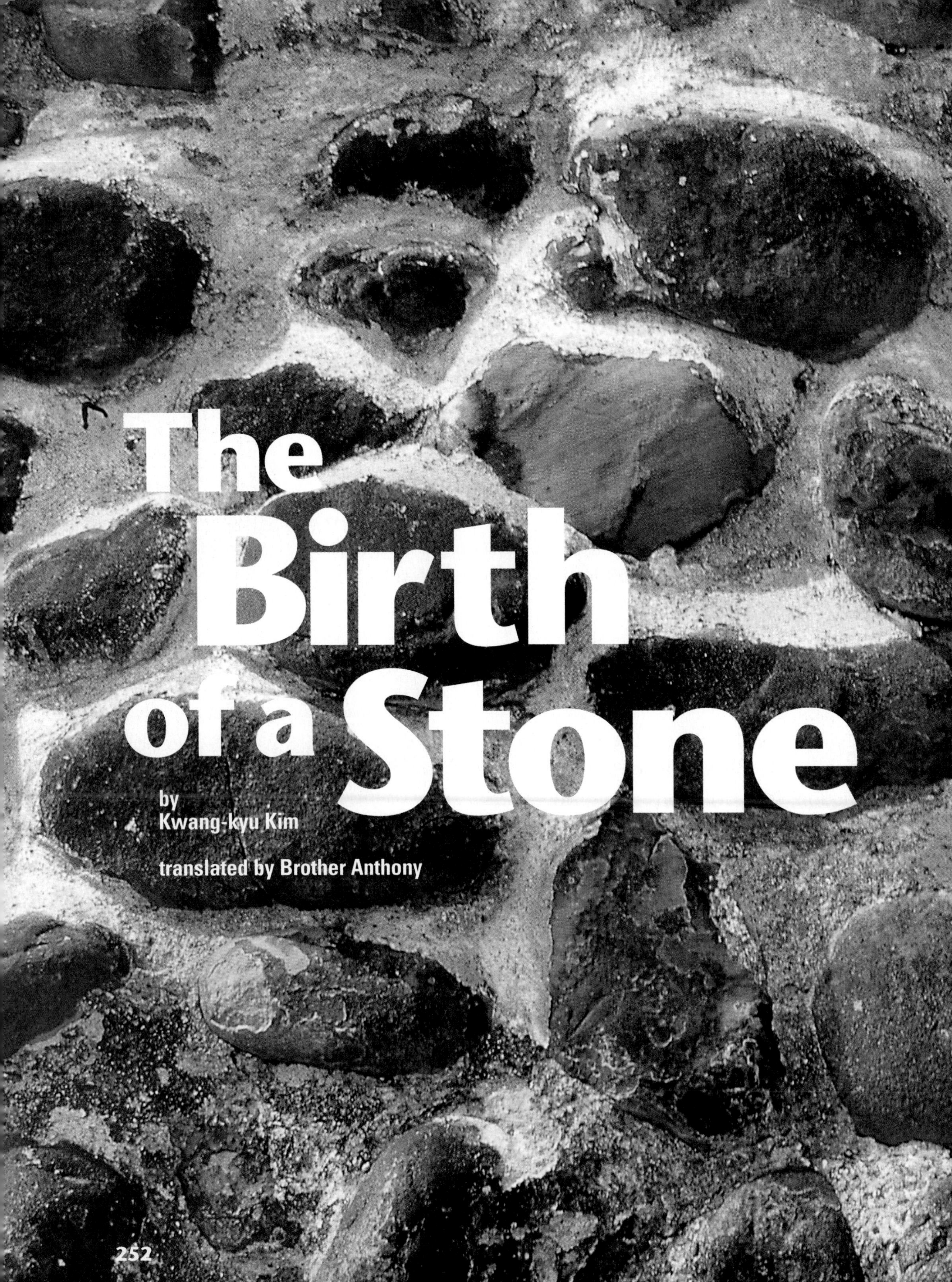

The Birth of a Stone

by
Kwang-kyu Kim

translated by Brother Anthony

In those deep mountain ravines
I wonder if there are stones
that no one has ever visited?
I went up the mountain
in quest of a stone no one had ever seen
from the remotest of times

Under ancient pines
on steep pathless slopes
there was a stone
I wonder
how long
this stone all thick with moss
has been
here?

Two thousand years? Two million? Two billion?
No
Not at all
If really till now no one
has ever seen this stone
it is only
here
from now on
This stone
was only born
the moment I first saw it

Return to the Titanic

from *Exploring the Titanic* by Robert D. Ballard
illustrations of the *Titanic* by Ken Marschall

People said the Titanic, *a luxurious steamship, was unsinkable. On its first voyage in 1912, the* Titanic *sank, killing more than fifteen hundred people. For nearly seventy-five years, the wreckage lay hidden at the bottom of the Atlantic Ocean. Then, in 1985, a team of French and American scientists used a robot to find the* Titanic. *Dr. Robert Ballard, one of the American scientists, returned a year later to explore the ship's remains.*

With a big grin, I turned and gave the "thumbs up" sign for good luck to the crew standing on the deck of our new research ship, *Atlantis II.* In stocking feet I began to climb down the ladder inside *Alvin,* our tiny submarine. It was July 13, 1986, almost a year after our French-American expedition had first found the *Titanic* and taken photographs of her. Unfortunately, our French colleagues were not able to join us this year. I would miss my friend Jean-Louis.

We had steamed out to where the *Titanic* lay in the treacherous North Atlantic. Now it was time to take a closer look at her.

Our goal was to dive two and a half miles into the pitch-black freezing depths to where the *Titanic* lay. Then we would try to land *Alvin* on her decks. If all went well, we would be the first human beings in seventy-four years to see the legendary ship at close range.

We closed *Alvin*'s hatch, and I exchanged glances with my pilot and co-pilot as we felt our submarine gently rocking back and forth. We knew that meant we were now dangling half over the deck of *Atlantis II* and half over the water—one of the most dangerous moments of a dive. Should the sub suddenly fall, we could all get badly hurt.

But we hit the water safely. Then our lift line was released, and divers swarmed over the sub checking everything, including *Jason Junior*, or *JJ*. *JJ* was our remote-controlled underwater robot, who was attached to the outside of *Alvin* in a special garage. He operated on a long cable attached to our sub and was equipped with still and video cameras. With his help we hoped to explore inside the wreck below.

The three of us were crammed into the tiny cabin, our inner space capsule. Hemmed in by panels of instruments, we had no room to stretch out or stand up. We were like three sardines in a

Inside the *Alvin*'s cramped pressure sphere, pilot Dudley Foster checks the submarine's depth while I talk to the *Atlantis II* on the underwater telephone.

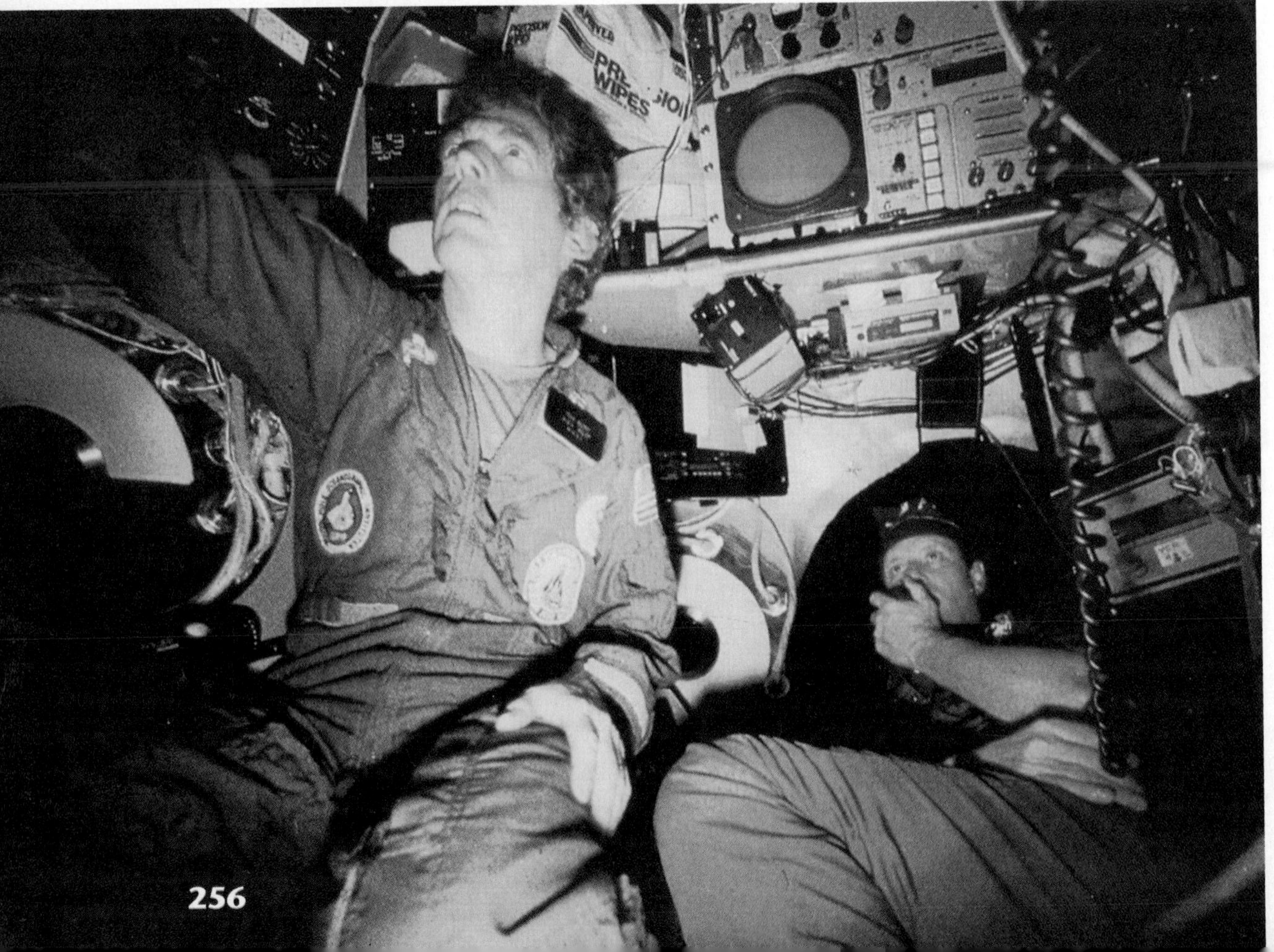

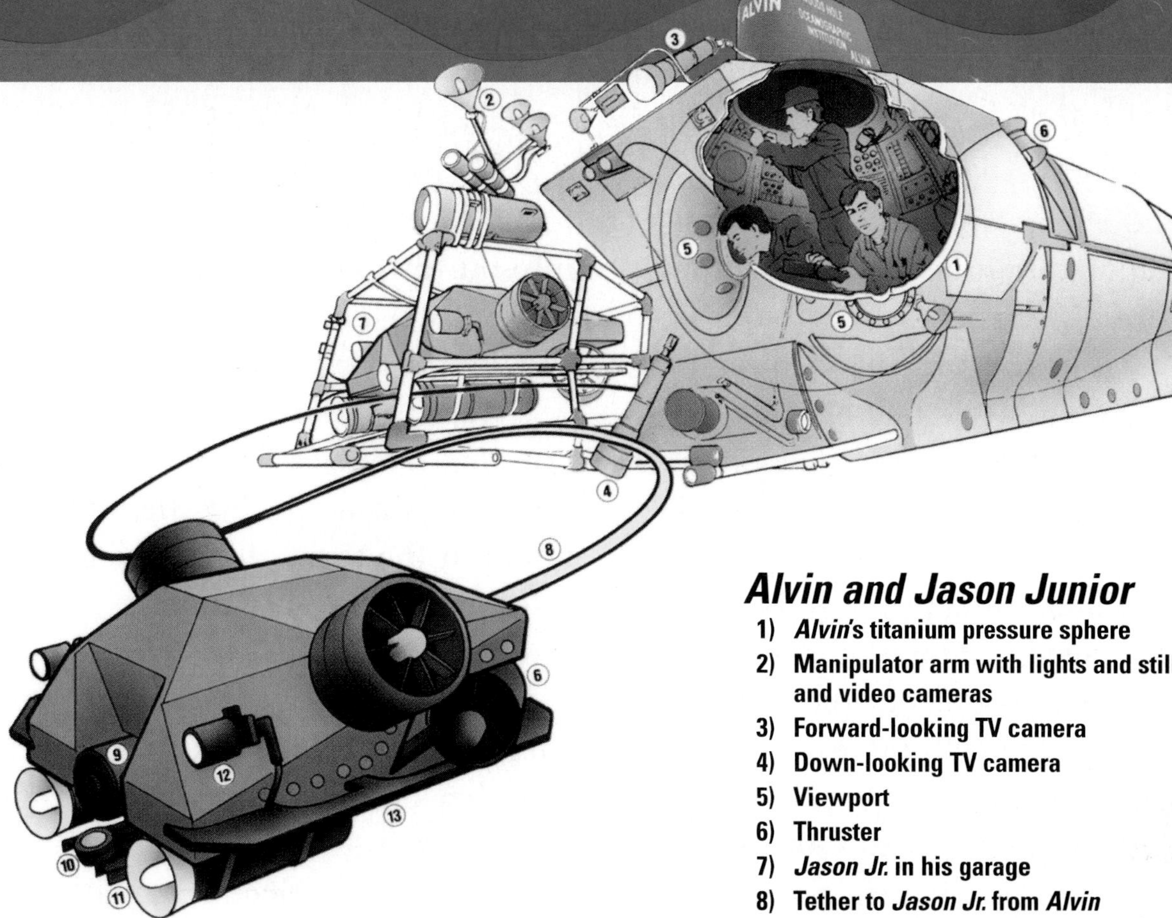

Alvin* and *Jason Junior

1) ***Alvin*'s titanium pressure sphere**
2) **Manipulator arm with lights and still and video cameras**
3) **Forward-looking TV camera**
4) **Down-looking TV camera**
5) **Viewport**
6) **Thruster**
7) ***Jason Jr.* in his garage**
8) **Tether to *Jason Jr.* from *Alvin***
9) **Still and video cameras**
10) **Compass**
11) **Strobe light**
12) **Light**
13) **Docking rail**

spherical can. It was warm and stuffy, but the ice-cold water outside would soon cool *Alvin*'s hull, both outside and inside.

Daylight began to fade into deeper and deeper blues as our sub reached its maximum descent speed of 100 feet per minute. It would take us two and a half hours to reach the bottom. There was little talking as we fell swiftly into utter darkness. Soft music played on the sub's stereo.

Suddenly, a white-tipped shark appeared outside my window and disappeared just as quickly. Sharks often swim by *Alvin* to investigate the noise. It was comforting to know that two inches of metal protected us. I remembered the time a swordfish had attacked *Alvin* and got its sword stuck in the sub.

The long fall to the bottom is usually a lulling experience. The interior gets darker and darker and begins to cool until, after less than fifteen minutes, the sub has reached a depth of 1,200 feet and total darkness.

To conserve power, *Alvin*'s outside lights are left off. The only illumination inside comes from three small red lights.

But this time we had technical problems to worry about. First, we discovered that *Alvin*'s sonar had stopped working. Probably either the cold seawater or the increasing pressure had damaged it. Sonar guided us by bouncing electronic sound waves off anything in our path. Without sonar we couldn't see beyond a few yards. Our surface navigator on board *Atlantis II* would have to guide us to the *Titanic* with his sonar and our sub-to-ship telephone.

A few minutes later, at about 2,000 feet, we passed through what is known as a deep-scattering layer, because it shows up like a cloudy blur on sonar. In fact, the cloud is made up of thousands and thousands of tiny creatures that live at this depth of the ocean. Many of them glow in the dark, their small bodies exploding like fireworks as they become aware of our presence. When I first saw these creatures, they reminded me of a tiny passenger train with lighted windows passing by at night.

By the time we had passed 5,000 feet, almost one hour into our dive, it was getting cold in the sub. We put on our first layers of extra clothing. I was wearing a wool hat from my sons' hockey team to keep my head warm. During the long hours in the tiny cabin, my legs often fell asleep, and sometimes I'd get a bad cramp in my hip. At times like that, *Alvin*'s cabin was more like a torture chamber than a space capsule.

Ten minutes later, at 6,000 feet, our pilot noticed that the instrument panel was showing a saltwater leak into the battery banks that power the sub. Our time on the bottom of the ocean would have to be awfully short today. And to make things even worse, the surface navigator's sonar suddenly stopped working. That meant we were now almost completely blind.

Our lights pierced the blackness as the ocean bottom slowly emerged from the dark-green gloom below us. We'd arrived. The only trouble was, we didn't know where we were. All we could see through the portholes was our own shadow cast by *Alvin*'s lights, and some gently rolling ground covered with mud.

So close and yet so far away. The ship lay somewhere near us, probably no more than 400 feet—the length of two city blocks. But when you're more than two miles down in black murk, a few hundred feet without any guiding sonar might as well be a thousand miles.

I couldn't believe it. I'd waited thirteen long years for this moment, and now, a stone's throw away from my dream, I was trapped inside a sardine can on my hands and knees staring at nothing but mud.

Suddenly, a head-splitting alarm buzzer pierced the silence inside our tiny sub. The leak in our battery was getting to the critical point. We had very little time left if we were to get back to the surface without damaging *Alvin.* Quickly, we decided to guess where the *Titanic* might be and blindly go there in a last-ditch throw of the dice.

437 ft/133m
This is the deepest a scuba diver has ever gone.

1,500 ft/465 m
Naval submarines dive no deeper than this. There is no light below this level.

3,028 ft/940 m
Pioneer underwater explorers William Beebe and Otis Barton reached this depth in a ball-shaped bathysphere in 1930.

1 mile/1,609 m
Many sea creatures here are transparent or can glow in the dark.

2 miles/3,218 m
The water temperature at this depth stays a few degrees above the freezing point.

12,460 ft/3,965 m
The water pressure where the Titanic lies is approximately 6,000 lbs per square inch.

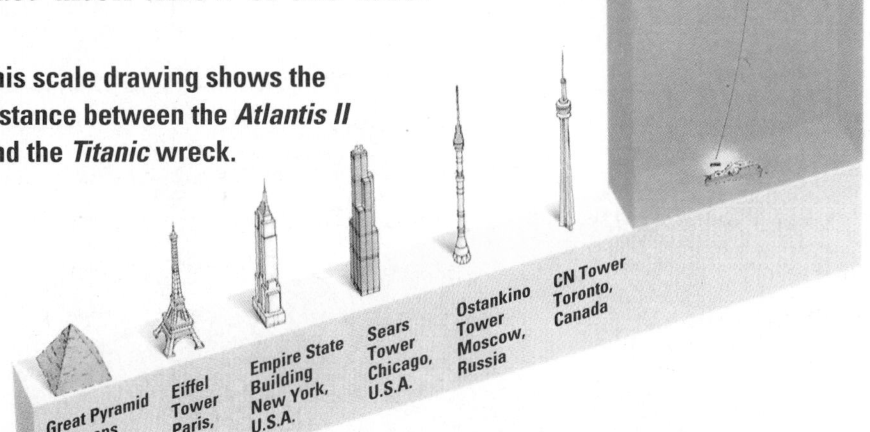

This scale drawing shows the distance between the *Atlantis II* and the *Titanic* wreck.

Alvin now gently touched the bottom with its single runner, like a one-legged skier, and we began to inch along. The shrill alarm was starting to drive us crazy, and the tension in the sub was heavy. Our time was running out fast. It was going to be a very close call if we hoped to see the *Titanic*.

Then our surface navigator called in on the telephone with the good news that his sonar was working again, and that "the *Titanic* should be about fifty yards west of us."

We turned the sub and strained our eyes to see out the portholes. Now the bottom began to look strange. It began to slope sharply upward, as though it had been bulldozed into place. My heartbeat quickened.

"Come right," I said to the pilot. "I think I see a wall of black just on the other side of that mud mound."

Then, directly in front of us, there it was: an endless slab of rusted steel rising out of the bottom—the massive hull of the *Titanic*! I felt like a space voyager peering at an alien city wall on some empty planet. Slowly, I let out my breath; I didn't realize I had been holding it.

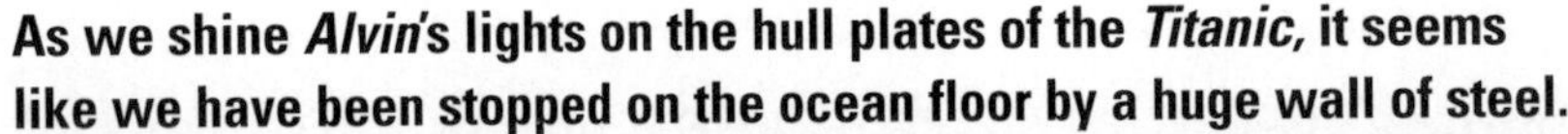

As we shine *Alvin*'s lights on the hull plates of the *Titanic,* it seems like we have been stopped on the ocean floor by a huge wall of steel.

As *Alvin*'s lights glow from above, *Jason Junior* explores the *Titanic*'s starboard anchor.

But one look at the fabulous wreck was all I got. Our pilot quickly dropped *Alvin*'s weights, clicked off that horrible alarm, and we went hurtling toward the surface. One moment longer on the bottom, and *Alvin*'s power system would have been in extreme danger.

All we had to show for six hours' work was a brief glimpse of the *Titanic*. But my dream had finally come true.

I was in a grim mood when I stepped out of the sub onto the deck of the *Atlantis II*. "I saw the ship for about ten seconds," I said. "But we've got a sick puppy here, and we've got to fix it." If we wanted to dive the next day, we had to take care of our growing list of technical problems. While I slept, our team of experts worked through the night to cure our sick submarine.

Luckily it was all systems go the next morning, and we were full of confidence as we began a second dive. Our goal was to check out possible landing sites for *Alvin* on the decks of the *Titanic*.

Our second view of the *Titanic* was breathtaking. As we glided soundlessly across the ocean bottom, the razor's edge of the bow loomed out of the darkness. The great ship towered above us. Suddenly it seemed to be coming right at us, about to run us over. My first reaction was that we had to get out of the way. But the

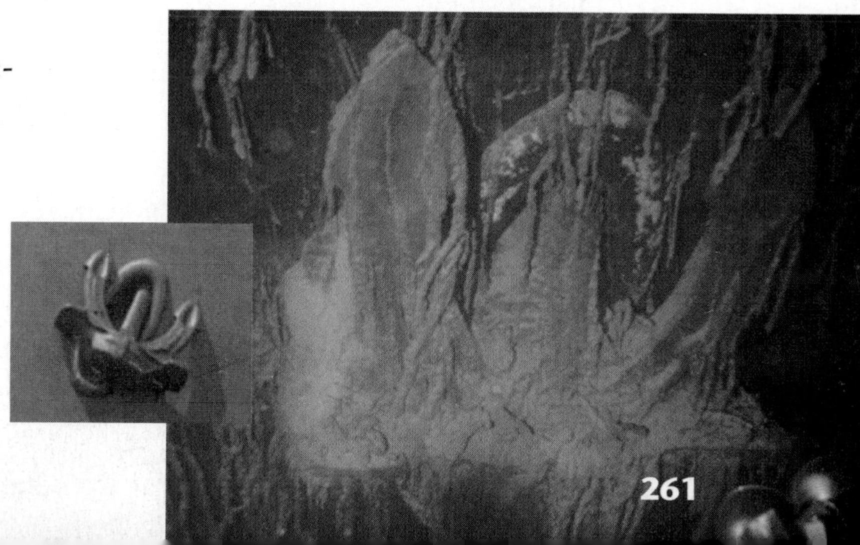

The port anchor as it appeared when the *Titanic* was launched (*inset*). At right, the port anchor today, encrusted with rust.

Titanic wasn't going anywhere. As we gently brought our sub closer, we could see the bow more clearly. Both of her huge anchors were still in place. But the bow was buried more than sixty feet in mud, far too deep for anyone to pull her out of the ooze.

It looked as though the metal hull was slowly melting away. What seemed like frozen rivers of rust covered the ship's side and spread out over the ocean bottom. It was almost as if the blood of the great ship lay in pools on the ocean floor.

As *Alvin* rose in slow motion up the ghostly side of the ship, I could see our lights reflecting off the still-unbroken glass of the *Titanic*'s portholes. They made me think of cats' eyes gleaming in the dark. In places the rust formations over the portholes looked like eye-lashes with tears, as though the *Titanic* were crying. I could also see a lot of reddish-brown stalactites of rust over the wreck, like long icicles. I decided to call them "rusticles." This rust turned out to be very fragile. If touched by our sub, it disappeared like a cloud of smoke.

As we rose further and began to move across the mighty forward deck, I was amazed at the sheer size of everything: giant bollards and shiny bronze capstans that were used for winding ropes and cables; the huge links of the anchor chains. When you were there on the spot, the ship was truly titanic.

I strained to get a good look at the deck's wood planking, just four feet below us. Then my heart dropped to my stomach. "It's gone!" I muttered. Most of the *Titanic*'s wooden deck had been eaten away. Millions of little wood-eating worms had done more damage than the iceberg and the salt water. I began to wonder whether the metal deck below the destroyed wood planking would support our weight when *Alvin* landed.

We would soon find out. Slowly we moved into position to make our first landing test on the forward deck just next to the fallen mast. As we made our approach, our hearts beat quickly. We knew there was a real risk of crashing through the deck. The sub settled down, making a muffled crunching noise. If the deck gave way, we'd be trapped in collapsing wreckage. But it held, and we settled firmly. That meant there was a good chance that the *Titanic*'s decks would support us at other landing sites.

We carefully lifted off and turned toward the stern. The dim outline of the ship's superstructure came into view: first B Deck, then A, finally the Boat Deck—the top deck where the bridge was located. It was here that the captain and his officers had guided the ship across the Atlantic. The wooden wheelhouse was gone, probably knocked away in the sinking. But the bronze telemotor control to which the ship's wheel had once been attached stood intact, polished to a shine by the current. We then safely tested this second landing site.

I had an eerie feeling as we glided along exploring the wreck. As I peered through my porthole, I could easily imagine people walking along the deck and looking out the windows of the ship that I was looking into. Here I was at the bottom of the ocean looking at a kind of time capsule from history.

Suddenly, as we rose up the port side of the ship, the sub shuddered and made a clanging noise. A waterfall of rust covered our portholes. "We've hit something!" I exclaimed. "What is it?"

***Jason Junior* illuminates a pillar still standing in the foyer of the Grand Staircase. *Alvin* has landed on the Boat Deck beside the collapsed roof that once held the glass dome over the staircase. From inside the submarine we guide *JJ* down the staircase shaft as far as B Deck.**

"I don't know," our pilot replied. "I'm backing off." Unseen overhangs are the nightmare of the deep-sub pilot. Carefully, the pilot backed away from the hull and brought us slowly upward. Then, directly in front of our forward port-hole, a big lifeboat davit slid by. We had hit one of the metal arms that held the lifeboats as they were lowered. This davit was one of the two that had held boat No. 8, the boat Mrs. Straus had refused to enter that night. She was the wife of the owner of Macy's department store in New York. When she had been offered a chance to save herself in one of the lifeboats, she had turned to her husband and said, "We have been living together for many years. Where you go, I go." Calmly, the two of them had sat down on a pile of deck chairs to wait for the end.

Now, as we peered out our portholes, it seemed as if the Boat Deck were crowded with passengers. I could almost hear the cry, "Women and children first!"

We knew from the previous year's pictures that the stern had broken off the ship, so we continued back to search for the severed end of the intact bow section. Just beyond the gaping hole where the second funnel had been, the deck began to plunge down at a dangerous angle. The graceful lines of the ship disappeared in a twisted mess of torn steel plating, upturned portholes, and jumbled wreckage. We saw enough to know that the decks of the ship had collapsed in on one another like a giant accordion. With an unexpectedly strong current pushing us toward this twisted wreckage, we veered away and headed for the surface.

The next day we landed on the deck next to the very edge of the Grand Staircase, which had once been covered by an elegant glass dome. The dome hadn't

The Grand Staircase as it appeared in 1912

survived the plunge, but the staircase shaft had, and to me it still represented the fabulous luxury of the ship. *Alvin* now rested quietly on the top deck of the R.M.S. *Titanic* directly above the place where three elevators had carried first-class passengers who did not wish to use the splendid Grand Staircase.

We, however, would take the stairs with *JJ* the robot, our R2D2 of the deep. This would be the first deep-water test for our remote-controlled swimming eyeball, and we were very nervous about it. No one knew whether *JJ*'s motors could stand up to the enormous ocean pressure of more than 6,000 pounds per square inch.

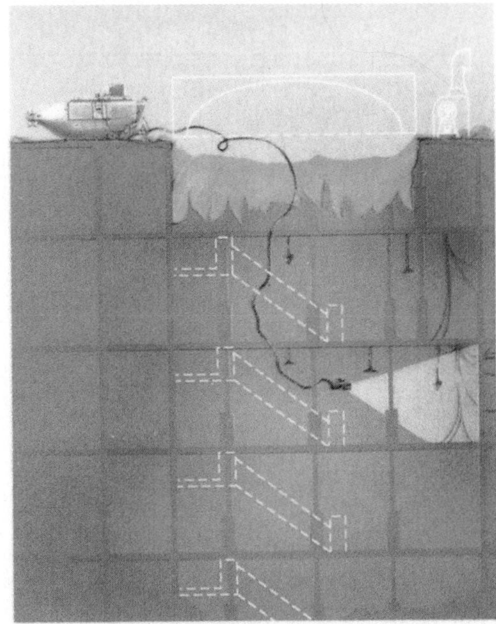

The illustration shows a cross-section of *JJ*'s descent, with an outline of the original staircase.

Traces of the staircase's former elegance can be seen in the light fixture from which a piece of coral has sprouted.

Using a control box with a joystick that operated like a video game, the operator cautiously steered *JJ* out of his garage attached to the front of *Alvin.* Slowly *JJ* went inching down into the yawning blackness of the Grand Staircase. More and more cable was let out as he dropped deeper and deeper.

We could see what *JJ* was seeing on our video in the sub. But at first *JJ* could see nothing. Then, as he dropped deeper, a room appeared off the port-side foyer on A Deck. *JJ* swung around and our co-pilot saw something in the distance. "Look at that," he said softly. "Look at that chandelier."

Now I could see it, too. "No, it can't be a chandelier," I said. "It couldn't possibly have survived."

I couldn't believe my eyes. The ship had fallen two and a half miles, hitting the bottom with the force of a train running into a mountain, and here was an almost perfectly preserved light fixture! *JJ* left the stairwell and started to enter the room, managing to get within a foot of the fixture. To our astonishment, we saw a feathery piece of coral sprouting from it. We could even see the sockets where the light bulbs had been fitted! "This is fantastic," I exulted.

Top: A window from Captain Smith's quarters.
Bottom: JJ tries to go in for a closer look.

"Bob, we're running short of time. We have to return to the surface." Our pilot's words cut like a knife through my excitement. Here we were deep inside the *Titanic,* actually going down the Grand Staircase, but we had used up all the time that we had to stay safely on the bottom. I knew our pilot was just following orders, but I still wanted to shout in protest.

Our little robot soldier emerged from the black hole and shone his lights toward us, bathing the interior of the sub in an unearthly glow. For a moment it felt as if an alien spaceship were hovering nearby. But that feeling quickly gave way to one of victory, thanks to our little friend. *JJ* had been a complete success.

On our next day's dive, we crossed over what had once been Captain Smith's cabin. Its outer wall now lay collapsed on

The *Titanic's* Bridge in 1986

With its wheelhouse washed away and the foremast lying across it, the bridge is a changed scene today.

1) Telemotor without wheel
2) Remains of base of wheelhouse
3) Fallen foremast
4) Mast light
5) Dislodged lifeboat davits
6) First-class staterooms
7) Collapsed bridge cab
8) Hole where forward funnel stood
9) No. 2 lifeboat davit
10) Cargo cranes
11) Cargo hatch No. 3

The wooden ship's wheel (*far left*) has disappeared but its bronze telemotor control (*left*) still stands on the bridge.

The ghostly open window of a first-class stateroom

Jason Jr. now went for a stroll along the Boat Deck. As he slowly made his way along, he looked in the windows of several first-class cabins as well as into some passageways, including one that still bore the words, "First-Class Entrance." As *JJ* passed by the gymnasium windows, I could see bits and pieces of equipment amid the rubble, including some metal grillwork that had been part of the electric camel, an old-fashioned exercise machine. We could also see various wheel shapes and a control lever. Much of the gym's ceiling was covered with rust. This was where the gym instructor, dressed in white flannel trousers, had urged passengers to try the gym machines. And, on the last night, passengers had gathered here for warmth as the lifeboats were being lowered.

I could see *JJ* far off down the deck, turning this way and that to get a better view inside doorways and various windows. It was almost as though our little robot had a mind of his own.

But now we had to bring him home. We had been on the *Titanic* for hours. Once again it was time to head back to the surface.

The morning of July 18 was lovely and warm, but I felt edgy about the day's mission. We had decided to visit the *Titanic*'s debris field. Along the 1,970 feet that separated the broken-off bow and stern pieces of the wreck, there was a large scattering of all kinds of objects from the ship. Everything from lumps of coal to wrought-iron deck benches had fallen to the bottom as she broke in two and sank. But I was anxious about what we might find down there among the rubble. I had often been asked about the possibility of finding human bodies. It was a chilling thought. We had not seen any signs of human remains so far, but I knew that if we were to find any, it would most likely be during this dive.

***JJ* looks in one of the gymnasium windows. (*Inset*) The gymnasium in 1912.**

As the first fragments of wreckage began to appear on the bottom, I felt like we were entering a bombed-out museum. Thousands upon thousands of objects littered the rolling fields of ocean bottom, many of them perfectly preserved. The guts of the *Titanic* lay spilled out across the ocean floor. Cups and saucers, silver serving trays, pots and pans, wine bottles, boots, chamber pots, space heaters, bathtubs, suitcases, and more.

Then, without warning, I found myself looking into the ghostly eyes of a small, white smiling face. For a split second I thought it was a skull—and it really scared me. Then I realized I was looking at a doll's head, its hair and clothes gone.

My shock turned to sadness as I began to wonder who had owned this toy. Had the girl survived in one of the lifeboats? Or had she clutched the doll tightly as she sank in the icy waters?

We moved on through this amazing scenery. There were so many things scattered about that it became difficult to keep track of them. We came across one of the ship's boilers, and there on top of it sat an upright rusty metal cup like the ones the crew had used. It looked as though it had been placed there by a stoker moments before water had burst into the boiler room. It was astonishing to

The Bow Section of the *Titanic*

1) The curved edge of the open A-Deck forward promenade.
2) Rusticles hang from the windows of the enclosed A-Deck promenade.
3) This winch was used only once to raise the lifeboats after a test launch in port.
4) A rusticle hangs over the glass of a C-Deck porthole.
5) Anchor chains went around this windlass.
6) *JJ* examines a bollard on the Forecastle Deck.
7) The arm of a lifeboat davit with its block and pulley still attached. Other similar davit arms are indicated on the painting.

think that in fact this cup had just fluttered down that night to land right on top of a boiler.

Then in the light of *Alvin*'s headlights, we spotted a safe ahead of us. I had heard about the story of fabulous treasure, including a leather-bound book covered with jewels, being locked in the ship's safes when she sank. Here was the chance of a lifetime, and I wanted to get a good look at it.

The safe sat there with its door face up. The handle looked as though it was made of gold, although I knew it had to be brass. Next to it, I could see a small circular gold dial, and above both a nice shiny gold crest.

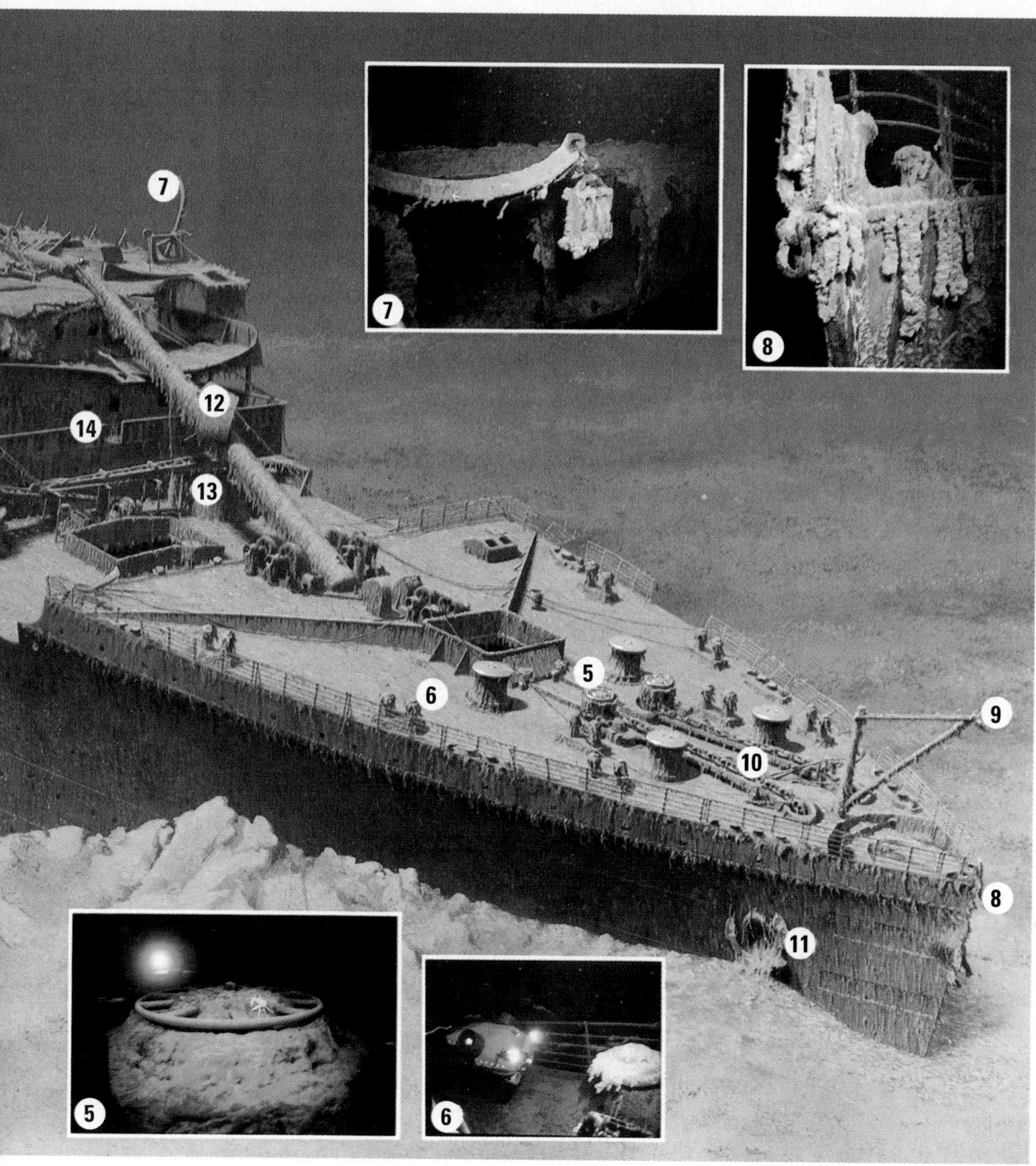

8) Rusticles adorn the prow of the *Titanic.*
9) The anchor crane.
10) Anchor chains on the forecastle.
11) The starboard anchor.
12) The crow's nest on the fallen foremast.
13) Cranes that lowered cargo into the holds.
14) A closed gate between third- and first-class areas.
15) The telemotor that once held the ship's wheel.
16) The collapsed roof of the Grand Staircase.
17) The gymnasium.
18) An opened joint in the ship's structure.
19) A lifeboat davit missing its arm.
20) Hull plates possibly damaged by the iceberg.

Why not try to open it? I watched as *Alvin*'s sample-gathering arm locked its metal fingers onto the handle. Its metal wrist began to rotate clockwise. To my surprise, the handle turned easily. Then it stopped. The door just wouldn't budge. It was rusted shut. I felt as if I'd been caught with my hand in the cookie jar. Oh, well, I thought, it was probably empty, anyway. In fact, when we later looked at the video footage we had taken, we could see that the bottom of the safe had rusted out. Any treasure should have been spread around nearby, but there was none to be seen. Fortunately, my promise to myself not to bring back anything from the *Titanic* was not put to the test.

Two days passed before I went down to the *Titanic* again. After the rest, I was raring to go at it once more. This time we were going to explore the torn-off stern section that lay 1,970 feet away from the bow. It had been very badly damaged during the plunge to the bottom. Now it lay almost unrecognizable amidst badly twisted pieces of wreckage. We planned to land *Alvin* on the bottom directly behind the stern section and then send *JJ* in under the overhanging hull. Unless the *Titanic*'s three huge propellers had fallen off when she sank, I figured they still ought to be there, along with her enormous 101-ton rudder.

We made a soft landing on the bottom, and discovered that one of *JJ*'s motors wouldn't work. Our dive looked like a washout. I sat glumly staring out of my viewport at the muddy bottom. Suddenly the mud started to move! Our pilot was slowly inching *Alvin* forward on its single ski right under the dangerous overhanging stern area. He was taking the sub itself to search for the huge propellers. Was he crazy? What if a piece of wreckage came crashing down? But our pilot was a professional, so I figured he must know exactly what he was doing.

I could see an area ahead covered with rusticles that had fallen from the rim of the stern above. Until now we had had ocean above us. Crossing this point was like taking a dangerous dare. Once on the other side, there was no sure way of escaping if disaster struck. None of us spoke. The only sound in the sub was our breathing.

Slowly a massive black surface of steel plating seemed to inch down toward us overhead. The hull seemed to be coming at us from all sides. As we looked closely, we could see that like the bow, the stern section was buried deep in the mud—forty-five feet or so. Both the middle and the starboard propellers were under the mud. Only about sixteen feet of the massive rudder could be seen rising out of the ooze.

"Let's get out of here," I said. Ever so gently, *Alvin* retraced the path left by its ski.

As we crossed over from the area covered with rusticles into the clear, we sighed with relief. We were out of danger. All of us were glad that this adventure was over.

Before we left the bottom this time, however, there was one mission that I wanted to complete. I wanted to place a memorial plaque on the twisted and tangled wreckage of the stern, in memory of all those lost on the *Titanic*. Those who had died had gathered on the stern as the ship had tilted bow first. This had been their final haven. So we rose up the wall of steel to the top of the stern. With great care, *Alvin*'s mechanical arm plucked the plaque from where it had been strapped outside the sub, and gently released it. We watched as it sank quietly to the deck of the stern.

As we lifted off and began our climb to the surface, our camera kept the plaque in view as long as possible. As we rose, it grew smaller and smaller, until finally it was swallowed in the gloom.

We made two more trips down to the *Titanic*. At the end of the final dive, I knew I had visited the great ship for the last time. Two and a half hours later when we reached the surface, everybody on the *Atlantis II* prepared to head for home. Later that night there would be a party on board, but through it all I was still thinking about the *Titanic*: of the people who built her, sailed on her, and died when she went down.

The memorial plaque (*shown in photograph*) for victims of the *Titanic* reads as follows:

In Memory of Those Souls Who Perished
with the "Titanic" April 14–15, 1912.
Dedicated to William M. Tantum, IV,
Whose Dream to Find the "Titanic"
has been Realized
by Dr. Robert D. Ballard.
The Officers and Members of the
Titanic Historical Society Inc. 1986.

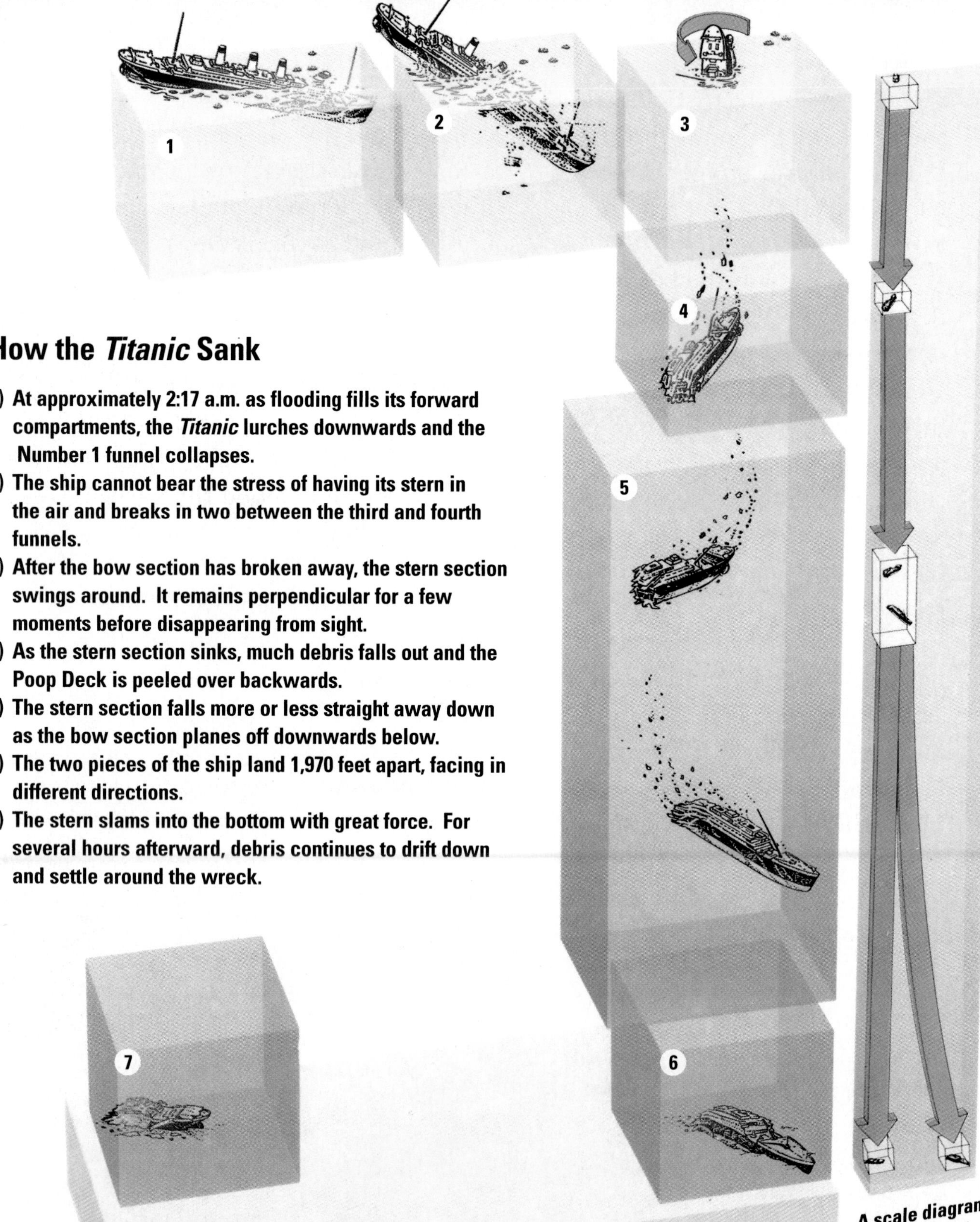

How the *Titanic* Sank

1) At approximately 2:17 a.m. as flooding fills its forward compartments, the *Titanic* lurches downwards and the Number 1 funnel collapses.
2) The ship cannot bear the stress of having its stern in the air and breaks in two between the third and fourth funnels.
3) After the bow section has broken away, the stern section swings around. It remains perpendicular for a few moments before disappearing from sight.
4) As the stern section sinks, much debris falls out and the Poop Deck is peeled over backwards.
5) The stern section falls more or less straight away down as the bow section planes off downwards below.
6) The two pieces of the ship land 1,970 feet apart, facing in different directions.
7) The stern slams into the bottom with great force. For several hours afterward, debris continues to drift down and settle around the wreck.

A scale diagram of the descent of the wreck.

IN RESPONSE

A *Titanic* Visit

Suppose Robert Ballard is coming to your school to discuss his exploration of the *Titanic*. Advertise Dr. Ballard's speech in a poster that includes information as well as pictures.

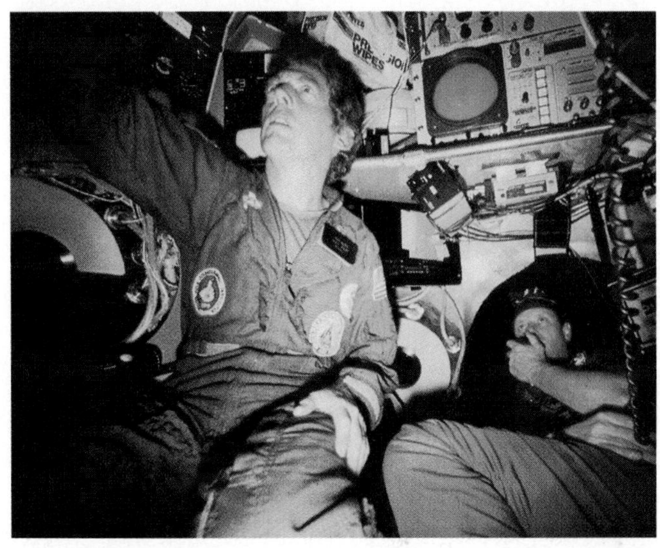

Think Like a Scientist

Imagine that Dr. Ballard and Dr. Urquhart ("Tracking the Monarch Butterflies") meet at a convention on scientific discovery. With a friend, take the roles of the two scientists. Discuss the difficulties of your long search and the excitement you felt when you finally reached your goal.

AUTHOR AT WORK

Robert Ballard, a marine geologist, grew up in Southern California with the ocean beach as his playground. As a teenager, he loved to scuba dive. As an adult, Mr. Ballard says that he has spent more hours in the deep ocean than any other scientist. In *Exploring the Titanic,* he writes: "The bottom of the ocean is a peaceful place. In future, when I think of the *Titanic,* I will see her bow sitting upright on the bottom, finally at rest."

Other Books by . . .

Robert D. Ballard

The Lost Wreck of the Isis
by Robert D. Ballard with Rick Archbold, Scholastic/Madison Press, 1990

Exploring the Bismarck
by Robert D. Ballard with Rick Archbold, Scholastic/Madison Press, 1991

Library Link "Return to the *Titanic*" was taken from *Exploring the Titanic* by Robert D. Ballard. You might enjoy reading the entire book to find out more about the famous ship.

Protecting the Titanic

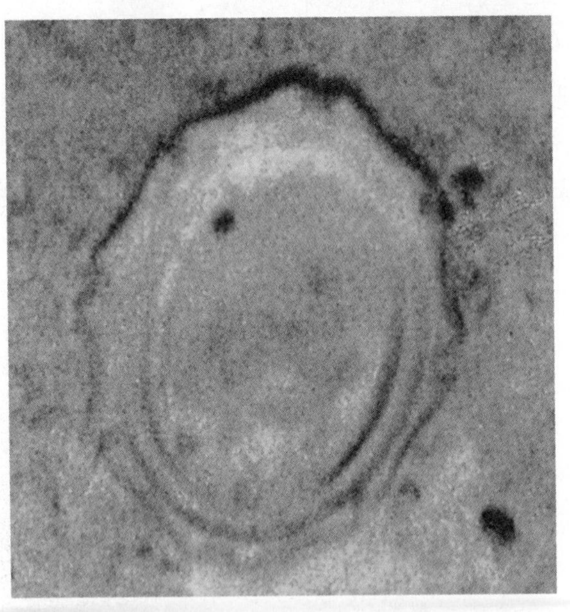

Many items from the *Titanic* rest on the ocean floor. They include a metal plate (*above*) and a safe (*below*).

Do you think people should disturb the remains of the *Titanic*?

After Robert Ballard explored the *Titanic*, a group of French researchers visited the great ship's remains. This group took objects from the ship, including china and a stained-glass window.

No—Leave the Ship in Peace

Dr. Robert Ballard says it's all right for scientists to visit the *Titanic*. However, he believes they should not take anything from the ship.

In his book *Exploring the Titanic*, Ballard says new expeditions should leave the ship in peace. He was angry when he learned the French group took items from the ship. "In my opinion, this was done purely for profit and shows a great disrespect for the grave site of the victims of the disaster," Ballard explains.

This first-class deck chair was found among the floating debris after the *Titanic* sank (*left*). *Titanic* survivors view artifacts in a museum (*right*). One week after the disaster, this watch was retrieved from the area where the ship sank (*below*).

Yes—Put the Objects in a Museum

Members of the French expedition say it is wrong to leave the objects on the ocean floor. Time, water, and sea animals are ruining the ship and the things on it, the explorers insist.

Bruno Chomel de Varagnes, who led the French expedition, says that objects from the *Titanic* can help people learn more about the great ship. That's why his team allowed museums to display the objects. "The best memorial that can be made for the *Titanic* is to put them in a museum so that everyone can see them," Chomel de Varagnes says.

Look Again

Artists often look at everyday things in a new way. Sometimes you have to look closely at a piece of art to discover what it's really about.

Some people say dogs see with their noses. What do you think they mean? Did the artist show that idea here? How?

Sculpture by Alan Rath (United States),
***Hound,* 1990**

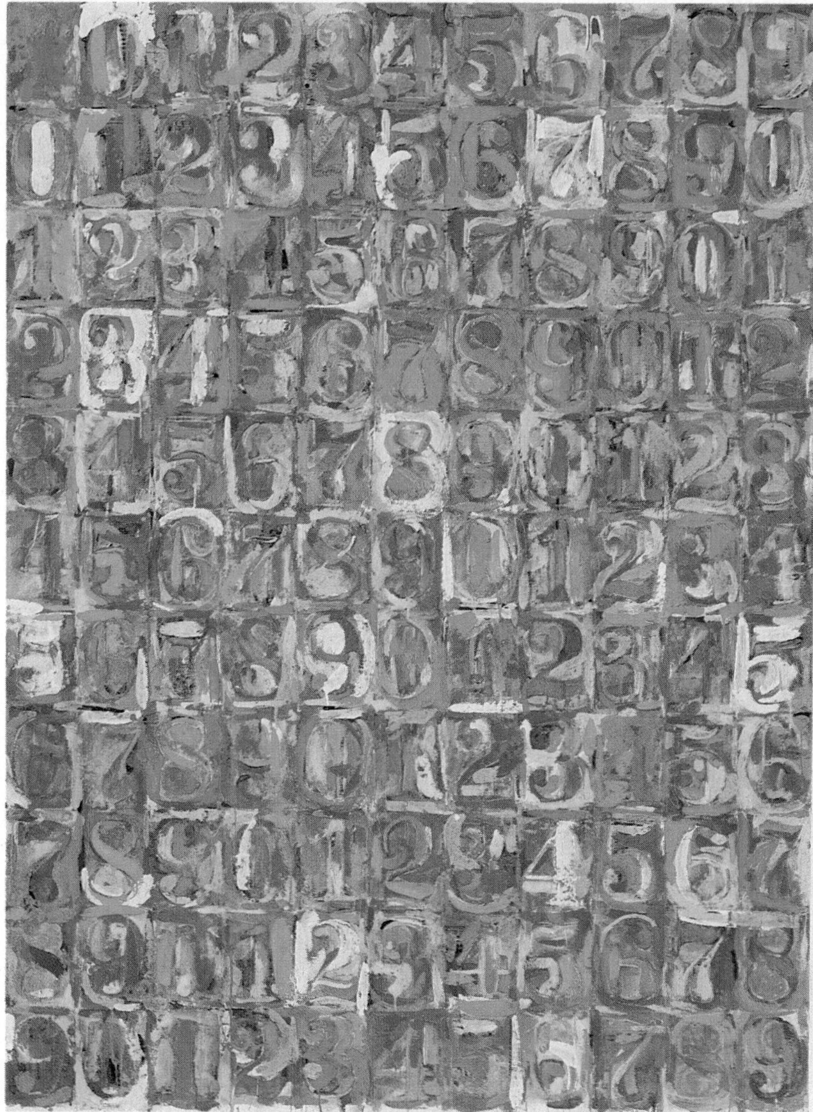

Painting by Jasper Johns (United States), ***Numbers in Color,*** **1959**

This painting mixes colors and numbers in an unusual way. What patterns can you see when you look closely?

This sculpture is made of things other people have thrown away. What everyday objects do you recognize?

Sculpture by Larry Beck (Inuit),
Punk Walrus Inua, **1986**

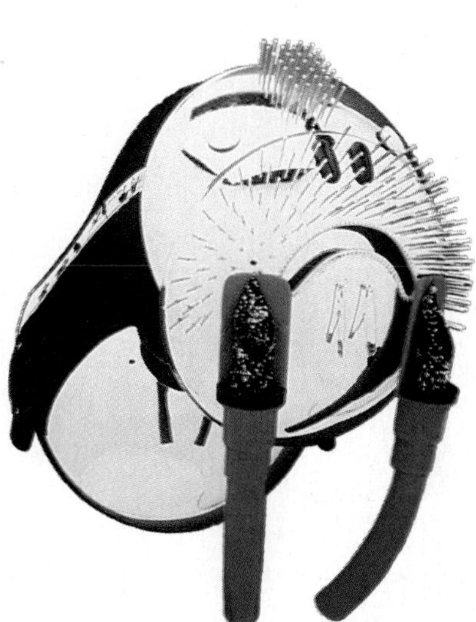

Express **Yourself**

A missing dog, a cloud of butterflies, a sunken ship: anything can turn up when people look closely and ask questions. In Looking Below the Surface, you met characters who solved mysteries and made discoveries. Some people did it by looking at familiar things in a new way. Others took a different path to the same place.

A Detective's Steps

Mysteries and detective stories usually follow a sequence of steps or events. With a partner, discuss the events in Caro's story ("The Secret Among the Stones") and Ali Baba's adventure ("Ali Baba and the Missing Glass Slipper"). How many events take place before each character makes a discovery? Which character does the fastest detective work—Ali Baba or Caro? Defend your choice with examples from the story.

Tragedy or Triumph?

"There was tragedy here, not triumph," Ardath Mayhar writes of Caro's discovery ("The Secret Among the Stones"). Is there also a tragedy or a sadness in "Return to the *Titanic*" and in "Tracking the Monarch Butterflies"? Is there a triumph? In a small group, look back at the selections and discuss your answers.

Investigate the Characters

The main characters in each selection helped solve important mysteries. In a small group, discuss at least three qualities that helped each person solve a mystery. What traits did the characters have in common? Which trait do you think is most important for a detective or scientist? Why?

Stories with Suspense

Robert Ballard's story ("Return to the *Titanic*") has many exciting moments. Ardath Mayhar's ("The Secret Among the Stones") does, too. Which writer does a better job of creating suspense? Use examples from the stories to explain your choice. Do you think suspense is an important part of a mystery story? Why?

Living Mysteries

Some stories in this theme feature animals doing surprising things. Look back at the stories for examples of mysterious things that creatures do. Choose the animal that you are most curious about, and record your questions. If you were a scientist, how might you find the answers? Use your own knowledge and what you've learned in this theme to make a plan.

More Books for You to Enjoy

What Eric Knew

by James Howe, Atheneum, 1985

Does the figure in the cemetery have anything to do with Eric's unexplained accident? Mystery and intrigue are in store for Sebastian Barth when cryptic messages arrive from Eric, and Barth sets out to discover who pushed Eric down the stairs.

Dinosaurs Walked Here and Other Stories Fossils Tell

by Patricia Lauber, Bradbury Press, 1987

From dinosaur eggs to woolly mammoths frozen in tar, this is the story of how fossils are formed and what they can tell us about life long ago.

Math Mini-Mysteries

by Sandra Markle, Atheneum, 1993

Problem solving is fun with puzzles and games. Learn how to predict when the wind is best for kite flying. Discover how you can find a champion tree or match snowflakes. Calculate how much it costs to feed zoo animals, and try a recipe for zoo bread.

The Village of Blue Stone

by Stephen Trimble, illustrated by Jennifer Owings Dewey and Deborah Reade, Macmillan, 1990

Meet farmers, artists, and families who lived nine hundred years ago in Cliff Palace, an Anasazi community. The author uses information discovered through archaeology to give you a glimpse of an ancient people now known as the Pueblo.

Steal Away Home

by Lois Ruby, Macmillan, 1994

Dana is startled to discover a skeleton in a sealed-up room of an old house in Lawrence, Kansas. Her attempt to identify the skeleton leads her to the days of the Underground Railroad and a conductor named Lizbet Charles.

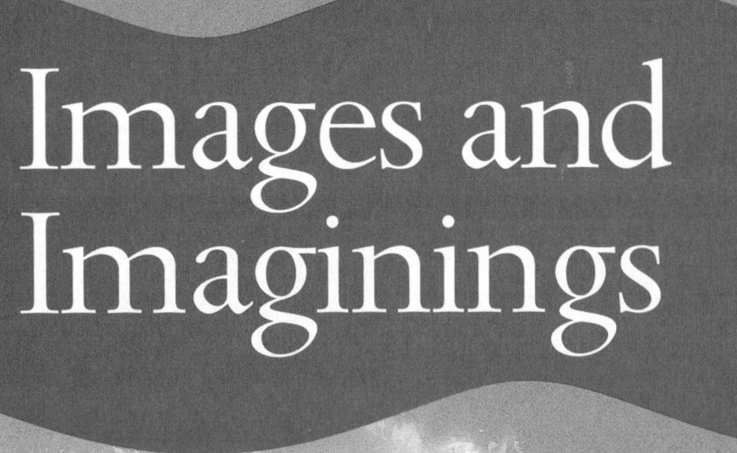

Images and Imaginings

Theme

4

“An idea came into my head”

—Malick Fall
“Empty Head”

Theme 4

Images and Imaginings

CONTENTS

Theme Trade Books

Jacques-Henri Lartigue: Boy With a Camera
by John Cech
Jacques-Henri looked for unusual ways to photograph his family and friends. This real-life account takes a look at life in France during the early 1900's.

The House I Live In: At Home in America
by Isadore Seltzer
What kind of house do you live in? This introduction to house design describes many kinds of American houses. Some will look familiar; others may look completely unfamiliar.

Theme Magazine

Did Atlantis really exist? Can you dream up a wacky world of your own? What's the fuss over virtual reality? Imagine what you can find out in *Mind Zone* Theme Magazine!

AWARD WINNER

MILO'S MYSTERIOUS GIFT

from *The Phantom Tollbooth*
by Norton Juster

There was once a boy named Milo who didn't know what to do with himself—not just sometimes, but always.

When he was in school he longed to be out, and when he was out he longed to be in. On the way he thought about coming home, and coming home he thought about going. Wherever he was he wished he were somewhere else, and when he got there he wondered why he'd bothered. Nothing really interested him—least of all the things that should have.

"It seems to me that almost everything is a waste of time," he remarked one day as he walked dejectedly home from school. "I can't see the point in learning to solve useless problems, or subtracting turnips from turnips, or knowing where Ethiopia is or how to spell February." And, since no one bothered to explain otherwise, he regarded the process of seeking knowledge as the greatest waste of time of all.

As he and his unhappy thoughts hurried along (for while he was never anxious to be where he was going, he liked to get there as quickly as possible) it seemed a great wonder that the world, which was so large, could sometimes feel so small and empty.

"And worst of all," he continued sadly, "there's nothing for me to do, nowhere I'd care to go, and hardly anything worth seeing." He punctuated this last thought with such a deep sigh that a house sparrow singing nearby stopped and rushed home to be with his family.

Without stopping or looking up, he rushed past the buildings and busy shops that lined the street and in a few minutes reached home—dashed through the lobby—hopped onto the elevator—two, three, four, five, six, seven, eight, and off again—opened the apartment door—rushed into his room—flopped dejectedly into a chair, and grumbled softly, "Another long afternoon."

He looked glumly at all the things he owned. The books that were too much trouble to read, the tools he'd never learned to use, the small electric automobile he hadn't driven in months—or was it years?—and the hundreds of other games and toys, and bats and balls, and bits and pieces scattered around him. And then, to one side of the room, just next to the phonograph, he noticed something he had certainly never seen before.

Who could possibly have left such an enormous package and such a strange one? For, while it was not quite square, it was definitely not round, and for its size it was larger than almost any other big package of smaller dimension that he'd ever seen.

Attached to one side was a bright-blue envelope which said simply: "FOR MILO, WHO HAS PLENTY OF TIME."

Of course, if you've ever gotten a surprise package, you can imagine how puzzled and excited Milo was; and if you've never gotten one, pay close attention, because someday you might.

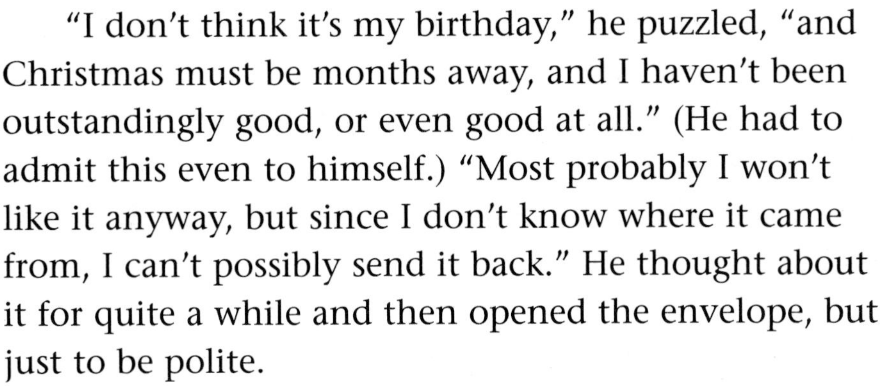

"I don't think it's my birthday," he puzzled, "and Christmas must be months away, and I haven't been outstandingly good, or even good at all." (He had to admit this even to himself.) "Most probably I won't like it anyway, but since I don't know where it came from, I can't possibly send it back." He thought about it for quite a while and then opened the envelope, but just to be polite.

"ONE GENUINE TURNPIKE TOLLBOOTH," it stated—and then it went on:

"EASILY ASSEMBLED AT HOME, AND FOR USE BY THOSE WHO HAVE NEVER TRAVELED IN LANDS BEYOND."

"Beyond what?" thought Milo as he continued to read.

"THIS PACKAGE CONTAINS THE FOLLOWING ITEMS:

"One (1) genuine turnpike tollbooth to be erected according to directions.

"Three (3) precautionary signs to be used in a precautionary fashion.

"Assorted coins for use in paying tolls.

"One (1) map, up to date and carefully drawn by master cartographers, depicting natural and man-made features.

"One (1) book of rules and traffic regulations, which may not be bent or broken."

And in smaller letters at the bottom it concluded:

"Results are not guaranteed, but if not perfectly satisfied, your wasted time will be refunded."

Following the instructions, which told him to cut here, lift there, and fold back all around, he soon had the tollbooth unpacked and set up on its stand. He fitted the windows in place and attached the roof, which extended out on both sides and fastened on the coin box. It was very much like the tollbooths he'd seen many times on family trips, except of course it was much smaller and purple.

"What a strange present," he thought to himself. "The least they could have done was to send a highway with it, for it's terribly impractical without one." But since, at the time, there was nothing else he wanted to play with, he set up the three signs,

SLOW DOWN APPROACHING TOLLBOOTH

PLEASE HAVE YOUR FARE READY

HAVE YOUR DESTINATION IN MIND

and slowly unfolded the map.

As the announcement stated, it was a beautiful map, in many colors, showing principal roads, rivers and seas, towns and cities, mountains and valleys, intersections and detours, and sites of outstanding interest both beautiful and historic.

The only trouble was that Milo had never heard of any of the places it indicated, and even the names sounded most peculiar.

"I don't think there really is such a country," he concluded after studying it carefully. "Well, it doesn't matter anyway." And he closed his eyes and poked a finger at the map.

"Dictionopolis," read Milo slowly when he saw what his finger had chosen. "Oh, well, I might as well go there as anywhere."

He walked across the room and dusted the car off carefully. Then, taking the map and rule book with him, he hopped in and, for lack of anything better to do, drove slowly up to the tollbooth. As he deposited his coin and rolled past he remarked wistfully, "I do hope this is an interesting game, otherwise the afternoon will be so terribly dull."

Suddenly he found himself speeding along an unfamiliar country highway, and as he looked back over his shoulder neither the tollbooth nor his room nor even the house was anywhere in sight. What had started as make-believe was now very real.

"What a strange thing to have happen," he thought (just as you must be thinking right now). "This game is much more serious than I thought, for here I am riding on a road I've never seen, going to a place I've never heard of, and all because of a tollbooth which came from nowhere. I'm certainly glad that it's a nice day for a trip," he concluded hopefully, for, at the moment, this was the one thing he definitely knew.

The sun sparkled, the sky was clear, and all the colors he saw seemed to be richer and brighter than he could ever remember. The flowers shone as if they'd been cleaned and polished, and the tall trees that lined the road shimmered in silvery green.

"WELCOME TO EXPECTATIONS," said a carefully lettered sign on a small house at the side of the road.

"INFORMATION, PREDICTIONS, AND ADVICE CHEERFULLY OFFERED. PARK HERE AND BLOW HORN."

With the first sound from the horn a little man in a long coat came rushing from the house, speaking as fast as he could and repeating everything several times:

"My, my, my, my, my, welcome, welcome, welcome, welcome to the land of Expectations, to the land of Expectations, to the land of Expectations. We don't get many travelers these days; we certainly don't get many travelers these days. Now what can I do for you? I'm the Whether Man."

"Is this the right road for Dictionopolis?" asked Milo, a little bowled over by the effusive greeting.

"Well now, well now, well now," he began again, "I don't know of any wrong road to Dictionopolis,

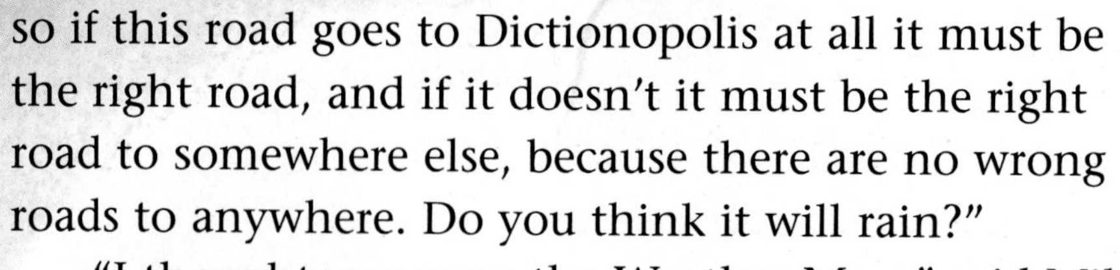

so if this road goes to Dictionopolis at all it must be the right road, and if it doesn't it must be the right road to somewhere else, because there are no wrong roads to anywhere. Do you think it will rain?"

"I thought you were the Weather Man," said Milo, very confused.

"Oh no," said the little man, "I'm the Whether Man, not the Weather Man, for after all it's more important to know whether there will be weather than what the weather will be." And with that he released a dozen balloons that sailed off into the sky. "Must see which way the wind is blowing," he said, chuckling over his little joke and watching them disappear in all directions.

"What kind of a place is Expectations?" inquired Milo, unable to see the humor and feeling very doubtful of the little man's sanity.

"Good question, good question," he exclaimed. "Expectations is the place you must always go to before you get to where you're going. Of course, some people never go beyond Expectations, but my job is to hurry them along whether they like it or not. Now what else can I do for you?" And before Milo could reply he rushed into the house and reappeared a moment later with a new coat and an umbrella.

"I think I can find my own way," said Milo, not at all sure that he could. But, since he didn't understand the little man at all, he decided that he might as well move on—at least until he met someone whose sentences didn't always sound as if they would make as much sense backwards as forwards.

"Splendid, splendid, splendid," exclaimed the Whether Man. "Whether or not you find your own way, you're bound to find some way. If you happen to find my way, please return it, as it was lost years ago.

I imagine by now it's quite rusty. You did say it was going to rain, didn't you?" And with that he opened the umbrella and walked with Milo to the car.

"I'm glad you made your own decision. I do so hate to make up my mind about anything, whether it's good or bad, up or down, in or out, rain or shine. Expect everything, I always say, and the unexpected never happens. Now please drive carefully; good-by, good-by, good-by, good . . ." His last good-by was drowned out by an enormous clap of thunder, and as Milo drove down the road in the bright sunshine he could see the Whether Man standing in the middle of a fierce cloudburst that seemed to be raining only on him.

The road dipped now into a broad green valley and stretched toward the horizon. The little car bounced along with very little effort, and Milo had hardly to touch the accelerator to go as fast as he wanted. He was glad to be on his way again.

"It's all very well to spend time in Expectations," he thought, "but talking to that strange man all day would certainly get me nowhere. He's the most peculiar person I've ever met," continued Milo—unaware of how many peculiar people he would shortly encounter.

As he drove along the peaceful highway he soon fell to daydreaming and paid less and less attention to where he was going. In a short time he wasn't paying any attention at all, and that is why, at a fork in the road, when a sign pointed to the left, Milo went to the right, along a route which looked suspiciously like the wrong way.

Things began to change as soon as he left the main highway. The sky became quite gray and, along with it, the whole countryside seemed to lose its color and assume the same monotonous tone. Everything was quiet, and even the air hung heavily. The birds sang only gray songs and the road wound back and forth in an endless series of climbing curves.

Mile after

mile after

mile after

mile he drove, and now, gradually the car went slower and slower, until it was hardly moving at all.

"It looks as though I'm getting nowhere," yawned Milo, becoming very drowsy and dull. "I hope I haven't taken a wrong turn."

Mile after

mile after

mile after

mile, and everything became grayer and more monotonous. Finally the car just stopped altogether, and, hard as he tried, it wouldn't budge another inch.

"I wonder where I am," said Milo in a very worried tone.

"You're . . . in . . . the . . . Dol . . . drums," wailed a voice that sounded far away.

He looked around quickly to see who had spoken. No one was there, and it was as quiet and still as one could imagine.

"Yes . . . the . . . Dol . . . drums," yawned another voice, but still he saw no one.

"WHAT ARE THE DOLDRUMS?" he cried loudly, and tried very hard to see who would answer this time.

"The Doldrums, my young friend, are where nothing ever happens and nothing ever changes."

This time the voice came from so close that Milo jumped with surprise, for, sitting on his right shoulder, so lightly that he hardly noticed, was a small creature exactly the color of his shirt.

"Allow me to introduce all of us," the creature went on. "We are the Lethargarians, at your service."

Milo looked around and, for the first time, noticed dozens of them—sitting on the car, standing in the road, and lying all over the trees and bushes. They were very difficult to see, because whatever they happened to be sitting on or near was exactly the color they happened to be. Each one looked very much like the other (except for the color, of course) and some looked even more like each other than they did like themselves.

"I'm very pleased to meet you," said Milo, not sure whether or not he was pleased at all. "I think I'm lost. Can you help me please?"

"Don't say 'think,'" said one sitting on his shoe, for the one on his shoulder had fallen asleep. "It's against the law." And he yawned and fell off to sleep, too.

"No one's allowed to think in the Doldrums," continued a third, beginning to doze off. And as each one spoke, he fell off to sleep and another picked up the conversation with hardly any interruption.

"Don't you have a rule book? It's local ordinance 175389-J."

Milo quickly pulled the rule book from his pocket, opened to the page, and read, "Ordinance 175389-J: It shall be unlawful, illegal, and unethical to think, think of thinking, surmise, presume, reason, meditate, or speculate while in the Doldrums. Anyone breaking this law shall be severely punished!"

"That's a ridiculous law," said Milo, quite indignantly. "Everybody thinks."

"We don't," shouted the Lethargarians all at once.

"And most of the time *you* don't," said a yellow one sitting in a daffodil. "That's why you're here. You weren't thinking, and you weren't paying attention either. People who don't pay attention often get stuck in the Doldrums." And with that he toppled out of the flower and fell snoring into the grass.

Milo couldn't help laughing at the little creature's strange behavior, even though he knew it might be rude.

"Stop that at once," ordered the plaid one clinging to his stocking. "Laughing is against the law. Don't you have a rule book? It's local ordinance 574381-W."

Opening the book again, Milo found Ordinance 574381-W: "In the Doldrums, laughter is frowned upon and smiling is permitted only on alternate Thursdays. Violators shall be dealt with most harshly."

"Well, if you can't laugh or think, what can you do?" asked Milo.

"Anything as long as it's nothing, and everything as long as it isn't anything," explained another. "There's lots to do; we have a very busy schedule—

"At 8 o'clock we get up, and then we spend

"From 8 to 9 daydreaming.

"From 9 to 9:30 we take our early midmorning nap.

"From 9:30 to 10:30 we dawdle and delay.

"From 10:30 to 11:00 we take our late early morning nap.

"From 11:00 to 12:00 we bide our time and then eat lunch.

"From 1:00 to 2:00 we linger and loiter.

"From 2:00 to 2:30 we take our early afternoon nap.

"From 2:30 to 3:30 we put off for tomorrow what we could have done today.

"From 3:30 to 4:00 we take our early late afternoon nap.

"From 4:00 to 5:00 we loaf and lounge until dinner.

"From 6:00 to 7:00 we dillydally.

"From 7:00 to 8:00 we take our early evening nap, and then for an hour before we go to bed at 9:00 we waste time.

"As you can see, that leaves almost no time for brooding, lagging, plodding, or procrastinating, and if we stopped to think or laugh, we'd never get nothing done."

"You mean you'd never get anything done," corrected Milo.

"We don't want to get anything done," snapped another angrily; "we want to get nothing done, and we can do that without your help."

"You see," continued another in a more conciliatory tone, "it's really quite strenuous doing nothing all day, so once a week we take a holiday and go nowhere, which was just where we were going when you came along. Would you care to join us?"

"I might as well," thought Milo; "that's where I seem to be going anyway."

"Tell me," he yawned, for he felt ready for a nap now himself, "does everyone here do nothing?"

"Everyone but the terrible watchdog," said two of them, shuddering in chorus. "He's always sniffing around to see that nobody wastes time. A most unpleasant character."

"The watchdog?" said Milo quizzically.

"THE WATCHDOG," shouted another, fainting from fright, for racing down the road barking furiously and kicking up a great cloud of dust was the very dog of whom they had been speaking.

"RUN!"

"WAKE UP!"

"RUN!"

"HERE HE COMES!"

"THE WATCHDOG!"

Great shouts filled the air as the Lethargarians scattered in all directions and soon disappeared entirely.

"R-R-R-G-H-R-O-R-R-H-F-F," exclaimed the watchdog as he dashed up to the car, loudly puffing and panting.

Milo's eyes opened wide, for there in front of him was a large dog with a perfectly normal head, four feet, and a tail—and the body of a loudly ticking alarm clock.

"What are you doing here?" growled the watchdog.

"Just killing time," replied Milo apologetically. "You see—"

"KILLING TIME!" roared the dog—so furiously that his alarm went off. "It's bad enough wasting time without killing it." And he shuddered at the thought. "Why are you in the Doldrums anyway—don't you have anywhere to go?"

"I was on my way to Dictionopolis when I got stuck here," explained Milo. "Can you help me?"

"Help you! You must help yourself," the dog replied, carefully winding himself with his left hind leg. "I suppose you know why you got stuck."

"I guess I just wasn't thinking," said Milo.

"PRECISELY," shouted the dog as his alarm went off again. "Now you know what you must do."

"I'm afraid I don't," admitted Milo, feeling quite stupid.

"Well," continued the watchdog impatiently, "since you got here by not thinking, it seems reasonable to expect that, in order to get out, you must start thinking." And with that he hopped into the car.

"Do you mind if I get in? I love automobile rides."

Milo began to think as hard as he could (which was very difficult, since he wasn't used to it). He thought of birds that swim and fish that fly. He thought of yesterday's lunch and tomorrow's dinner. He thought of words that began with J and numbers that end in 3. And, as he thought, the wheels began to turn.

"We're moving, we're moving," he shouted happily.

"Keep thinking," scolded the watchdog.

The little car started to go faster and faster as Milo's brain whirled with activity, and down the road they went. In a few moments they were out of the Doldrums and back on the main highway. All the colors had returned to their original brightness, and as they raced along the road Milo continued to think of all sorts of things; of the many detours and wrong turns that were so easy to take, of how fine it was to be moving along, and, most of all, of how much could be accomplished with just a little thought. And the dog, his nose in the wind, just sat back, watchfully ticking.

IN RESPONSE

What Nonsense!

Characters in "Milo's Mysterious Gift" often say ridiculous things and make them sound sensible. Find something a character says that you think is nonsense. In writing, explain why it makes no sense.

Milo in the Doldrums

In the Doldrums, Milo meets creatures who are much like himself. With a partner, list words or phrases that describe both Milo and the Lethargarians. Does your list help explain why Milo ends up in the Doldrums? Next, list ways that Milo and the Lethargarians are different. Discuss how these differences help Milo escape the Doldrums.

AUTHOR AT WORK

Norton Juster is an architect and a part-time author who writes in the morning as often as he can. When the writing gets difficult, Mr. Juster chews on his pencil.

He began *The Phantom Tollbooth* as a short story. "I didn't know I was writing a book," Mr. Juster says. "I thought I was just writing something to amuse myself."

Mr. Juster has written four other books for children. In addition, he has turned *The Phantom Tollbooth* into an opera.

★ **Award-winning Author**

Another Book by . . .

Norton Juster

Alberic the Wise
by Norton Juster,
illustrated by
Leonard Baskin,
Picture Book Studio,
1992

Library Link "Milo's Mysterious Gift" was taken from *The Phantom Tollbooth* by Norton Juster. You might enjoy reading the entire book to find out whether Milo reaches Dictionopolis.

Peach Blossom Spring

retold by Fergus M. Bordewich
illustrated by Yang Ming-Yi

One day a fisherman from the city of Wu-ling was rowing along an unfamiliar stream. He was paying no attention to how far he was going, when suddenly he came to a grove of blossoming peach trees stretching along both banks.

Their falling blossoms swirled and danced in the summer breeze, and their fragrance was so delicious that he stopped to enjoy it. After awhile he discovered a spring at the end of the grove. Nearby a cave led into the mountainside. A faint light seemed to come from within, and he decided to see where it led.

At first the cave was so narrow that the fisherman could hardly get through, but after he had continued for some distance the passageway opened up into daylight.

As the fisherman emerged, a hidden valley appeared before him, as if in a dream. Tidy cottages stood amid rich fields and beautiful ponds. Farmers were stacking hay on curving terraces, bending and folding, bending and folding, chattering cheerfully to each other as they worked.

Even the trees seemed friendly. There were pomegranates and palms, plum trees and willows. There were forests of slender bamboo, and strange feathery trees that the fisherman had never seen before in the outside world.

Wrens and swallows chirped and twittered among the branches, while flocks of colorful birds wheeled and whirled high overhead. Some of them had tiny flutes tied to their wings, so that as they swooped and dove, the air hummed and whistled with a delicate music more beautiful than anything the fisherman had ever heard.

When the farmers saw the fisherman, they gathered around excitedly and asked where he had come from. When he told them, they were astonished. They knew nothing of the outside world, and none of them had ever seen a stranger before.

They explained that the valley's fields always produced just enough to eat, that the weather in the valley was always just right, and that everyone there treated his neighbors with just the proper amount of kindness and respect.

"We call our valley Peach Blossom Spring," said one.

All the villagers in turn invited the fisherman to their homes for food and drink. They explained that their grandparents' grandparents' grandparents had come to the valley to escape the cruelty of an ancient emperor. After reaching the valley, they had never left it again.

The fisherman related all that had happened in the hundreds of years since their ancestors had come to Peach Blossom Spring. The villagers were astonished at what he told them.

"People wear silk robes embroidered with dragons now, and they eat silkworm pie for dinner," the fisherman boasted, although he was rather poor and could not afford such luxuries himself. "They have more than one hundred different kinds of tea to drink, and they print whole stories on paper with blocks of

wood, and when they make war, they have a powder that can blow up a whole town!"

The villagers sighed and murmured at everything they heard.

"Why should we ever leave here," they said to each other. "What the stranger tells us sounds wonderful indeed, but we could never be as happy anywhere else."

It surprised the fisherman that although there were huge carp swimming in the ponds, none of his hosts ate fish.

"No one here knows how to catch them," the villagers said sadly.

"Let me show you," the fisherman offered.

The next day he dropped a line into a pond and soon pulled up a wriggling carp. The villagers said they had never tasted anything so good in their lives!

"Please stay here with us," the villagers pleaded.

The fisherman thought of his poor home in the city, with its crowds and its noise. Then he looked around him at the happy villagers and the sunny fields, and at the wonderful birds making their strange music overhead.

"I'll just go home and get my things," the fisherman said eagerly.

"It is very difficult to find this valley," the villagers warned him. "You must promise not to tell anyone that we are here, or you will never be able to find your way back at all."

The fisherman gave them his word that he wouldn't tell a soul.

"Of course not!" Little Wang replied.

A little farther along the way, they ran into Lanky Li, the proprietor of their favorite teahouse.

"Where are you going?" Lanky Li asked, curiously eyeing the two men who were loaded down with all the fisherman's nets and fishing lines and floats.

The fisherman sighed. As long as he had already told Little Wang, he decided it wouldn't make much difference if he told someone else.

Lanky Li's jaw fell open when he heard about Peach Blossom Spring.

"Won't you please allow me to come with you?" Lanky Li begged.

"How can we say no?" Little Wang whispered to the fisherman.

"All right," the fisherman sighed. "But let's hurry before we meet anyone else."

A little farther down the road, as luck would have it, they encountered Fat Chang, who made the tastiest spicy bean curd in the city. Before anyone could stop him Lanky Li had blurted out the story of Peach Blossom Spring.

"Think how nice it would be to have Fat Chang's bean curd when we get to Peach Blossom Spring," Little Wang said.

That made sense to the fisherman, so he told Fat Chang to gather up his pots and pans and join them too.

By the time the fisherman, Little Wang, Lanky Li and Fat Chang reached the river, hundreds of people

were tagging along behind them. Some were carrying their belongings in great heaps on their backs. Others were tugging heavily laden donkeys. Still others were pushing wheelbarrows piled high with furniture. There were rich people and poor people, and old people and young people, and whole families with their babies. All of them were shoving and yelling at each other to get out of the way.

What would the villagers say? the fisherman wondered and worried. How would all these people even fit into Peach Blossom Spring?

It took dozens of boats to carry everyone. More and more joined them, until by the time they arrived

at the forest of peach trees, there was a traffic jam of boats that extended for miles along the stream.

"Hurry up! Hurry up!" people kept shouting at the fisherman. "We're hungry and tired. Won't we ever get to Peach Blossom Spring?"

The fisherman was suddenly confused. Nothing looked quite the way he had remembered it. He searched for the markers he had left, but everything was covered with peach blossoms as far as the eye could see.

The city people were very impatient. They jumped out of their boats and ran off in every direction,

scattering peach blossoms and branches and stones until any hope of finding the markers was gone. The fisherman now knew that they would never find Peach Blossom Spring.

Sighing, he sat down in his little boat, dropped a line in the water, and sat watching the peach blossoms as they drifted in the summer breeze like snow. It was the most beautiful sight he had ever seen.

Many people who have heard the fisherman's tale have set off in search of Peach Blossom Spring. But no one has ever found it.

IN RESPONSE

Home Sweet Home

Imagine you are the fisherman and have spent one year in Peach Blossom Spring. What do you like about living there? What do you miss about your old home? Write your thoughts in a letter to your friend.

What Might Have Been

What might have happened if the crowd of people had reached Peach Blossom Spring? Discuss your ideas in a small group. Think about how the people might have felt when they first saw the hidden valley. How might the people already living there have reacted?

Lessons to Learn

The fisherman in this story and Milo ("Milo's Mysterious Gift") both make a mistake and learn a lesson from their experiences in new lands. What mistake does each character make? What lesson does each learn? Which lesson do you think is more valuable? Why do you think so?

ILLUSTRATOR AT WORK

Yang Ming-Yi

Mr. Yang uses Chinese paints, inks, and brushes.

Yang Ming-Yi's ink and watercolor illustrations add a dreamy feeling to *Peach Blossom Spring.* Maybe it's because the artist imagines what he paints before his brush touches the paper.

As a boy in Suzhou,[1] China, Mr. Yang could look at a blank wall and find a different image in it every time. He saw forests, mountains, oceans, cities, animals, and flowers. "I was always eager to draw on paper the inspiration I got from the wall," he recalls. It was the beginning of his art career.

1 **Suzhou** (*SOO joh*)

Mr. Yang won his first art award when he was ten years old. He was the youngest artist ever to exhibit at the National Museum of China. He has won many more prizes and has illustrated four children's books since then.

In 1987 Mr. Yang moved to New York City, where he lives today. He came to the United States so he could share his art with other painters and also learn from them. At first Mr. Yang visited museums almost every day. He wanted to look at art that was different from traditional Chinese artwork.

Today Mr. Yang has a style all his own. Some of his images and techniques are modern. Yet he combines these with memories of his Chinese home. He still uses Chinese inks, brushes, and plain rice paper.

Other Books Illustrated by . . .

Yang Ming-Yi

The Shell Woman & the King, retold by Laurence Yep, illustrated by Yang Ming-Yi, Dial Books for Young Readers, 1993

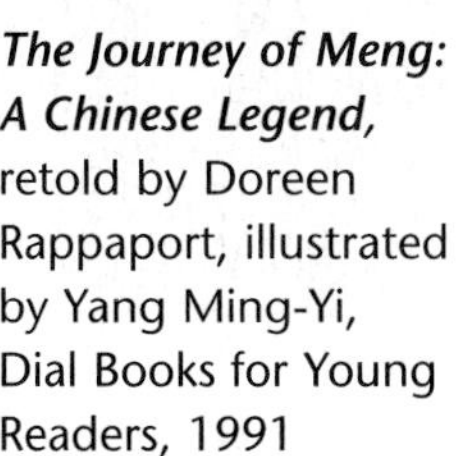

The Journey of Meng: A Chinese Legend, retold by Doreen Rappaport, illustrated by Yang Ming-Yi, Dial Books for Young Readers, 1991

FIRST MANNED FLIGHT TO VENUS

by Jan Minter

Characters
Two Astronauts
Ground Control Person
Venu, *a creature from Venus*

SCENE 1

Time: *The future.*

Setting: *Space capsule, center, and Houston ground control console, at left. Each area has its own set of spotlights.*

At rise: Two Astronauts *are strapped into spaceship seats, center, ready for take-off. They wear appropriate metallic spacesuits, and helmets with attached mouthpieces, which they lift to mouth when speaking to* **Ground Control. Ground Control Person** *sits at console, left.*

1st Astronaut (*To* **2nd Astronaut**): I'm nervous.

2nd Astronaut: Why? You've flown space missions before.

1st Astronaut: I have a strange feeling that we won't make it this time.

2nd Astronaut: That's silly. We've made many shots like this without a hitch. No need to worry.

1st Astronaut: I just know that we won't land on Venus. (*Petulantly*) I wanted to bring back one of those green rocks!

2nd Astronaut: Relax. You'll get your green rocks.

Ground Control: This is Houston Ground Control. Everything is A-O.K. from here. We're waiting for last checklist before continuing countdown.

1st Astronaut (*Into mouthpiece*)**:** Check, Houston. Everything on go. Continuing last checklist. (*To* **2nd Astronaut**) Left retro rocket.

2nd Astronaut: Check.

1st Astronaut: Right retro rocket.

2nd Astronaut: Check.

1st Astronaut: Backup cabin oxygen.

2nd Astronaut: Check.

1st Astronaut: Backup guidance mechanism.

2nd Astronaut: Check.

1st Astronaut: Backup tape deck.

2nd Astronaut: Check. (*Looks up suddenly*) Hey, what do you mean, backup tape deck? We don't have a tape deck on the checklist.

1st Astronaut: Oh, I meant to tell you about that. (*Holds up cassette player*) I put one in. I taped some music from the radio for us to listen to in our spare time.

2nd Astronaut: You shouldn't have done that. You know the rules. (*In a sing-song*) No personal paraphernalia on board.

1st Astronaut: I know. But I get bored on these long trips.

2nd Astronaut: Well, it's too late for Ground Control to do anything about it. (*Into mouthpiece*) Ground Control, we have completed last checklist. Everything A-O.K.

Ground Control: Last checklist completed. Holding for countdown. (*Pauses*) Beginning last countdown. Thirty, twenty-nine, twenty-eight . . . (*Pantomimes counting*)

1st Astronaut: I just know we won't make it to Venus.

Ground Control: Twenty-five, twenty-four, twenty-three . . .

2nd Astronaut: Stop that kind of talk, will you? We'll make it—and we'll be heroes. I can see our ticker tape parade now.

1st Astronaut: I feel as if something will keep us from ever setting down on Venus.

2nd Astronaut: Don't be silly. I can see the headlines when we get back. (*Raises hands as if reading newspaper*) "First Manned Flight to Venus Successful."

Ground Control: Eighteen, seventeen, sixteen, fifteen . . .

1st Astronaut: We won't make it.

2nd Astronaut (*Still pretending to read newspaper*)**:** "Astronauts

Honored for Actions Beyond the Call of Duty."

Ground Control: Twelve, eleven, ten, ignition.

1st Astronaut: We have ignition.

Ground Control: Everything on go and counting, eight, seven, six (**Two Astronauts** *brace themselves*), five, four, three, two, one. (*Loud*) Blastoff! (**Two Astronauts** *jerk backward, tilting seats, as sound of rocket engines is heard. They strain back against their chairs, acting out "gravity pull." Their arms shake with ship's vibrations. Portable spotlight is shaken to give effect of motion, then they gradually return chairs to original position.*) We have liftoff.

1st Astronaut (*Into microphone*)**:** Check. Ready for first phase rocket release.

Ground Control: First phase jettison completed.

1st Astronaut (*Rubbing back of neck*)**:** I've got a crick in my neck.

2nd Astronaut: You always get a crick in your neck. You can work it out when we get into orbit.

Ground Control: Earth orbit established.

2nd Astronaut (*Into microphone*)**:** Ground Control, our orbiting attitude is not correct. My instruments show we are off yaw by twenty-two hundredths. Ready for countdown for stabilization rocket.

Ground Control: You'll have to try for manual stabilization, Venus trip. Computer's stabilizer and backup not working.

1st Astronaut: See, I told you we'd have problems.

2nd Astronaut (*Into microphone*)**:** A-O.K., Ground Control. All systems go for manual stabilization. (*Pushes buttons with intense concentration, then sighs with relief*) Whew! That was close. (*Turns to* **1st Astronaut**) You'll get your green rocks.

Ground Control: Stabilization completed and locked in. Good work, Venus trip. Your earth orbit is half-way completed. How does Australia look? You should be directly over it.

2nd Astronaut (*Leaning to look out side porthole; into microphone*)**:** I can't see much but twinkling lights.

Ground Control: All right, Venus trip, we need to synchronize for release from earth orbit.

1st Astronaut: Ready, Ground Control.

Ground Control: Three, two, one. Synchronizing accomplished.

2nd Astronaut: Ready for countdown on engine ignition for release from earth orbit.

Ground Control: Countdown for ignition. And counting, five, four, three, two, one.

2nd Astronaut: Venus, here we

come! (**Two Astronauts** *freeze in position as lights go out. Curtain closes.*)

SCENE 2

Time: *Several days later.*
Setting: *Same as Scene 1, except that* **Ground Control,** *though in place, is blacked out.*
At rise: Venu *is concealed in control panel.* **2nd Astronaut** *rubs eyes and stretches, as if just waking.* **1st Astronaut,** *holding cassette player, is moving arms in rhythm to music on tape. He wears earplug and sound of music is not heard.*

2nd Astronaut (*Looking at control panel*): Hey, we're nearly there. Why didn't you wake me? (**1st Astronaut** *doesn't answer, but continues moving rhythmically*) Hey! (*Nudges* **1st Astronaut**)

1st Astronaut (*Removing earplug*): What did you say?

2nd Astronaut: I said, we're nearly there. Why didn't you wake me?

1st Astronaut: Sorry. I wasn't paying attention. (*Begins pushing buttons, etc.*) Ready for orbital approach to Venus. (*Happily*) I guess I'll get my green rocks after all.

2nd Astronaut: Sure you will. (*Into microphone*) Come in, Houston. This is Venus trip. Come in, Ground Control. (*Listens*) Come in, Ground Control, this is Venus trip. Do you copy? (*There is no answer.*)

1st Astronaut: Have we lost radio contact?

2nd Astronaut: It seems that way. (*Imitates* **1st Astronaut's** *musical arm movements*) Unless Ground Control is busy dancing, too. (*Into microphone*) Come in Houston. Do you read? Come in, Ground Control, this is Venus trip. (*Listens, then shakes head*) I guess we've lost them. The Venus atmosphere may have blocked the signal.

1st Astronaut: We'll have to make a landing without them. (*Checks instruments*) I'm ready when you and the computer are. Let's try for Venus orbit.

2nd Astronaut: According to the computer, we have correct trajectory for orbit and should fire in five seconds and counting. Ready? (**1st Astronaut** *makes circle with index finger and thumb.*)

1st Astronaut: Ready. Starting countdown. Five, four, three, two, one.

2nd Astronaut: Forward retro on.

1st Astronaut: Speed reduction accomplished. (*Worried*) That stabilizer is still not functioning. Can you do it manually?

2nd Astronaut: I'll give it a try. Fire left retro at count of three, two, one, fire. (*Pantomimes pulling trigger device*) Just a little more now. (*Relieved*) There!

1st Astronaut: Great! What a job! A thing of beauty. Orbit established.

2nd Astronaut: Wait! Something's wrong.

1st Astronaut: The orbit is fine.

2nd Astronaut: The instruments are flashing on and off like neon lights in Las Vegas. (*Alarmed*) The computer is going out. It's out altogether now. No power, none at all.

1st Astronaut (*Alarmed*)**:** There won't be any cabin oxygen.

2nd Astronaut: Switch to backup.

1st Astronaut: I already have. Everything is dead! (*Both push buttons frantically, then* **2nd Astronaut** *slumps in chair, sighs heavily.*)

2nd Astronaut: It's no use. Everything is out. We're just floating here, helpless.

1st Astronaut: We'll think of something. Maybe it's only temporary. Maybe we're caught in a magnetic field. That would neutralize our power.

2nd Astronaut: We'll make it, somehow. (*Warningly*) And if you say "I told you so," I'll choke you!

1st Astronaut: We don't have much time. It won't take long to use up the air we have in the cabin.

2nd Astronaut (*Sadly*)**:** I never thought it would end this way. I always thought I would be a hero with a ticker tape parade.

1st Astronaut: Hey, buddy. (*Slowly, with feeling*) I . . . well . . . I just wanted to tell you, you've been a real pal.

2nd Astronaut: I couldn't have had a better co-pilot. (*Trying to be more cheerful*) Now, what are we going to do?

1st Astronaut: We could play the cassette tapes.

2nd Astronaut: How can you think of music at a time like this?

1st Astronaut: We might as well. It's the only thing that works. (**1st Astronaut** *turns on tape player. Soft rock music is heard.* **Astronauts** *listen to music for a moment, then begin to cough a little, pull at collars, run hands over brows, etc.*)

2nd Astronaut: I'm really beginning to feel a change in our air supply. (*Suddenly,* **Venu,** *a small space creature or puppet in strange, bright-colored outfit, pops up dancing to music, from inside control panel.*)

1st Astronaut (*Startled*)**:** Do you see what I see?

2nd Astronaut: (*Slowly, with effort*): It's probably a figment of our imagination. When you run out of air, you imagine all sorts of crazy things.

1st Astronaut: Do you mean to tell me that both of us are imagining a little creature, dancing in front of us? (*To* **Venu**) Hello, Imagination.

Venu: My name is not Imagination, it's Venu. I like your music. (*Continues* *dancing until* **1st Astronaut** *turns music off.*) Why did you turn off the music?

2nd Astronaut: Who are you?

Venu: I told you, my name is Venu. If you will turn on the music, I'll turn on your cabin oxygen.

1st Astronaut: That's a deal! (*Turns the music on.* **Astronauts** *breathe deeply.*) Wow! Air! (**Venu** *dances.*)

2nd Astronaut (*To* **Venu**): How did you turn on our air?

Venu: The same way I turned it off.

1st Astronaut (*Shocked*): Did you turn our air off? Why?

Venu: So you couldn't land on my planet. (**1st Astronaut** *turns off music.*) Why do you keep turning off the music?

2nd Astronaut (*Angrily*): What do you mean, so we couldn't land on your planet? Where are you from?

Venu: From the planet you call Venus. You brought your ship into our realm, and we couldn't let you land.

1st Astronaut: Why not?

Venu (*Laughing*): Look at you! Look at me! You are too big. And we are too many.

1st Astronaut: Are there many more like you?

Venu: Millions and millions and millions.

2nd Astronaut: Are the other millions as small as you are?

Venu (*Giggling*): Yes, thank the stars. It is a good thing that we are not bigger. We are using up our resources too quickly as it is.

2nd Astronaut: By resources, do you mean minerals?

Venu: Yes, and energy sources and water and oxygen. If you were to land on our planet, you would crush thousands of us with your ship, and you are so big that you would scare us.

2nd Astronaut: And use up all your resources.

Venu: That's right. You two would use as much water and oxygen in one day as one of our biggest cities does.

1st Astronaut: That makes sense.

Venu: Good. Now you know why you have to stay out here in space. So, turn on your music.

2nd Astronaut: But, Venu, we can't stay out here too much longer. Our computer is down. We will run out of energy and die.

Venu: I thought you could produce all the energy you need.

1st Astronaut: Venu, can you turn all of our systems on?

Venu: Yes, I can—but I won't. If I do, you would land on our planet.

1st Astronaut: No, we promise you we won't land. We understand about your resources. On our planet we are exhausting our resources, too.

2nd Astronaut: We would like to go back home, and we can do that if you would turn our power on.

Venu: Will you send back others like yourself?

1st Astronaut: No, not if it will hurt you. But our planets might exchange information about saving energy and resources.

Venu: Perhaps. Your music is very pleasant. Let me listen to it a little longer.

1st Astronaut: All right. (*Turns on music.* **Venu** *hums and dances.*) How did you get here?

Venu (*Dancing*): I just beamed aboard.

1st Astronaut: Don't you have music on Venus?

Venu: Yes, but it's not good, like this. I like the beat—it's easy to dance to it.

2nd Astronaut: Venu, can you beam heavy things?

Venu: Yes, we can beam something as heavy as this ship, but we don't do it often, because it uses so much energy.

2nd Astronaut: Could you beam something this heavy? (*He picks up tape recorder.*)

Venu: Sure. That would be easy.

2nd Astronaut: Let's make a deal. We'll give you the music.

1st Astronaut: Hey, that's my tape recorder!

2nd Astronaut: It's the very least we can do to thank Venu for restoring our oxygen.

1st Astronaut: I suppose you're right. I can always get another one.

Venu (*Giggling and reaching for recorder*): Stars above! Goody, goody!

2nd Astronaut (*Drawing recorder back to him*): We'll give this to you, *if* you restore our power, so we can go home.

1st Astronaut: And while you're at it, I'd like a green rock from your planet, too.

Venu: Well, all right.

2nd Astronaut: Terrific!

1st Astronaut (*Handing batteries to* **Venu**): Here are the extra batteries.

Venu (*Puzzled*): Batteries? What are batteries?

1st Astronaut: When the machine won't play anymore, open it here (*Points to back of machine*), put in the batteries, and the music will play again. It's easy. (*Hands recorder to* **Venu**)

Venu: The others will probably be more interested in the batteries than the music. But I like the music. Thank you very much.

1st Astronaut: Wait! What about our power?

Venu: Have a nice trip home. You won't mind if I give you a little push, will you? (*Giggles*) Bye. (*She disappears into control panel.* **Astronauts** *suddenly jerk and bounce around in their seats.*)

2nd Astronaut: Hey, what's going on? (**Astronauts** *lean back in their chairs, indicating that ship is moving forward. Light flashes.*)

1st Astronaut: We're moving forward! Venu did it—she turned on our systems! (*Move chairs back to upright positions. Lights come up again on* **Ground Control.**)

Ground Control: Come in, Venus trip. Can you read me? Come in. We are picking you up on scan. Are you there?

2nd Astronaut (*To* **1st Astronaut**): Everything is working! (*Into microphone*) Yes, we hear you, Ground Control. Everything on go for return trip. Landing on Venus was not feasible.

1st Astronaut (*Dreamily*): She was nice.

Ground Control: Glad to hear you, Venus trip. (*Pause*) Your stabilizer works now! How did you fix it?

2nd Astronaut: You wouldn't believe us if we told you. (*To* **1st Astronaut**) We have a lot to tell the scientists back home.

1st Astronaut: She liked my music!

2nd Astronaut: Liked it so well that we'll have peace and quiet all the way home.

1st Astronaut: Speaking of home, I'm ready to go. (*Finds rock on control panel. Pleased*) Look! A little green rock. She remembered, after all!

Ground Control: Roger, Venus trip. Glad to have you aboard. All systems are go for the return flight home. *(Curtain)*

THE END

IMAGES

FROM *A SHORT WALK AROUND THE PYRAMIDS & THROUGH THE WORLD OF ART*

BY PHILIP M. ISAACSON

1. Fitz Hugh Lane (United States), *Owl's Head,* 1862

This is a sublime moment (1). We are back in 1862, standing along the shore of a small island in Penobscot Bay, Maine. Ahead of us is a finger of land called Owl's Head, and beyond, in the distance, are the Camden Hills. It is sunset. Light, like a phantom, slides across the bay, tracing the edges of all that it touches. The still ship, the man leaning on the pole, the line of houses are locked in that light-filled moment. Does it look real? Yes, but somehow it isn't quite what we have seen in nature. The water, the high clouds, the reflections are familiar; still, we have a feeling that they, the ship, the boatman in his red shirt, the stillness, and the pure light are so perfect that the moment could never have happened. We have a feeling that it is partly an illusion.

We have been looking at a painting by Fitz Hugh Lane. It is called *Owl's Head,* and it is one of many that he painted of the same scene. In his imagination, Lane saw the bay as an enchanted place, and he painted it according to that private vision. He moved the Camden Hills from their true location (far to the right of the lighthouse); he lowered the Head a bit; and he put in a square-sailed vessel and a boatman. And he joined all of this together by a light that is so clear, so weightless, that it is magical.

Therefore, although Lane's scene—a landscape—is beautiful, it isn't really what he saw from that island. It's what he saw in his imagination. Like the carvers of the Elgin Marbles,* he has given us something idealized. *Owl's Head* is another reminder that artists invent and change forms to express their imagination and their feelings.

* A group of ancient Greek sculptures of gods and goddesses.

2. **Marsden Hartley (United States), *After the Storm, Vinalhaven,* 1938**

In this painting we're still on the Maine coast, but on an island called Vinalhaven (2). It is about the year 1938, and instead of a quiet, light-washed bay, we find granite and dark water. Black pines notch the sky, and they, the rocks, and the water seem roughly painted, almost crude. The painting is called *After the Storm, Vinalhaven.* In it, painter Marsden Hartley . . . describes his feelings about a place made of hard granite, near a sea that is often unfriendly. Unlike *Owl's Head,* this painting doesn't look at all real; still, through its raw, powerfully painted forms and its simple, vivid colors, we sense the stern character of that rugged island.

So we see that two artists may have quite different feelings about a similar place. One, Fitz Hugh Lane, is moved by the calm, quiet side of nature; the other, Marsden Hartley, by its dramatic side. Both artists tell us about their feelings, and although one painting is more realistic than the other, neither copies nature. Through a delicate wash of light, Lane shows us a moment that never quite happened in a place that seems quite real; through simple, rugged shapes, Hartley tells us about the rough power in the natural world and, perhaps, in himself.

This is our third landscape (3). It was painted by April Gornik, and its title is *Fresh Light.* In it, the field, the trees around it, and the sky are softened by damp summer light. The light gives the painting an air of emptiness, as though no one has ever walked in this lonely place. *Fresh Light* is not like *Owl's Head* or *After the Storm, Vinalhaven.* We're certain that each of those places exists. In *Fresh Light* we're not so certain, and its painter doesn't give us the answer; she provides us with a glimpse of a soft moment in nature and then asks us to decide the question for ourselves.

3. April Gornik (United States), *Fresh Light,* 1987

4. Ellen Phelan (United States), *After Atget,* 1984

Does this place exist (4)? Before we try to answer, we must decide what we're looking at. It's a painting by Ellen Phelan and is called *After Atget.* "Atget" refers to Eugène Atget, a photographer who lived in Paris and who, from about 1900 to 1927, produced carefully composed photographs taken along country roads in France and in the streets of Paris. Ellen Phelan admires them. Her painting was probably inspired by one of Atget's photographs of an old French road. It is almost entirely abstract; still, in its dancing planes of color we can find forms that remind us of a road, trees, and the bright, wet sunshine that follows a rain. The landscape doesn't look real, but the forms are so bold that we feel that such a place must exist. The forms are only hints, but we accept them—and with them the reality of the place.

5. Frank Stella (United States), *Chocorua II,* 1966

This is a painting (5) by Frank Stella and it is even more abstract than *After Atget.* In that painting, with the help of our imagination, we could find the road and follow it through the trees and into the distance. Here there is no distance. Instead of being able to look into a scene, our eyes stop at the face of the canvas.

Up to now we have used paintings as windows to peer into a story. We cannot do that with this work because its flat bands of color do not lead our eye beyond the surface of the canvas, and its unusual shape even reminds us of sculpture. Can we find a story in its stiff forms? . . .

The title, *Chocorua II,* gives us a hint. Chocorua is the name of a pyramid-shaped mountain rising amid the lakes in eastern New Hampshire. Nearby is the Saco River, and beyond the river is the dark Pemigewasset Wilderness. Knowing this, we can find symbols that remind us of a triangular peak, a fast-moving yellow river, and, finally, a deep green wilderness. Like the forms in all of the paintings that we have looked at in this chapter, the symbols in *Chocorua II* join to give us the feeling of a landscape.

Will we always be able to find a story in paintings? Perhaps not. There are many reasons for creating art, and telling a story is only one of them. For example, an artist can paint simply to express feelings or just for the pleasure of painting, without describing something exactly.

6. Jackson Pollock (United States), *Composition with Pouring II,* 1943

Look at this painting by Jackson Pollock (6). Its name, *Composition with Pouring II,* tells us that it was made by pouring and perhaps by spattering paint on a canvas. It has no story to relate other than that of the many complicated routes the painter's hand took as he created the work. In following the trails on the face of *Composition,* we feel close to the very act of painting. They make us feel that Pollock is still near the picture and that we are near to him.

So we must learn to enjoy some paintings for the feelings created by their forms and colors alone . . . .

IN RESPONSE

Colors and Shapes

This selection ends by saying, "So we must learn to enjoy some paintings for the feelings created by their forms and colors alone." Look back at the paintings. What feelings do you get from the colors and shapes in each one? Which painting gives you the strongest feeling? Why?

Find the Best Story

The author thinks of some paintings as "windows to peer into a story." Which painting in this essay do you think tells the best story? Why? Write the story that you see in the painting you chose.

AUTHOR AT WORK

Philip M. Isaacson is an art critic for the *Maine Sunday Telegram.* He enjoys using his experience to introduce young people to the world of art.

Mr. Isaacson lives in Lewiston, Maine, with his wife and three children.

★ Award-winning Author

Another Book by . . .

Philip M. Isaacson

Round Buildings, Square Buildings, & Buildings That Wiggle Like a Fish, written with photographs by Philip M. Isaacson, Knopf, 1988

Library Link "Images" was taken from *A Short Walk Around the Pyramids & Through the World of Art* by Philip M. Isaacson. You might enjoy reading the entire book to find out more about art.

Where Ideas Come From

Ideas for artwork often come from an artist's surroundings or are drawn from personal experiences. Some artists make images that look very real. Others use imagination to show their ideas or emotions.

Maria Izquierdo painted many pictures of fruits and vegetables in her native Mexico. Look at the objects on the table and the details in the tablecloth. What do they tell you about her surroundings?

Painting by Maria Izquierdo (Mexican),
***Bodegón con Fresas* (*Still Life with Strawberries*), 1952**

Painting by Bert G. Phillips (United States),
***Our Washerwoman's Family,* 1918**

Bert Phillips painted scenes in New Mexico for sixty years. Who are the people in this scene? What can you tell about them from their facial expressions, their clothes, and the objects around them?

Quilt by Faith Ringgold (United States), *The Sunflowers Quilting Bee at Arles,* 1991

These works of art tell stories about each artist's culture and experience. What clues about the artist's background do you see in each piece? Can you find a story in any of the pieces? Describe what you find.

Marc Chagall, *I and the Village,* 1911, oil on canvas, 6′ 3 5/8″ x 59 5/8.″ The Museum of Modern art, New York, Mrs. Simon Guggenheim Fund. Photograph © 1996 The Museum of Modern Art, New York/© 1995 Artists Rights Society (ARS), New York/ADAGP, Paris

Painting by Marc Chagall (Russian), *I and the Village,* 1911

Sculpture by Kristine Yuki Aono (United States), *Obasan/Grandma Kimono,* 1992

Maria Izquierdo's Mexico

As a girl, Maria Izquierdo[1] loved the circus that came each year to her pueblo[2] in the Mexican state of Jalisco.[3] The town became a festival with colorful decorations and people celebrating. The circus brought performers, games, and hot-air balloon rides.

Ms. Izquierdo left her small pueblo behind and moved to Mexico City in 1923. Still, she thought about the people and places she had known as a child. She remembered people living in the simple way their ancestors had. She recalled the food they ate and objects they kept in their homes. She thought about how they prayed and how they celebrated.

Ms. Izquierdo began to paint what she remembered. She painted open cupboards filled

***Alacena (Cupboard),* 1952**

1 **Izquierdo** (*ees KYEHR doh*)
2 **pueblo** (*PWEHB loh*) village, town
3 **Jalisco** (*hah LEES koh*)

El Circo (The Circus), 1939

with fruits and vegetables, small statues, and handmade Mexican crafts. She painted household altars with flickering candles. Some of her paintings show circus performers. Others show peasant women and scenes from village life.

Some Mexican artists she knew painted famous people and important events. Ms. Izquierdo believed that the ordinary people and everyday scenes she painted were more important. "I try to make my work reflect the true Mexico which I feel and love," she said.

Mis Sobrinas (My Nieces), 1940

AWARD WINNER

LAFFF

by Lensey Namioka

In movies, geniuses have frizzy white hair, right? They wear thick glasses and have names like Dr. Zweistein.

Peter Lu didn't have frizzy white hair. He had straight hair, as black as licorice. He didn't wear thick glasses, either, since his vision was normal.

Peter's family, like ours, had immigrated from China, but they had settled here first. When we moved into a house just two doors down from the Lus, they gave us some good advice on how to get along in America.

I went to the same school as Peter, and we walked to the school bus together every morning. Like many Chinese parents, mine made sure that I worked very hard in school.

In spite of all I could do, my grades were nothing compared to Peter's. He was at the top in all his classes. We walked to the school bus without talking because I was a little scared of him. Besides, he was always deep in thought.

Peter didn't have any friends. Most of the kids thought he was a nerd because they saw his head always buried in books. I didn't think he even tried to join the rest of us or cared what the others thought of him.

Then on Halloween he surprised us all. As I went down the block trick-or-treating, dressed as a zucchini in my green sweats, I heard a strange, deep voice behind me say, "How do you do."

I yelped and turned around. Peter was wearing a long, black Chinese gown with slits in the sides. On his head he had a little round cap, and down each side of his mouth drooped a thin, long mustache.

"I am Dr. Lu Manchu, the mad scientist," he announced, putting his hands in his sleeves and bowing.

He smiled when he saw me staring at his costume. I smiled back. I knew he was making fun of the way some kids believed in stereotypes about Chinese people. Still his was a scary smile, somehow.

Some of the other kids came up, and when they saw Peter, they were impressed. "Hey, neat!" said one boy.

I hadn't expected Peter to put on a costume and go trick-or-treating like a normal kid. So maybe he did want to join the others after all—at least some of the time. After that night he wasn't a nerd anymore. He was Dr. Lu Manchu. Even some of the teachers began to call him that.

When we became too old for trick-or-treating, Peter was still Dr. Lu Manchu. The rumor was that he was working on a fantastic machine in his parents' garage. But nobody had any idea what it was.

One evening, as I was coming home from a baby-sitting job, I cut across the Lus' backyard. Passing their garage, I saw through a little window that the light was on. My curiosity got the better of me, and I peeked in.

I saw a booth that looked like a shower stall. A stool stood in the middle of the stall, and hanging

over the stool was something that looked like a great big shower head.

Suddenly a deep voice behind me said, "Good evening, Angela." Peter bowed and smiled his scary smile. He didn't have his costume on and he didn't have the long, droopy mustache. But he was Dr. Lu Manchu.

"What are you doing?" I squeaked.

Still in his strange, deep voice, Peter said, "What are *you* doing? After all, this is my garage."

"I was just cutting across your yard to get home. Your parents never complained before."

"I thought you were spying on me," said Peter. "I thought you wanted to know about my machine." He hissed when he said the word *machine*.

Honestly, he was beginning to frighten me. "What machine?" I demanded. "You mean this shower-stall thing?"

He drew himself up and narrowed his eyes, making them into thin slits. "This is my time machine!"

I goggled at him. "You mean . . . you mean . . . this machine can send you forward and backward in time?"

"Well, actually, I can only send things forward in time," admitted Peter, speaking in his normal voice again. "That's why I'm calling the machine LAFFF. It stands for Lu's Artifact For Fast Forward."

Of course Peter always won first prize at the annual statewide science fair. But that's a long way from making a time machine. Minus his mustache and long Chinese gown, he was just Peter Lu.

"I don't believe it!" I said. "I bet LAFFF is only good for a laugh."

"Okay, Angela. I'll show you!" hissed Peter.

He sat down on the stool and twisted a dial. I heard some *bleep*s, *cheep*s, and *gurgle*s. Peter disappeared.

He must have done it with mirrors. I looked around the garage. I peeked under the tool bench. There was no sign of him.

"Okay, I give up," I told him. "It's a good trick, Peter. You can come out now."

Bleep, cheep, and *gurgle* went the machine, and there was Peter, sitting on the stool. He held a red rose in his hand. "What do you think of that?"

I blinked. "So you produced a flower. Maybe you had it under the stool."

"Roses bloom in June, right?" he demanded.

That was true. And this was December.

"I sent myself forward in time to June when the flowers were blooming," said Peter. "And I picked the rose from our yard. Convinced, Angela?"

It was too hard to swallow. "You said you couldn't send things back in time," I objected. "So how did you bring the rose back?"

But even as I spoke I saw that his hands were empty. The rose was gone.

"That's one of the problems with the machine," said Peter. "When I send myself forward, I can't seem to stay there for long. I snap back to my own time after only a minute. Anything I bring with me snaps back to its own time, too. So my rose has gone back to this June."

I was finally convinced, and I began to see possibilities. "Wow, just think: If I don't want to do the dishes, I can send myself forward to the time when the dishes are already done."

"That won't do you much good," said Peter. "You'd soon pop back to the time when the dishes were still dirty."

Too bad. "There must be something your machine is good for," I said. Then I had another idea. "Hey, you can bring me back a piece of fudge from the future, and I can eat it twice: once now, and again in the future."

"Yes, but the fudge wouldn't stay in your stomach," said Peter. "It would go back to the future."

"That's even better!" I said. "I can enjoy eating the fudge over and over again without getting fat!"

It was late, and I had to go home before my parents started to worry. Before I left, Peter said, "Look, Angela, there's still a lot of work to do on LAFFF. Please don't tell anybody about the machine until I've got it right."

A few days later I asked him how he was doing.

"I can stay in the future time a bit longer now," he said. "Once I got it up to four minutes."
"Is that enough time to bring me back some fudge from the future?" I asked.

"We don't keep many sweets around the house," he said. "But I'll see what I can do."

A few minutes later, he came back with a spring roll for me. "My mother was frying these in the kitchen, and I snatched one while she wasn't looking."

I bit into the hot, crunchy spring roll, but before I finished chewing, it disappeared. The taste of soy sauce, green onions, and bean sprouts stayed a little longer in my mouth, though.

It was fun to play around with LAFFF, but it wasn't really useful. I didn't know what a great help it would turn out to be.

Every year our school held a writing contest, and the winning story for each grade got printed in our school magazine. I wanted desperately to win. I worked awfully hard in school, but my parents still thought I could do better.

Winning the writing contest would show my parents that I was really good in something. I love writing stories, and I have lots of ideas. But when I actually write them down, my stories never turn out as good as I thought. I just can't seem to find the right words, because English isn't my first language.

I got an honorable mention last year, but it wasn't the same as winning and showing my parents my name, Angela Tang, printed in the school magazine.

The deadline for the contest was getting close, and I had a pile of stories written, but none of them looked like a winner.

Then, the day before the deadline, *boing,* a brilliant idea hit me.

I thought of Peter and his LAFFF machine.

I rushed over to the Lus' garage and, just as I had hoped, Peter was there, tinkering with his machine.

"I've got this great idea for winning the story contest," I told him breathlessly. "You see, to be certain of winning, I have to write the story that would be the winner."

"That's obvious," Peter said dryly. "In fact, you're going around in a circle."

"Wait, listen!" I said. "I want to use LAFFF and go forward to the time when the next issue of the school magazine is out. Then I can read the winning story."

After a moment Peter nodded. "I see. You plan to write down the winning story after you've read it and then send it in to the contest."

I nodded eagerly. "The story would *have* to win, because it's the winner!"

Peter began to look interested. "I've got LAFFF to the point where I can stay in the future for seven minutes now. Will that be long enough for you?"

"I'll just have to work quickly," I said.

Peter smiled. It wasn't his scary Lu Manchu smile, but a nice smile. He was getting as excited as I was. "Okay, Angela. Let's go for it."

He led me to the stool. "What's your destination?" he asked. "I mean, *when's* your destination?"

Suddenly I was nervous. I told myself that Peter had made many time trips, and he looked perfectly healthy.

Why not? What have I got to lose—except time?

I took a deep breath. "I want to go forward three weeks in time." By then I'd have a copy of the new school magazine in my room.

"Ready, Angela?" asked Peter.

"As ready as I'll ever be," I whispered.

Bleep, cheep, and *gurgle.* Suddenly Peter disappeared.

What went wrong? Did Peter get sent by mistake, instead of me?

Then I realized what had happened. Three weeks later in time Peter might be somewhere else. No wonder I couldn't see him.

There was no time to be lost. Rushing out of Peter's garage, I ran over to our house and entered through the back door.

Mother was in the kitchen. When she saw me, she stared. "Angela! I thought you were upstairs taking a shower!"

"Sorry!" I panted. "No time to talk!"

I dashed up to my room. Then I suddenly had a strange idea. What if I met *myself* in my room? Argh! It was a spooky thought.

There was nobody in my room. Where was I? I mean, where was the I of three weeks later?

Wait. Mother had just said she thought I was taking a shower. Down the hall, I could hear the water running in the bathroom. Okay. That meant I wouldn't run into me for a while.

I went to the shelf above my desk and frantically pawed through the junk piled there. I found it! I found the latest issue of the school magazine, the one with the winning stories printed in it.

How much time had passed? Better hurry.

The shower had stopped running. This meant the other me was out of the bathroom. Have to get out of here!

Too late. Just as I started down the stairs, I heard Mother talking again. "Angela! A minute ago you were all dressed! Now you're in your robe again and your hair's all wet! I don't understand."

I shivered. It was scary, listening to Mother talking to myself downstairs. I heard my other self answering something, then the sound of her—my—steps coming up the stairs. In a panic, I dodged into the spare room and closed the door.

I heard the steps—my steps—go past and into my room.

The minute I heard the door of my room close, I rushed out and down the stairs.

Mother was standing at the foot of the stairs. When she saw me, her mouth dropped. "But . . . but . . . just a minute ago you were in your robe and your hair was all wet!"

"See you later, Mother," I panted. And I ran.

Behind me I heard Mother muttering, "I'm going mad!"

I didn't stop and try to explain. I might go mad, too.

It would be great if I could just keep the magazine with me. But, like the spring roll, it would get carried back to its own time after a few minutes. So the next best thing was to read the magazine as fast as I could.

It was hard to run and flip through the magazine at the same time. But I made it back to Peter's garage and plopped down on the stool.

At last I found the story: the story that had won the contest in our grade. I started to read.

Suddenly I heard *bleep, cheep,* and *gurgle,* and Peter loomed up in front of me. I was back in my original time again.

But I still had the magazine! Now I had to read the story before the magazine popped back to the future. It was hard to concentrate with Peter jumping up and down impatiently, so different from his usual calm, collected self.

I read a few paragraphs, and I was beginning to see how the story would shape up. But before I got any further, the magazine disappeared from my hand.

So I didn't finish reading the story. I didn't reach the end, where the name of the winning writer was printed.

That night I stayed up very late to write down what I remembered of the story. It had a neat plot, and I could see why it was the winner.

I hadn't read the entire story, so I had to make up the ending myself. But that was okay, since I knew how it should come out.

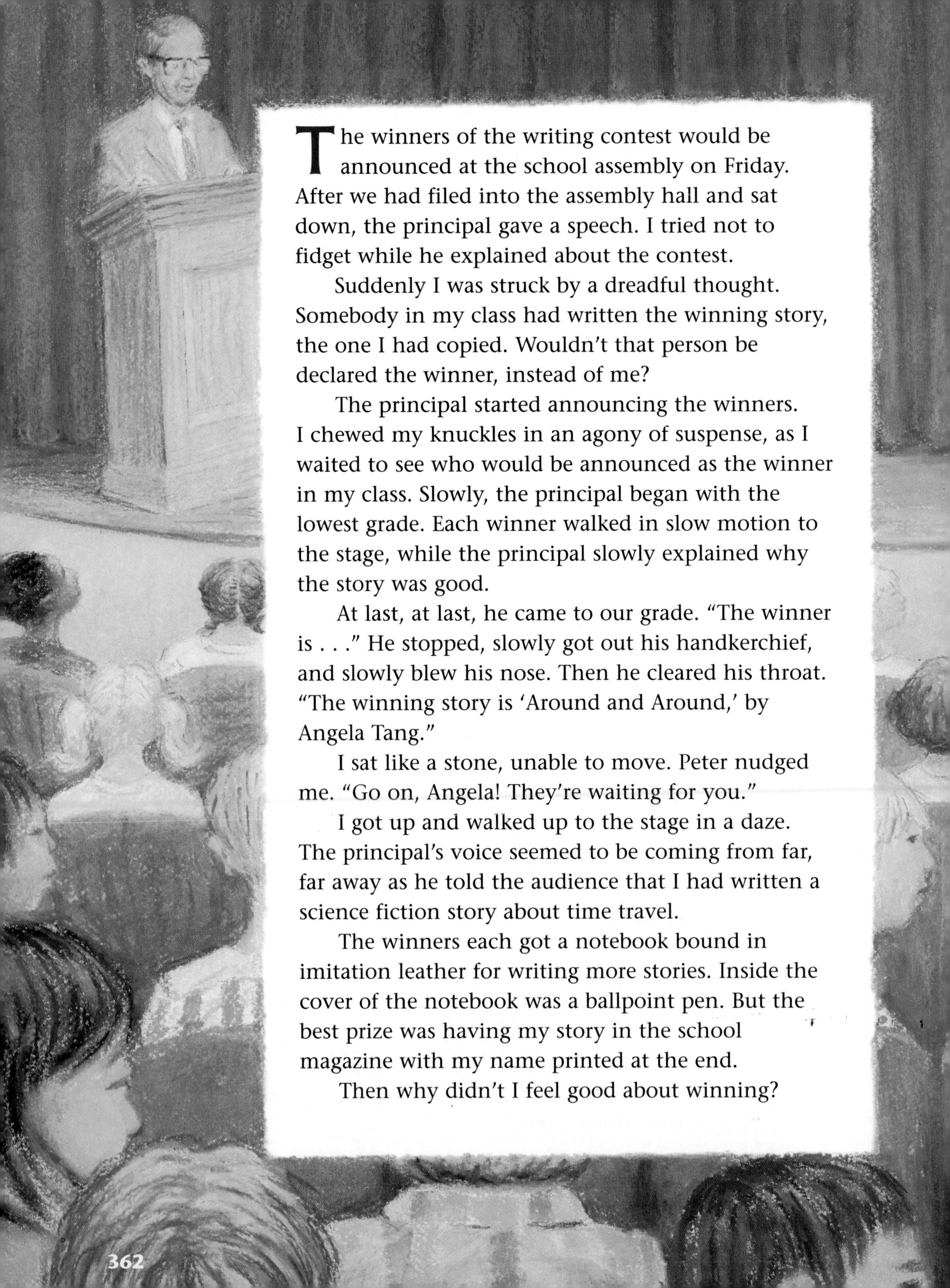

The winners of the writing contest would be announced at the school assembly on Friday. After we had filed into the assembly hall and sat down, the principal gave a speech. I tried not to fidget while he explained about the contest.

Suddenly I was struck by a dreadful thought. Somebody in my class had written the winning story, the one I had copied. Wouldn't that person be declared the winner, instead of me?

The principal started announcing the winners. I chewed my knuckles in an agony of suspense, as I waited to see who would be announced as the winner in my class. Slowly, the principal began with the lowest grade. Each winner walked in slow motion to the stage, while the principal slowly explained why the story was good.

At last, at last, he came to our grade. "The winner is . . ." He stopped, slowly got out his handkerchief, and slowly blew his nose. Then he cleared his throat. "The winning story is 'Around and Around,' by Angela Tang."

I sat like a stone, unable to move. Peter nudged me. "Go on, Angela! They're waiting for you."

I got up and walked up to the stage in a daze. The principal's voice seemed to be coming from far, far away as he told the audience that I had written a science fiction story about time travel.

The winners each got a notebook bound in imitation leather for writing more stories. Inside the cover of the notebook was a ballpoint pen. But the best prize was having my story in the school magazine with my name printed at the end.

Then why didn't I feel good about winning?

After assembly, the kids in our class crowded around to congratulate me. Peter formally shook my hand. "Good work, Angela," he said, and winked at me.

That didn't make me feel any better. I hadn't won the contest fairly. Instead of writing the story myself, I had copied it from the school magazine.

That meant someone in our class—one of the kids here—had actually written the story. Who was it?

My heart was knocking against my ribs as I stood there and waited for someone to complain that I had stolen his story.

Nobody did.

As we were riding the school bus home, Peter looked at me. "You don't seem very happy about winning the contest, Angela."

"No, I'm not," I mumbled. "I feel just awful."

"Tell you what," suggested Peter. "Come over to my house and we'll discuss it."

"What is there to discuss?" I asked glumly. "I won the contest because I cheated."

"Come on over, anyway. My mother bought a fresh package of humbow in Chinatown."

I couldn't turn down that invitation. Humbow, a roll stuffed with barbecued pork, is my favorite snack.

Peter's mother came into the kitchen while we were munching, and he told her about the contest.

Mrs. Lu looked pleased. "I'm very glad, Angela. You have a terrific imagination, and you deserve to win."

"I like Angela's stories," said Peter. "They're original."

It was the first compliment he had ever paid me, and I felt my face turning red.

After Mrs. Lu left us, Peter and I each had another humbow. But I was still miserable. "I wish I had never started this. I feel like such a jerk."

Empty Head

An idea came
Into my head
So slender
So slight
An idea came
Fleetingly
Fearfully
Came to alight
It wheeled about
Stretched itself out
An idea came
That I wanted to stay
But it brushed my hand
And taking its flight
Through my fingers
Slipped away.

—Malick Fall
translated from the French by John Reed
and Clive Wake

Dreams

Hold fast to dreams
For if dreams die
Life is a broken-winged bird
That cannot fly.

Hold fast to dreams
For when dreams go
Life is a barren field
Frozen with snow.

—Langston Hughes

Express **Yourself**

How can you travel great distances without budging from your seat? It's simple. The selections in Images and Imaginings have already taken you to faraway places and have shown you new ways of looking at things. Your own imagination can take you even further.

Imagine a New Ending

What if the dog ("Milo's Mysterious Gift") hadn't helped Milo leave the Doldrums? What if another student had claimed authorship of Angela's story ("LAFFF")? Can you imagine these stories ending differently? Write a new ending for one of the stories. Use your own ideas and what you know about the characters to help you.

The Right Road

One of the road signs at the beginning of Milo's journey says, "Have your destination in mind." Yet the Whether Man tells him, "There are no wrong roads to anywhere." Which statement do you think the main characters in "LAFFF" and "First Manned Flight to Venus" would prefer? In a small group, discuss the answer. Which quote do you prefer? Explain your choice.

Picture a Setting

The authors and illustrators in this theme took you to lands beyond, such as China, Venus, and the future. They tried to help you make mental pictures of each place. Which story best helped you imagine the setting? Explain your choice with examples of images, descriptive writing, or dialogue from the story.

Why Aren't They Welcome?

In "Peach Blossom Spring," the villagers don't want the fisherman to tell anyone about their valley. In "Last Manned Flight to Venus," Venu doesn't want the astronauts to land on her planet. What reasons does Venu give? Which ones might apply to the villagers? to our planet? Why? Discuss your answers with a partner.

The Artist Inside You

In "Images" and "Where Ideas Come From" (Fine Art Portfolio), you saw how artists use their imagination to make ordinary places and things look extraordinary. If you were an artist, what real place might you choose as a subject? How would you make it look different? Write or draw your thoughts. Use your own ideas and examples from the two selections.

More Books for You to Enjoy

Bright Shadow

by Avi, Aladdin, 1994

Morwenna, a servant in the king's castle, meets a wizard who gives her five magic wishes. The wishes may be the answer to Morwenna's dreams, or they may become a terrible burden.

Time Out

by Helen Cresswell, illustrated by Peter Elwell, Macmillan, 1990

Tweeny Wilks lives with her parents in 1887. When her family's vacation plans are ruined by a fire, Tweeny and her parents use an old book of magic spells to take a trip—one hundred years into the future.

Augusta & Trab

by Christopher de Vinck, Four Winds Press, 1993

To fill the emptiness created by her mother's death, ten-year-old Augusta dreams up fantastic adventures. Then she and her cat, Trab, set off on an extraordinary journey that leads them to a very special place.

Starting Home: The Story of Horace Pippin, Painter

by Mary E. Lyons, Charles Scribner's Sons, 1993

African American folk artist Horace Pippin brings everyday happenings and historic moments to life in his paintings. The self-taught artist is driven by his burning desire to fulfill a dream.

Something New Begins: New & Selected Poems

by Lilian Moore, illustrated by Mary J. Dunton, Atheneum, 1982

This sparkling collection of poems will provide you with a new look at the ordinary and the extraordinary.

Learning from Nature

Theme
5
“Let Nature be
your teacher.”
— William Wordsworth

Theme 5

Learning from Nature

CONTENTS

Theme Trade Books

Surtsey: The Newest Place on Earth
by Kathryn Lasky
An undersea volcano erupts in 1963 and breaks through the water's surface to form a new island. This is the true story of Surtsey, an island that may hold clues about the beginning of life on earth.

Waterman's Boy
by Susan Sharpe
Ben Warren's father works as a waterman fishing in Chesapeake Bay. When Ben meets David Watchman, a scientist, he begins to learn why the crab population his father depends on is dying.

Theme Magazine

Do all birds fly south for the winter? How did dogs become man's best friend? The answers to these and other nature questions are waiting for you in the Theme Magazine *Bio Zone*.

The Dolphins Led Me Home

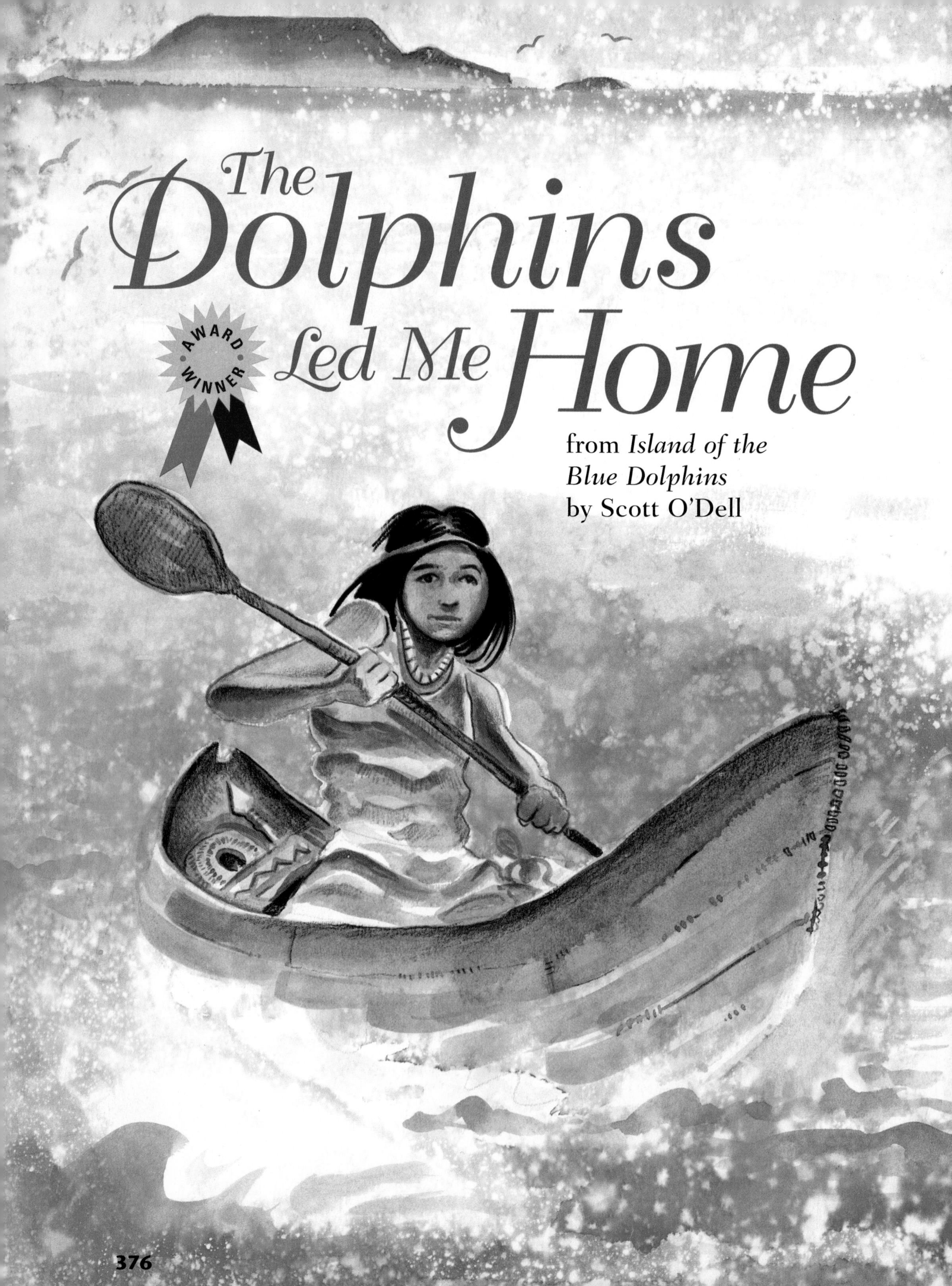

from *Island of the Blue Dolphins*
by Scott O'Dell

When Karana was a girl, a group of visiting hunters attacked the island where she lived. Her people, the Ghalas-at, fled. They accidentally left behind Karana's younger brother, so she swam back to the island to be with him. After a pack of wild dogs kills her brother, Karana tries to sail to the mainland in an old, abandoned canoe.

The sun was in the west when I left the shore. The sea was calm behind the high cliffs. Using the two-bladed paddle I quickly skirted the south part of the island. As I reached the sandspit the wind struck. I was paddling from the back of the canoe because you can go faster kneeling there, but I could not handle it in the wind.

Kneeling in the middle of the canoe, I paddled hard and did not pause until I had gone through the tides that run fast around the sandspit. There were many small waves and I was soon wet, but as I came out from behind the spit the spray lessened and the waves grew long and rolling. Though it would have been easier to go the way they slanted, this would have taken me in the wrong direction. I therefore kept them on my left hand, as well as the island, which grew smaller and smaller, behind me.

At dusk I looked back. The Island of the Blue Dolphins had disappeared. This was the first time that I felt afraid.

There were only hills and valleys of water around me now. When I was in a valley I could see nothing and when the canoe rose out of it, only the ocean stretching away and away.

Night fell and I drank from the basket. The water cooled my throat.

The sea was black and there was no difference between it and the sky. The waves made no sound among themselves, only faint noises as they went under the canoe or struck against it. Sometimes the noises seemed angry and at other times like people laughing. I was not hungry because of my fear.

The first star made me feel less afraid. It came out low in the sky and it was in front of me, toward the east. Other stars began to appear all around, but it was this one I kept my gaze upon. It was in the figure that we call a serpent, a star which shone green and which I knew. Now and then it was hidden by mist, yet it always came out brightly again.

Without this star I would have been lost, for the waves never changed. They came always from the same direction and in a manner that kept pushing me away from the place I wanted to reach. For this reason the canoe made a path in the black water like a snake. But somehow I kept moving toward the star which shone in the east.

This star rose high and then I kept the North Star on my left hand, the one we call "the star that does not move." The wind grew quiet. Since it always died down when the night was half over, I knew how long I had been traveling and how far away the dawn was.

About this time I found that the canoe was leaking. Before dark I had emptied one of the baskets in which food was stored and used it to dip out the water that came over the sides. The water that now moved around my knees was not from the waves.

I stopped paddling and worked with the basket until the bottom of the canoe was almost dry. Then I searched around, feeling in the dark along the smooth planks, and found the place near the bow where the water was seeping through a crack as long as my hand and the width of a finger. Most of the time it was out of the sea, but it leaked whenever the canoe dipped forward in the waves.

The places between the planks were filled with black pitch which we gather along the shore. Lacking this, I tore a piece of fiber from my skirt and pressed it into the crack, which held back the water.

Dawn broke in a clear sky and as the sun came out of the waves I saw that it was far off on my left. During the night I had drifted south of the place I wished to go, so I changed my direction and paddled along the path made by the rising sun.

There was no wind on this morning and the long waves went quietly under the canoe. I therefore moved faster than during the night.

I was very tired, but more hopeful than I had been since I left the island. If the good weather did not change I would cover many leagues before dark. Another night and another day might bring me within sight of the shore toward which I was going.

Not long after dawn, while I was thinking of this strange place and what it would look like, the canoe began to leak again. This crack was between the same planks, but was a larger one and close to where I was kneeling.

The fiber I tore from my skirt and pushed into the crack held back most of the water which seeped in whenever the canoe rose and fell with the waves. Yet I could see that the planks were weak from one end to the other, probably from the canoe being stored so long in the sun, and that they might open along their whole length if the waves grew rougher.

It was suddenly clear to me that it was dangerous to go on. The voyage would take two more days, perhaps longer. By turning back to the island I would not have nearly so far to travel.

Still I could not make up my mind to do so. The sea was calm and I had come far. The thought of turning back after all this labor was more than I could bear. Even greater was the thought of the deserted island I would return to, of living there alone and forgotten. For how many suns and how many moons?

The canoe drifted idly on the calm sea while these thoughts went over and over in my mind, but when I saw the water seeping through the crack again, I picked up the paddle. There was no choice except to turn back toward the island.

I knew that only by the best of fortune would I ever reach it.

The wind did not blow until the sun was overhead. Before that time I covered a good distance, pausing only when it was necessary to dip water from the canoe. With the wind I went more slowly and had to stop more often because of the water spilling over the sides, but the leak did not grow worse.

This was my first good fortune. The next was when a swarm of dolphins appeared. They came swimming out of the west, but as they saw the canoe they turned around in a great circle and began to follow me. They swam up slowly and so close that I could see their eyes, which are large and the color of the ocean. Then they swam on ahead of the canoe, crossing back and forth in front of it, diving in and out, as if they were weaving a piece of cloth with their broad snouts.

Dolphins are animals of good omen. It made me happy to have them swimming around the canoe, and though my hands had begun to bleed from the chafing of the paddle, just watching them made me forget the pain. I was very lonely before they appeared, but now I felt that I had friends with me and did not feel the same.

The blue dolphins left me shortly before dusk. They left as quickly as they had come, going on into the west, but for a long time I could see the last of the sun shining on them. After night fell I could still see them in my thoughts and it was because of this that I kept on paddling when I wanted to lie down and sleep.

More than anything, it was the blue dolphins that took me back home.

Fog came with the night, yet from time to time I could see the star that stands high in the west, the red star called Magat which is part of the figure that looks like a crawfish and is known by that name. The crack in the planks grew wider so I had to stop often to fill it with fiber and to dip out the water.

The night was very long, longer than the night before. Twice I dozed kneeling there in the canoe, though I was more afraid than I had ever been. But the morning broke clear and in front of me lay the dim line of the island like a great fish sunning itself on the sea.

I reached it before the sun was high, the sandspit and its tides that bore me into the shore. My legs were stiff from kneeling and as the canoe struck the sand I fell when I rose to climb out. I crawled through the shallow water and up the beach. There I lay for a long time, hugging the sand in happiness.

I was too tired to think of the wild dogs. Soon I fell asleep.

I was awakened by the waves dragging at my feet. Night had come, but being too tired to leave the sandspit, I crawled to a higher place where I would be safe from the tide, and again went to sleep.

In the morning I found the canoe a short distance away. I took the baskets, my spear, and the bow and arrows, and turned the canoe over so that the tides could not take it out to sea. I then climbed to the headland where I had lived before.

I felt as if I had been gone a long time as I stood there looking down from the high rock. I was happy to be home. Everything that I saw—the otter playing in the kelp, the rings of foam around the rocks that guarded the harbor, the gulls flying, the tides moving past the sandspit—filled me with happiness.

I was surprised that I felt this way, for it was only a short time ago that I had stood on this same rock and felt that I could not bear to live here another day.

I looked out at the blue water stretching away and all the fear I had felt during the time of the voyage came back to me. On the morning I first sighted the island and it had seemed like a great fish sunning itself, I thought that someday I would make the canoe over and go out once more to look for the country that lay beyond the ocean. Now I knew that I would never go again.

The Island of the Blue Dolphins was my home; I had no other. It would be my home until the white men returned in their ship. But even if they came soon, before next summer, I could not live without a roof or a place to store my food. I would have to build a house. But where?

That night I slept on the rock and the next day I began the search. The morning was clear, but to the north banks of clouds hung low. Before long they would move in across the island and behind them many other storms were waiting. I had no time to waste.

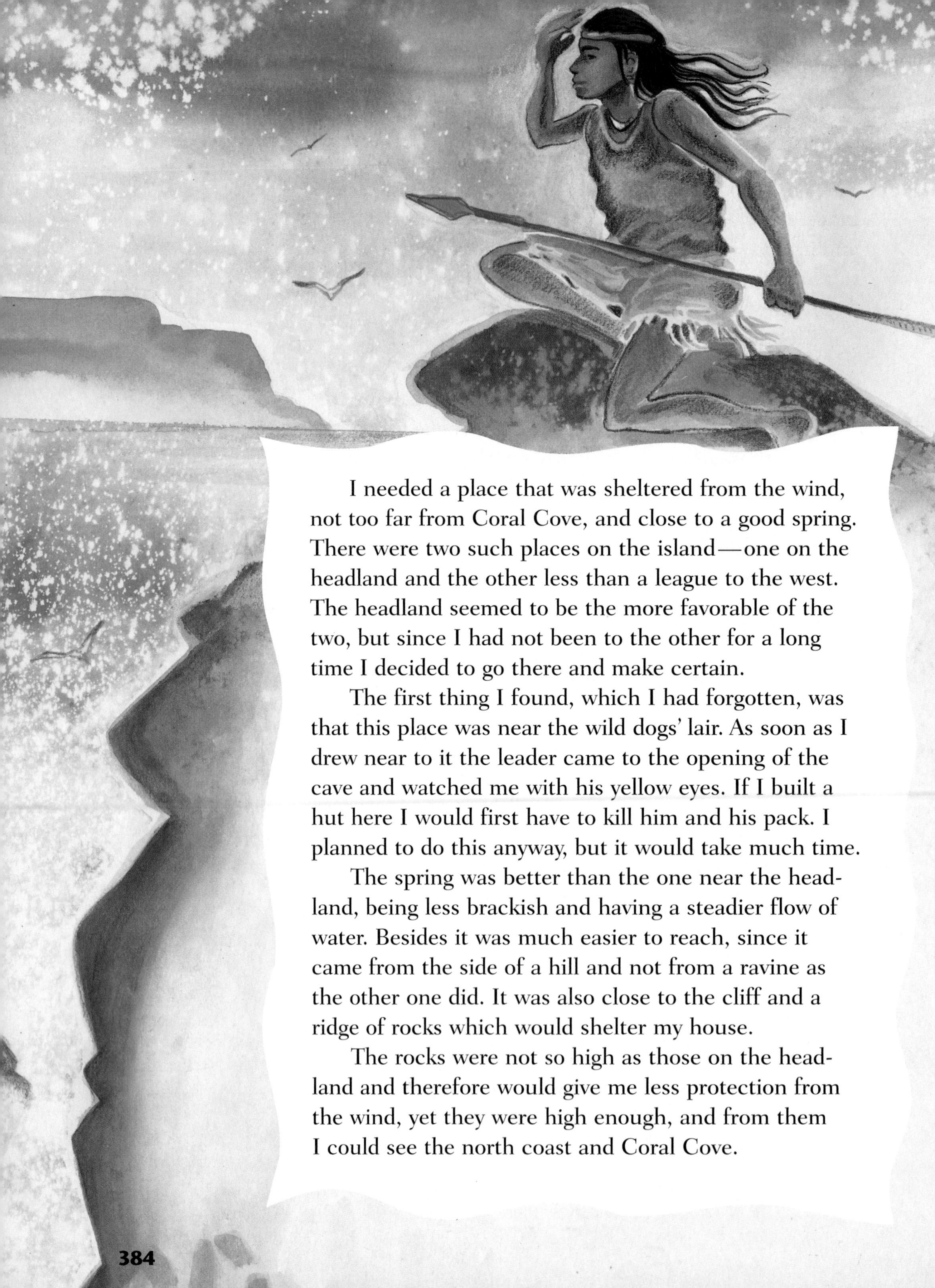

I needed a place that was sheltered from the wind, not too far from Coral Cove, and close to a good spring. There were two such places on the island—one on the headland and the other less than a league to the west. The headland seemed to be the more favorable of the two, but since I had not been to the other for a long time I decided to go there and make certain.

The first thing I found, which I had forgotten, was that this place was near the wild dogs' lair. As soon as I drew near to it the leader came to the opening of the cave and watched me with his yellow eyes. If I built a hut here I would first have to kill him and his pack. I planned to do this anyway, but it would take much time.

The spring was better than the one near the headland, being less brackish and having a steadier flow of water. Besides it was much easier to reach, since it came from the side of a hill and not from a ravine as the other one did. It was also close to the cliff and a ridge of rocks which would shelter my house.

The rocks were not so high as those on the headland and therefore would give me less protection from the wind, yet they were high enough, and from them I could see the north coast and Coral Cove.

The thing that made me decide on the place to build my house was the sea elephants.

The cliffs here fell away easily to a wide shelf that was partly covered when the tide came in. It was a good place for sea elephants because they could crawl halfway up the cliff if the day were stormy. On fair days they could fish among the pools or lie on the rocks.

The bull is very large and often weighs as much as thirty men. The cows are much smaller, but they make more noise than the bulls, screaming and barking through the whole day and sometimes at night. The babies are noisy, too.

On this morning the tide was low and most of the animals were far out, just hundreds of specks against the waves, yet the noise they made was deafening. I stayed there the rest of the day, looking around, and that night. At dawn when the clamor started again I left and went back to the headland.

There was another place to the south where I could have built my house, near the destroyed village of Ghalas-at, but I did not want to go there because it would remind me of the people who were gone. Also the wind blew strong in this place, blowing against the dunes which cover the middle part of the island so that most of the time sand is moving everywhere.

Rain fell that night and lasted for two days. I made a shelter of brush at the foot of the rock, which kept off some of the water, and ate the food I had stored in the basket. I could not build a fire because of the rain and I was very cold.

On the third day the rain ceased and I went out to look for things which I would need in building the house. I likewise needed poles for a fence. I would soon kill the wild dogs, but there were many small red foxes on the island. They were so numerous that I could never hope to get rid of them either by traps or with arrows. They were clever thieves and nothing I stored would be safe until I had built a fence.

The morning was fresh from the rain. The smell of the tide pools was strong. Sweet odors came from the wild grasses in the ravines and from the sand plants on the dunes. I sang as I went down the trail to the beach and along the beach to the sandspit. I felt that the day was an omen of good fortune.

It was a good day to begin my new home.

Many years before, two whales had washed up on the sandspit. Most of the bones had been taken away to make ornaments, but ribs were still there, half-buried in the sand.

These I used in making the fence. One by one I dug them up and carried them to the headland. They were long and curved, and when I had scooped out holes and set them in the earth they stood taller than I did.

I put the ribs together with their edges almost touching, and standing so that they curved outward, which made them impossible to climb. Between them I wove many strands of bull kelp, which shrinks as it dries and pulls very tight. I would have used seal sinew to bind the ribs together, for this is stronger than kelp, but wild animals like it and soon would have gnawed the fence down. Much time went into its building. It would have taken me longer except that the rock made one end of the fence and part of a side.

For a place to go in and out, I dug a hole under the fence just wide and deep enough to crawl through. The bottom and sides I lined with stones. On the outside I covered the hole with a mat woven of brush to shed the rain, and on the inside with a flat rock which I was strong enough to move.

I was able to take eight steps between the sides of the fence, which gave me all the room I would need to store the things I gathered and wished to protect.

I built the fence first because it was too cold to sleep on the rock and I did not like to sleep in the shelter I had made until I was safe from the wild dogs.

The house took longer to build than the fence because it rained many days and because the wood which I needed was scarce.

There was a legend among our people that the island had once been covered with tall trees. This was a long time ago, at the beginning of the world when Tumaiyowit[1] and Mukat[2] ruled. The two gods quarreled about many things. Tumaiyowit wished people to die. Mukat did not. Tumaiyowit angrily went down, down to another world under this world, taking his belongings with him, so people die because he did.

In that time there were tall trees, but now there were only a few in the ravines and these were small and crooked. It was very hard to find one that would make a good pole. I searched many days, going out early in the morning and coming back at night, before I found enough for the house.

---

1 **Tumaiyowit** *(too my yoh wiht)*

2 **Mukat** *(moo kaht)*

I used the rock for the back of the house and the front I left open since the wind did not blow from this direction. The poles I made of equal length, using fire to cut them as well as a stone knife which caused me much difficulty because I had never made such a tool before. There were four poles on each side, set in the earth, and twice that many for the roof. These I bound together with sinew and covered with female kelp, which has broad leaves.

The winter was half over before I finished the house, but I slept there every night and felt secure because of the strong fence. The foxes came when I was cooking my food and stood outside gazing through the cracks, and the wild dogs also came, gnawing at the whale ribs, growling because they could not get in.

I shot two of them, but not the leader.

While I was building the fence and the house, I ate shellfish and perch which I cooked on a flat rock. Afterwards I made two utensils. Along the shore there were stones that the sea had worn smooth. Most of them were round, but I found two with hollow places in the center which I deepened and broadened by rubbing them with sand. Using these to cook in, I saved the juices of the fish, which are good and were wasted before.

For cooking seeds and roots I wove a tight basket of fine reeds, which was easy because I had learned how to do it from my sister Ulape. After the basket had dried in the sun, I gathered lumps of pitch on the shore, softened them over the fire, and rubbed them on the inside of the basket so that it would hold water. By heating small stones and dropping them into a mixture of water and seeds in the basket I could make gruel.

I made a place for fire in the floor of my house, hollowing it out and lining it with rocks. In the village of Ghalas-at we made new fires every night, but now I made one fire which I covered with ashes when I went to bed. The next night I would remove the ashes and blow on the embers. In this way I saved myself much work.

There were many gray mice on the island and now that I had food to keep from one meal to the other, I needed a safe place to put it. On the face of the rock, which was the back wall of my house, were several cracks as high as my shoulder. These I cut out and smoothed to make shelves where I could store my food and the mice could not reach it.

By the time winter was over and grass began to show green on the hills my house was comfortable. I was sheltered from the wind and rain and prowling animals. I could cook anything I wished to eat. Everything I wanted was there at hand.

IN RESPONSE

Listening to Nature

"The first star made me feel less afraid," Karana says on her first night at sea. How does this comment show Karana's awareness of natural things? What other things in nature have an effect on her? Write about them and describe their effects on Karana. Then think about your own life. What things in nature affect you?

What Karana Needs

Karana plans carefully and works hard to make sure all of her needs are met. What needs does she have when she returns to the island? With a partner, make a list. Then discuss how Karana meets each of her needs.

AUTHOR AT WORK

Scott O'Dell as a child

Los Angeles was a frontier town when Scott O'Dell was born there in 1898. "It had more horses than automobiles, more jack rabbits than people," he once said. "The very first sound I remember was a wildcat scratching on the roof as I lay in bed."

His childhood memories of California include exploring coastal islands like the one where Karana lived.

Before he became a writer, Mr. O'Dell worked as a cameraman and a newspaper editor. He also served in the United States Air Force.

Mr. O'Dell published his first book, *Island of the Blue Dolphins,* when he was sixty-two years old. He went on to write twenty-five other children's books before he died in 1989.

Library Link

This story was taken from *Island of the Blue Dolphins* by Scott O'Dell. You might enjoy reading the entire book to find out what else happens to Karana on the island.

Other Books by . . .

Scott O'Dell

Sing Down the Moon by Scott O'Dell, Dell Publishing, 1970

Zia by Scott O'Dell, Dell Publishing, 1976

★ Award-winning Author

Desert Tortoise

by Byrd Baylor

I am the *old* one here.

Mice
and snakes
and deer
and butterflies
and badgers
come and go.
Centipedes
and eagles
come and go.

But tortoises
grow old
and *stay.*

Our lives stretch out.

I cross
the same arroyo
that I crossed
when I was young,
returning to
the same safe den
to sleep through
winter's cold.
Each spring,
I warm myself
in the same sun,
search for the same
long tender blades
of green,
and taste the same
ripe juicy cactus fruit.

I know
the slow
sure way
my world
repeats itself.
I know
how I fit in.

My shell still shows
the toothmarks
where a wildcat
thought he had me
long ago.
He didn't know
that I was safe
beneath
the hard brown rock
he tried to bite.

I trust that shell.
I move
at my own speed.

This
is a good place
for an old tortoise
to walk.

---

arroyo (*ah ROY oh*) a dry gully or a small stream

Looking for tracks in full Arctic gear, which includes handmade Inuit mukluks

WOLF WATCH

from *To the Top of the World*
text and photographs by Jim Brandenburg

The Ultimate Photograph

The leader of the wolf pack glanced back at me as I scrambled after him across the ice. He didn't appear to sense any danger. He just looked curious, maybe even a little amused, as if saying to himself, "*That* odd creature is really trying to sneak up on *me?*"

It was crazy to think that anyone bundled up in Arctic gear could escape a wolf's notice. Wolves are one of the most perceptive animals on earth, with extraordinary senses. But I couldn't help myself. My heart pounded with excitement because I sensed something about this wolf, whom I had nicknamed Buster (after my father). He was about to present me with the chance to take the greatest photograph of my life.

Buster was leading the pack to a favorite spot, an iceberg on which they often spent their time exploring, howling with one another, goofing off, napping. Since it was April, the wolves' iceberg was still shackled to the land by an eight-foot crust of ice. The altitude is irresistible to Arctic wolves. They seem to *like* climbing to the tops of things. From the heights, they can survey the territory and keep an eye on new developments.They had littered the iceberg with droppings—a KEEP OUT sign to other packs. And to me.

Now I needed to find my perfect vantage point, too. As I crouched and lumbered across the dry, Arctic snow, it squeaked like Styrofoam under my feet. The wolves were some 150 yards away from me. So I settled against a six- foot pressure (ice) ridge and began to shoot photographs frantically. My powerful lenses made

The perfect shot.

the wolves appear much closer than they were. As I reloaded my camera, Buster trotted over to a flat projection halfway up the iceberg. From this makeshift throne, he watched me. Suddenly, a single shaft of light illuminated the wolf while leaving the surrounding iceberg in blue, muted shadow. Nature had never provided me with a more perfectly composed photograph.

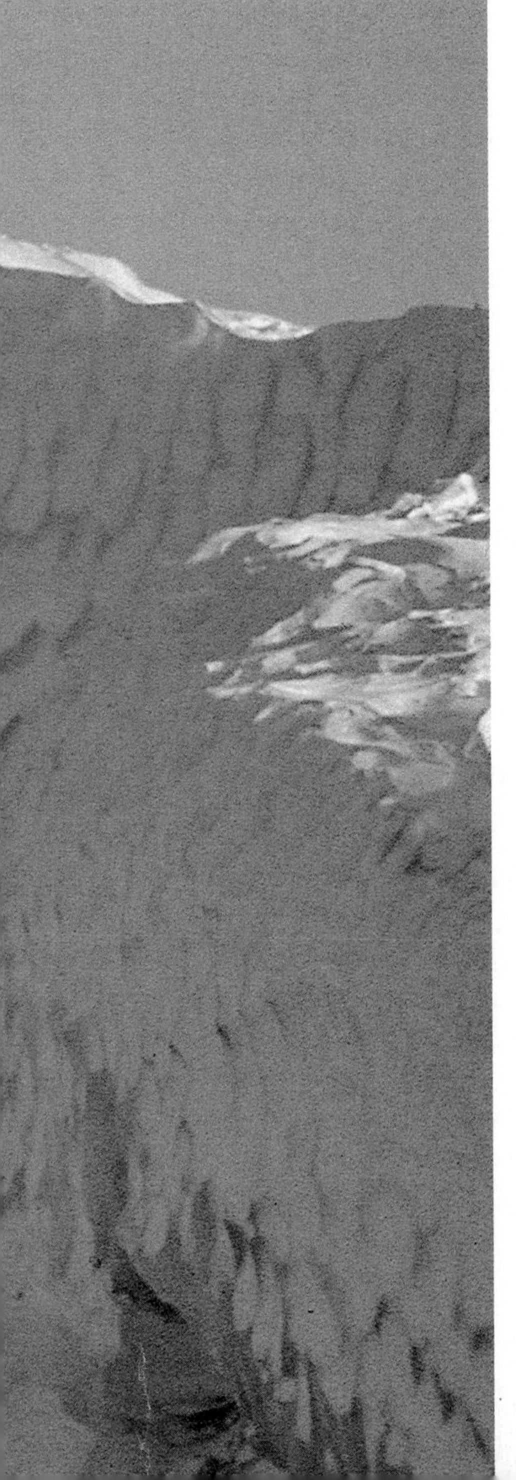

Buster sat there, in that perfect spot, for no more than thirty seconds. My thoughts raced ahead to when the editors at *National Geographic* would process my film. I was nervous and pessimistic about the outcome. Had the wind shaken the lens at the last second? Were the wolf's eyes open, or did I catch him blinking at the instant I snapped the shutter?

I found out later that, out of dozens of shots I'd taken of the lone wolf, only one turned out the way I had hoped it might.

Good photographs, like wolves, are elusive. Good photographs *of* wolves? Nearly impossible. I took this humbling realization as a challenge, which would inspire me in the long months to come.

Many people think Alaska is the most northerly part of North America, but Ellesmere Island, located in Canada's Northwest Territories, is actually several hundred miles farther north than any part of Alaska. From Ellesmere's tip to the North Pole measures some 500 miles across the Arctic Ocean.

During the winter, and for the first fifty or so days of "spring," such as it is, the water is frozen six to eight feet thick most of the way to the Pole. But this ice is nothing like the glassy ice familiar to skaters. Across its craggy, snow-blown surface, the ice cap is wrinkled with pressure ridges that make traveling on it difficult. Even worse are the frequent "leads"—yawning cracks in the ice that reveal open seawater.

I had taken other journeys into this treacherous, beautiful region during the first twenty years of my photographic career. Still, the *National Geographic* assignment to photograph the wildlife of Ellesmere Island, especially the wolves, was the fulfillment of a dream. And it all started when I first met my friend and fellow dreamer Will Steger. I think we each sensed something in the other: a kinship, a vision of the way we wanted to live our lives. Both of us had dreamed since childhood about testing ourselves, about danger, and about discovery. And we had found adventure wherever we could manage it.

The part of our conversation that I remember most vividly was about wolves. Arctic wolves. He had been dogsledding on Ellesmere with his wife two summers earlier. One morning they received a visitor.

"We woke up," Will told me, "and this large white head was staring at us through the flap of our tent. An Arctic wolf, as close to me as you are now. He showed no fear. He followed us for days, played with our dogs."

I was thrilled to think that a pack might exist that hadn't learned to fear humans. The images of that white wolf peering into Will Steger's tent and later playing with his dogs stuck stubbornly in my mind until I finally returned on assignment for *National Geographic* to follow the lives of these wolves for the whole Arctic summer. Even now, this time remains a highlight of my career, of my life.

Meeting the Family

One of my first concerns was about how much I might interfere with the lives of these wolves. Would my presence cause them to abandon their den and disappear?

During most of the year, a wolf pack roams over its entire territory, making wolf study almost impossible. But each spring, the pack stays in or near one place. The mother must take to the den to have her pups, and the behavior of the whole pack revolves around feeding their young and ensuring their safety. This phenomenon makes study easier, but it also is a uniquely sensitive time.

How could I make it clear to the pack that I meant them no harm? That I would keep my distance and simply observe?

At first, I did not set up a permanent campsite in case the pack fled and moved to another den. I approached the den cautiously, alert to any signs that my presence

Scruffy baby-sits puppies by the den's entrance.

The rocky outcropping at the den's entrance has been carved for eons by the winds of the High Arctic.

might be causing stress in the pack. But the wolves never appeared overly nervous or bothered.

The den was set high on a hill. At its opening, rocks formed a kind of porch on which the pack members spent much of their time. The den opened into the earth from an entryway just large enough to fit snugly around the mother wolf. A hungry polar bear, in other words, could not squeeze in to make a snack out of the growing pups.

Inside, a clean, bug-free layer of sand covered the ground leading into a cave twenty feet deep. The rock walls provided excellent protection from the bitter cold.

Pups spend their first weeks inside the den huddled around their mother, and each other, for warmth. I was eager and impatient for my first look at them. When they finally appeared outside the den, they proved well worth the wait.

There were six puppies, cute little gray bundles of fur waddling after the adults on short, fuzzy legs and oversized paws. I guessed that they were about five weeks old. It seemed impossible that by winter they'd be running alongside their parents.

Several days later, I set up a camera about fifty yards from the den and was shooting photographs of the wriggling ball of pups. All seven adults looked in my direction, stretched, howled a few times at the sky, and took off on a hunt. I couldn't believe it! Not one adult stayed behind to bark at me and keep me away from the den. They trusted me with their precious pups. Finally, after all those frustrating years of wolf pursuit, I would be able to get close to an entire pack. And what a family it was!

The way adult wolves are constantly caring for the young in their pack is only one of many similarities with human families. Wolves mate for life, and the whole pack functions as an extended family of aunts and uncles, brothers and sisters. They take turns baby-sitting and teaching the pups what they need to know.

Wolves have very individual personalities. Bison and musk-oxen all behave much the same within their herds. Not wolves. It probably has to do with their intelligence and gifts of perception.

At first, however, *my* perceptions were not up to the task of telling the seven wolves in this pack apart. But over the weeks of watching and listening to the wolves, I found myself more and more aware of their differences, like body scars, facial expressions, and coloring.

Minus 60 degrees Fahrenheit; the orange glow is a product of the low-hanging March sun.

Midback, the pack's best hare hunter, catches her prey and carries it with haughty pride to the grateful pups.

I also noticed that some of them behaved in dominant ways, bristling and cocky. Others were more submissive, cringing when in the presence of a "superior" and always trying to keep the peace. In other words, a hierarchy became apparent, a ranking of the wolves according to their power in relation to the others.

At the top was the alpha male, Buster. He was usually first to attack on a hunt and the first to eat after a kill. Buster's eyes were extremely expressive. Sometimes they were piercing, threatening. Other times they were amused, haughty, or quizzical. Weighing less than 100 pounds, he was not the largest of the pack. But he stood proudly on thin, long legs, taller than even the largest German shepherd.

Nearly his equal was the alpha female. I called her Midback because of a trail of dark fur running down her back. She was probably the most intelligent pack member. It was also clear that she was the *least* pleased to have me around. Midback's quickness and skill made her the best hunter among the pack.

Although scientists say that only the alpha pair has pups each spring, Midback was not the mother of the pups. There is no way to know why this alpha female did not give birth, but she was the most fiercely protective "parent" the pups had. She behaved like a dominant aunt who was often jealous of the pups' mother, whom I called, simply, Mom. Midback often rivaled Mom's authority over the pups.

Mom quickly became one of my favorites. She was a natural mother—gentle, tolerant, and devoted to the pups. Her facial expression can only be described as sweet and serene. And for some reason she seemed to have complete trust in humans. Maybe she simply got used to having me around because she was tied to the den.

Mom's serene disposition makes her the most tolerant member of the pack.

The other wolf that could most often be found with the pups was my other favorite. He was an "adolescent" wolf, probably from the previous year's litter. His position in the pack was at the opposite end from the alpha pair—the bottom. I called him Scruffy because he was always a mess. His summer coat

Scruffy, the pack's messiest member

was scraggly, with huge balls of hair hanging from virtually every part of his hide.

There was a kind of goofiness about Scruffy that endeared him to me, especially since he tended to follow me around a lot. He was usually left behind from a hunt, but baby-sitting was the perfect job for him because of his playfulness. It also gave him the chance to act dominantly over somebody, at least when Mom wasn't looking.

It was part of his job to play rough with the pups, knock them down hard enough to make them yelp. Though this kind of bullying may seem cruel, it is a necessary part of the pups' training. They have to learn the importance of knowing one's place in the hierarchy. This arrangement is crucial to the pack's unity and survival. Maintaining that ranking and its strict rules of behavior keeps the peace, avoids continual fights and injuries, maybe even death.

I knew less about the remaining three adults in the pack, mostly because they spent less time at the den site. Left Shoulder, a male named for a three-inch patch of missing fur on his left shoulder, was the largest, whitest wolf in the pack. Despite his size, he was submissive to the point of groveling in the presence of both Buster and Midback. The other two adults had even lower status in the pack, and I never got much of a sense of their personalities.

Many changes in the pack's membership would inevitably follow from one year to the next. But these seven adults and six pups made up the "family" as it existed one particular spring and summer on Ellesmere Island.

Living as Neighbors

While searching for an ideal campsite, I found a skull embedded in the powdery soil.

The story the skull told of the wolf's amazing survival skills intrigued me. Puncturing the lower jawbone was the

Puppies begin to practice howling very early in life; their amusing, high-pitched efforts add to the family songfest.

tip of a musk-ox horn that had broken off, probably during combat. Bone tissue had grown thick across the point of injury, showing that he had lived for at least several months after the battle. The simple act of chewing must have been terribly painful, but his worn teeth indicated that he was very old when he died.

The discovery of this skull gave me an unusual glimpse into the harsh lives these wolves lead. It also provided a symbolic site on which to stake my own territorial claim for the spring and summer.

This setting was a deep valley about a quarter-mile east of the den. A pair of binoculars allowed me to keep track of the pack's activities. My presence did not seem to affect the wolves in a negative way. They made regular trips to the camp, apparently to satisfy their curiosity. My goal was to blend in, to lie low without trying to hide or trick the wolves. There was, however, one unavoidable exception to this approach. It was my means of transportation, the Suzuki all-terrain vehicle (ATV).

The pack completely accepted my presence in their territory.

Two adults rest in cotton grass; in the balmy atmosphere, it is almost possible to forget about the swift and inevitable advance of winter.

I used this four-wheel buggy to carry my equipment and to keep up with the free-roaming pack. It's nothing for a wolf to travel forty miles at a steady pace of six miles per hour. It would have been impossible to keep up with them on foot.

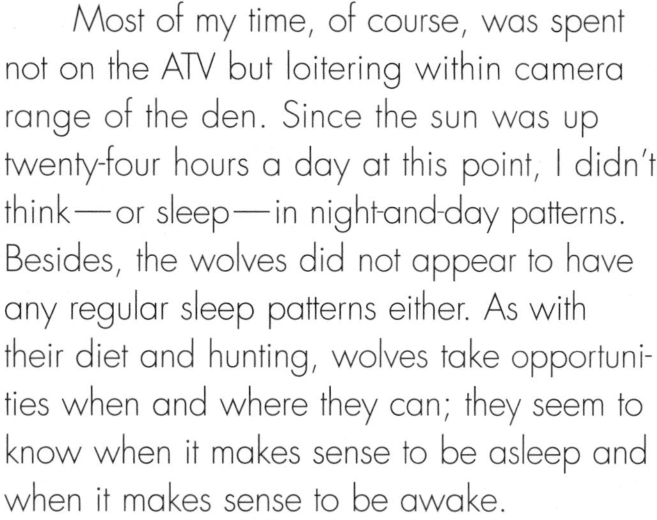

Most of my time, of course, was spent not on the ATV but loitering within camera range of the den. Since the sun was up twenty-four hours a day at this point, I didn't think—or sleep—in night-and-day patterns. Besides, the wolves did not appear to have any regular sleep patterns either. As with their diet and hunting, wolves take opportunities when and where they can; they seem to know when it makes sense to be asleep and when it makes sense to be awake.

Often I found myself staying up twenty hours or more at a stretch, fearful that if I did fall asleep, the wolves would do something never before documented and I'd miss it. I would grab my sleeping bag and telephoto lens and curl up on the hillside overlooking the den, taking catnaps and every now and then cocking an ear or raising an eyelid toward the activity across the way.

More than once I fell asleep in spite of myself, only to wake to the curious sniffing of a wolf a few yards away. It was satisfying, at these times, to know that the creatures whom I was observing were keeping a similarly watchful eye on me.

A few words here about anthropomorphism, the common practice of giving human characteristics and feelings to nonhumans. Throughout my career—even when I've felt closest to my wild subjects—I've always tried to preserve a boundary between us.

Yet, animals undoubtedly have more feelings than we give them credit for. To ignore this fact, or view their emotional range as smaller, *inferior* to ours, is just as wrong as thinking of them in strictly human terms.

I genuinely believe a magic exists in creatures as perceptive and intelligent as wolves, a magic that we may not be able to observe or measure in any scientific way.

Sometimes, during those days on Ellesmere, I would wonder how the wolves perceived me. Maybe they attributed wolflike feelings to my odd human behaviors. I wouldn't have been surprised.

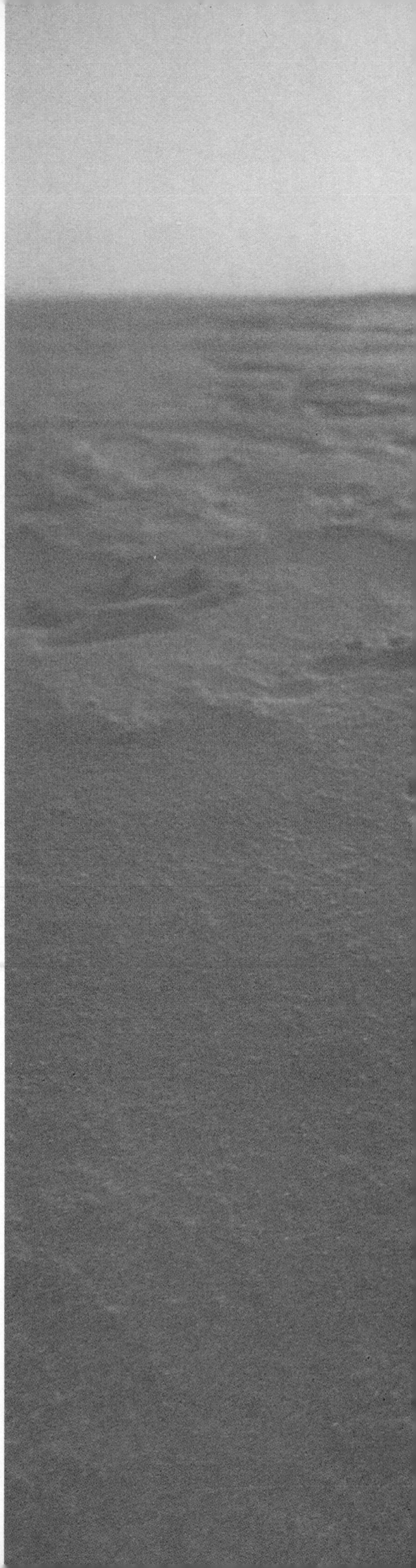

The Alligator and the Hunter

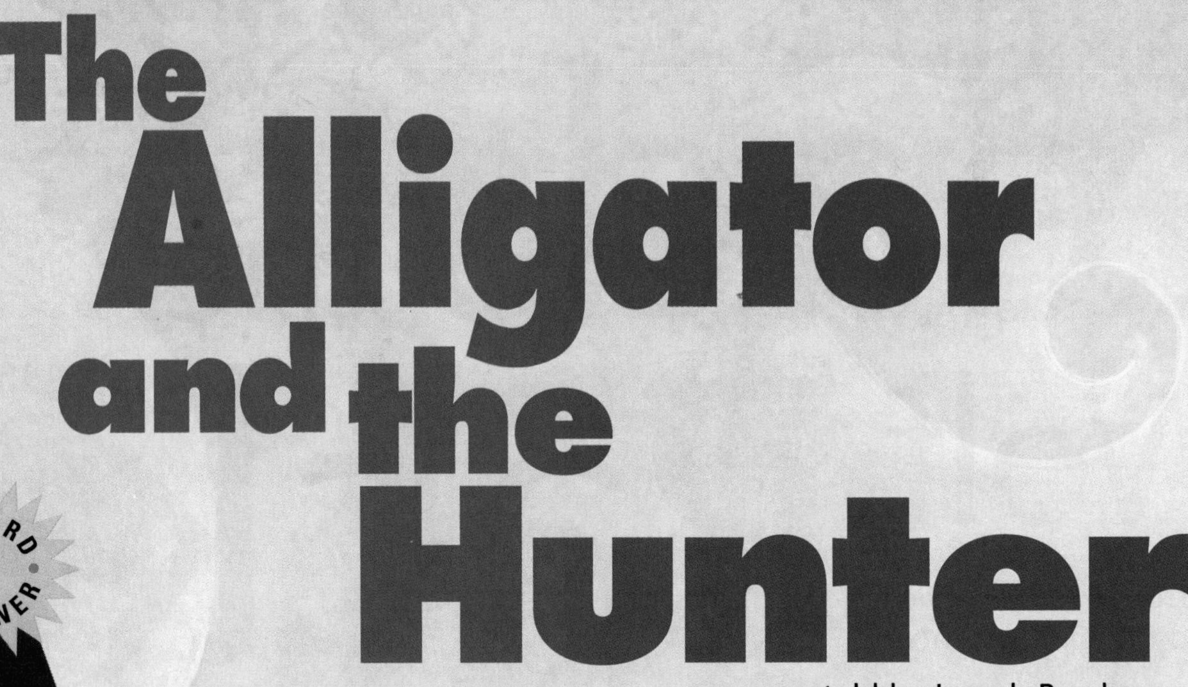

retold by Joseph Bruchac

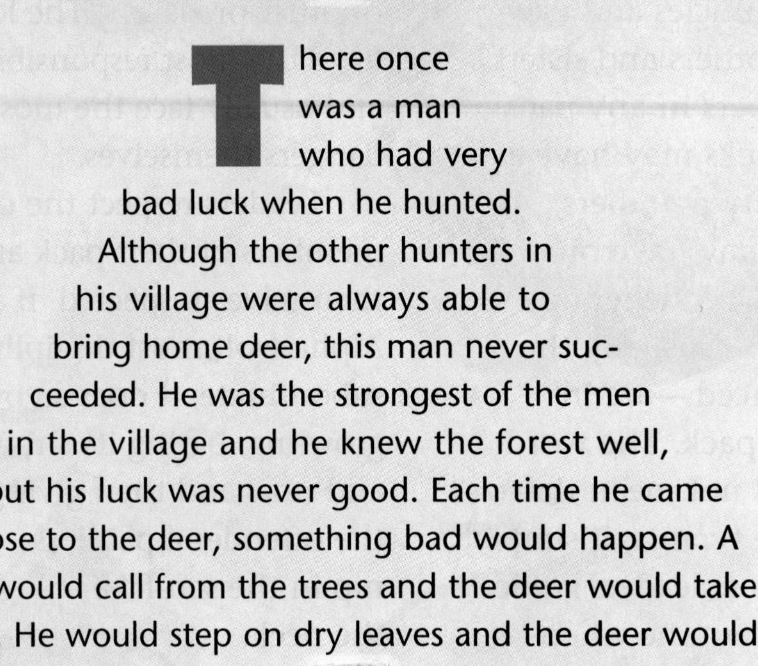

There once was a man who had very bad luck when he hunted. Although the other hunters in his village were always able to bring home deer, this man never succeeded. He was the strongest of the men in the village and he knew the forest well, but his luck was never good. Each time he came close to the deer, something bad would happen. A jay would call from the trees and the deer would take flight. He would step on dry leaves and the deer would

run before he could shoot. His arrow would glance off a twig and miss the deer. It seemed there was no end to his troubles. Finally the man decided he would go deep into the swamps where there were many deer. He would continue hunting until he either succeeded or lost his own life.

The man hunted for three days without success. At noon on the fourth day, he came to a place in the swamp where there had once been a deep pool. The late summer had been a very dry one, however, and now there was only hot sand where once there had been water. There, resting on the sand, was a huge alligator. It had been without water for many days. It was so dry and weak that it was almost dead. Although the hunter's own luck had been bad, he saw that this alligator's luck was even worse.

"My brother," said the man, "I pity you."

Then the alligator spoke. Its voice was so weak that the man could barely hear it. "Is there water nearby?" said the alligator.

"Yes," said the man. "There is a deep pool of clear cool water not far from here. It is just beyond that small stand of trees to the west. There the springs never dry up and the water always runs. If you go to that place, you will survive."

"I cannot travel there by myself," said the alligator. "I am too weak. Come close so I can talk to you. I will not harm you. Help me and I will also help you."

The hunter was afraid of the great alligator, but he came a bit closer. As soon as he was close, the alligator spoke again.

"I know that you are a hunter but the deer always escape from you. If you help me, I will make you a great hunter. I will give you the power to kill many deer."

This sounded good to the hunter, but he still feared the alligator's great jaws. "My brother," the man said, "I believe that you will help me, but you are still an alligator. I will carry you to that place, but you must allow me to bind your legs and bind your jaws so that you can do me no harm."

Immediately the alligator rolled over to its back and held up its legs. "Do as you wish," the alligator said.

The man bound the alligator's jaws firmly with his sash. He made a bark strap and bound the alligator's legs together. Then, with his great strength, he lifted the big alligator to his shoulders and carried it to the deep cool water where the springs never dried. He placed the alligator on its back close to the water and he untied its feet. He untied the alligator's jaws, but still held those jaws together with one hand. Then he jumped back quickly. The alligator rolled into the pool and dove underwater. It stayed under a long time and then came up. Three more times the alligator dove, staying down longer each time. At last it came to the surface and floated there, looking up at the hunter who was seated high on the bank.

"You have done as you said you would," said the alligator. "You have saved me. Now I shall help you, also. Listen closely to me now and you will become a great hunter. Go now into the woods with your bow and arrows. Soon you will meet a small doe. That doe has not yet grown large enough to have young

ones. Do not kill that deer. Only greet it and then continue on and your power as a hunter will increase. Soon after that you will meet a large doe. That doe has fawns and will continue to have young ones each year. Do not kill that deer. Greet it and continue on and you will be an even greater hunter. Next you will meet a small buck. That buck will father many young ones. Do not kill it. Greet it and continue on and your power as a hunter will become greater still. At last you will meet an old buck, larger than any of the others. Its time on Earth has been useful. Now it is ready to give itself to you. Go close to that deer and shoot it. Then greet it and thank it for giving itself to you. Do this and you will be the greatest of hunters."

The hunter did as the alligator said. He went into the forest and met the deer, killing only the old buck. He became the greatest of the hunters in his village. He told this story to his people. Many of them understood the alligator's wisdom and hunted in that way. That is why the Choctaws became great hunters of the deer. As long as they remembered to follow the alligator's teachings, they were never hungry.

The Deer Thief

retold by Rudolfo A. Anaya

A hunter was out hunting one day and killed a deer. Since it was very late in the day, he couldn't take the deer home, so he skinned it and hung it as high as he could from the branch of a tall pine tree. The following day he returned for his deer, but the deer was gone. He searched the area for tracks. He inspected everything very carefully, and then he went to the Justice of the Peace to seek redress.

The Justice of the Peace asked him if he had any idea who stole the deer. The hunter replied that he had not seen the thief and he didn't know who it was, but he could give an accurate description of the man who stole the deer.

"If you know something, tell me what kind of man he is," the Justice of the Peace said.

"Well, he is shorter than I. He is older, and he had a yellow bulldog with him."

"But how do you know all that?"

"I know he is shorter than I because he had to put some logs beneath the tree to reach the deer," replied the hunter.

"And how do you know he is old?"

"Because he took short steps, like an old man."

"And how do you know he had a yellow dog?"

"I followed his tracks and I found yellow hair where the dog passed beneath low branches."

"But how do you know it was a bulldog?" the exasperated judge asked.

"Because when the old man was lowering the deer, the dog sat nearby and the way the stub of his tail dug into the ground told me it was a bulldog."

The judge was convinced and granted permission to look for a man fitting that description. After searching for some time the hunter and the Justice of the Peace arrived at a house where they saw a yellow bulldog. They knocked on the door and a small, old man appeared. Then they searched his barn and found the stolen deer. So the hunter, by using his wits, had tracked down the thief who had stolen his deer.

Malinda Futrell

"Welcome to our garden," Malinda Futrell says warmly to passersby, who look with genuine curiosity at the sight of such lush, unexpected greenery.

Her friend and cofounder Nancy Paye unlocks the chain-link gate and opens it as wide as it will go. "This is city-owned land. We just manage it for the city. Good use of the land, don't you think?"

Every inch of space in this corner lot is used to cultivate the soil. Here, 105 "urban farmers" each pay twelve dollars a year to lease their tiny four-by-eight-foot plots.

"They can do anything they want with their land," Malinda says, her eyes sparkling as she surveys the diversity. "Each plot is a little thumbprint." Typical vegetable and flower plots are interspersed with meadows and wildflowers, peaceful corners bulging with fragrant herbs, and even a grape arbor. "There are many important things going on here. We've regenerated the soil and that's good. After all, God created healthy soil. It's up to us to take care of it. And the other thing is that all the people in the neighborhood are connecting to nature."

"Just nine years ago this corner was the neighborhood garbage dump as well as home to drug dealers and addicts," Malinda says.

"Most of us hated the place," Joanee Freedom, another garden cofounder, chimes in. "But one day I noticed a tomato plant growing right up out of all the trash. I couldn't believe my eyes! I immediately gathered up stones and bricks to make a little protective wall around the plant."

Nancy Paye

Soon thereafter a man named Charlie Paye cleared a small plot and planted a garden. It was his little creation that got Malinda thinking. A native of rural North Carolina, Malinda had come to the city in search of a better life, only to find herself longing for the land she'd left behind. "What was I doing here with all this noise and cement and no soil to dig my hands in?"

If he can do it, I sure can, Malinda thought, and within a matter of days she sought permission from the block association to start digging.

Avenue B urban gardeners sharing information

On July 19, 1983, "with beauty on my mind and love in my heart," a very determined Malinda began the back-breaking job of hauling away the rubble. For one whole year, she and two others labored. Gradually more neighbors pitched in, and the more space they cleared, the more they wanted to clear.

When the residents had the entire lot cleared, they sought help from a city gardening program called Operation Greenthumb, which leases more than 1,000 city-owned lots to 550 city gardens. "The only stipulation Greenthumb has," Malinda says, "is that we welcome the public inside several times a week. I try to have the gate open as much as we can. You know, beauty has a way of making people feel better."

Greenthumb encourages beautification, and it also encourages people to make vacant lots fruitful. Most of the city's gardens supply enough fresh produce that the gardeners, and many of their lucky friends, no longer need to purchase vegetables at the grocery store.

It was pretty obvious to the Greenthumb people that they had a woman of great will and determination in Malinda. They were quick to supply the initial topsoil, fencing, lumber, and assorted garden tools to get Malinda's garden going. Greenthumb even helped Malinda and her friends design their lot so they would have individual plots as well as common space.

Now, nine summers later, a full-fledged urban farm flourishes.

On this early September morning it is the turn of Malinda and fellow gardener Cheryl to act as water brigade. It's not a simple chore. There are no readily accessible spigots to connect the hose to. They have to drag hundreds of feet of hose out onto the city street and connect it to the corner hydrant. As the water begins gushing through, they fill up a dozen or so giant barrels from which the various plot owners fill up their watering cans.

Digging to make a beautiful garden

A group of preschoolers from P.S. 122 frolics into the garden. "Hey, garden mother," they shout to Malinda, "how are you today?" But they are too excited to wait for an answer and they run to their own plot.

"Look at these carrots," an excited little girl says, yanking a bunch out of the moist soil for everyone to see. Nearby a classmate is scavenging the string bean vines, collecting every last one.

Avenue B Garden has several school plots. "These kids don't get a chance to see where vegetables come from," says their teacher, Cheryl Marie Taylor. "Here they learn how things grow. We come once a week, first to plant, then to water and weed. Now, in the fall, harvest is the real fun part."

Life inside the fence is calm and peaceful. As the day goes on single men, mothers with children, older people, and families come and go. Some call the garden a refuge. Others refer to it as an oasis. It is definitely a place to feel safe from the turbulence of the city streets.

"After I'm in here for just a few minutes, I fail to hear the racket outside," one gardener says.

"It's my backyard," says another. "Sure beats sitting on my apartment steps."

Each farmer cares for his or her individual plot and part of the common space that needs tending. "Everyone is responsible for a section of the border," Malinda says. She walks along the carefully laid brick path, yanking out blades of grass that are peeking through the cracks. The border, with its eight-year growth of hemlocks and evergreens, hollyhocks and bushes, is responsible for the intimacy one feels in this magic place. "The border shuts out the world around us and allows us some peace."

Two mothers sit chatting under the shade of a weeping willow, while a single woman meditates in the corner of the communal herb garden. A family enjoys their breakfast in a patio space, while an earnest man is laying tile under a nearby grape arbor.

"God created his earth to look beautiful," Malinda says. "I think we're helping the cause."

Reclaiming the soil is the biggest challenge in the adverse conditions offered to city farmers. Each plot sits aboveground. The gardeners dig down two feet and replace the beaten earth with layers of fresh soil and compost. Additional soil, trucked in by Operation Greenthumb, tops off each plot.

Gardeners giving the tired city soil special care

A reward for hard work—a beautiful tomato

"When I put my hands in dirt," Malinda says, "I feel love. This is what we come from, you know. This is what we go back to.

"We don't add chemical fertilizer," she says, quick to point it out. "It isn't good for the earth, and besides, many people are allergic to it. We've found the stuff to be so strong that you can't plant for two or three weeks because it will burn the seeds and kill nearby healthy roots."

Instead of chemicals, the gardeners use cow and horse manure and peat moss. "Most soil is fixable," Malinda confidently states. "You just have to work with it."

Nearby sits a huge compost bin in which the gardeners place their vegetable and fruit peelings as well as fallen leaves, weeds, and grass clippings. Organic waste such as this constitutes a quarter of New York City's trash, and Avenue B Garden is doing its part to recycle.

By using compost, the gardeners are returning their organic matter to the soil, which in turn improves plant growth. "Everyone's a winner in the recycling process," Malinda points out.

Outside the garden are rows of bins for the neighborhood to dispose of their cans, bottles, and plastics. "We're trying to get the people beyond our garden to care," Malinda explains.

There seem to be as many different reasons for gardening as there are gardeners.

The Eros family waited a year for their plot. "This garden is the only way to survive New York City in the summer," Jeannie Eros says as she ties her morning glories to a newly erected trellis. "It's the biggest and safest yard we have to hang out in."

Clear across the garden a young man builds a Japanese-style garden where he hopes to come and meditate. "Because the city is so aggressive, I come here to calm down and find some peace," he says.

Nearby, a woman named Connie has stopped on her way to work to look at her wild meadow. "I've let all my various flowers and grasses grow from seed. It's a little bit of country on the Lower East Side," she says, delighted with her spot.

Nancy Paye and her husband, Charlie, eat out of their garden all year long. "It's multipurpose," Nancy says. "We get lots of gifts out of it, and we share the food with our neighbors . . . and the smells we get!" She squeezes a basil leaf between her fingers. "Fresh food! Nothing like it."

Just one plot over from the Payes' stands perhaps the most unique use of a four-by-eight-foot plot. A sculptor named Ed has constructed a work of art that stands approximately three stories high. "I got sick of all the broken toys and discarded treasures people put out for the garbagemen to pick up. To me, these things are beautiful. So little by little I began to cart the stuff off, and inspiration led me to build this sculpture." Ed climbs up the side of his piece of art, eventually perching himself on a platform. "This is one way of cleaning up the neighborhood, right?"

Ed's sculpture made from castoffs

Avenue B Garden bringing a city boy closer to nature

All over the city, community gardens are revitalizing the soil and uplifting human spirits. With Greenthumb's support, there are 100 gardens in Manhattan, 175 in the Bronx, 225 in Brooklyn, and 25 in Queens.

A Brooklyn gardener is busy bundling up produce for shut-ins and senior citizens. In the Bronx thirty to forty gardeners raise enough fruit and vegetables to supply the neighborhood throughout summer and fall.

As Malinda locks up at the end of each day she can feel satisfied because the garden has once more nourished and made people happy. "This process of giving life and defeating the obstacles given to us in the city is just plain energizing."

IN RESPONSE

Gardeners With a Cause

The people who rent plots in the city garden are learning about nature and also helping the planet. How are they helping it? What are they learning? Look back at the selection for examples. If you were to start a garden, what would be your main reason for doing it? Write a short paragraph.

Finding Inspiration

When Karana ("The Dolphins Led Me Home") has trouble at sea, she finds hope and inspiration in the dolphins. How does the garden in this story give people hope and inspiration? With a partner, find at least three examples.

Award-winning Gardener

Suppose a local environmental group gives Malinda Futrell an award for her work with the city garden. Design a plaque or trophy that she might receive. Be sure to include words or images that will help other people see what she has accomplished. Show the award to your class and explain your thinking behind it.

PHOTOGRAPHER AT WORK

George Ancona

For George Ancona, the photographer of "Farming on Avenue B," a book is much more than just a story with pictures. "A children's book," he says, "is like taking a child for a walk, hand in hand, and discovering something about our world."

He should know. Mr. Ancona has provided photographs for fifty children's books. Many of them he wrote himself.

Mr. Ancona became interested in photography as a boy in New York City. As an adult, he has traveled around the world taking pictures for his books. He got the idea to photograph the garden in "Farming on Avenue B" from one of his daughters, who lived a block away from the garden.

★ Award-winning Author and Photographer

George Ancona's tools (*below*): a small tape recorder, thumbnail sketches, film, and a camera

Before Mr. Ancona takes pictures for an assignment, he draws thumbnail sketches. If he's writing the story, he researches it and then writes a rough draft.

"I try to tell a story through pictures," he says. "I use words to round out the experience."

Mr. Ancona has also produced award-winning films, including some for *Sesame Street*. His top priority, however, is making children's books.

George Ancona creating a story with pictures

Other Books by . . .

George Ancona

My Camera, written with photographs by George Ancona, Crown, 1992

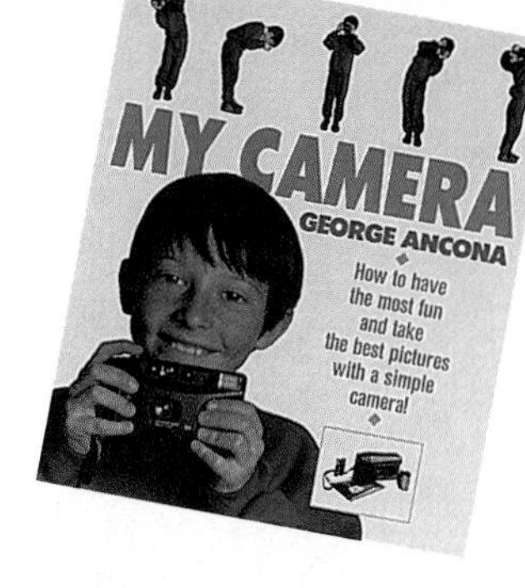

Powwow, written with photographs by George Ancona, Harcourt Brace, 1993

Library Link This article was taken from *Earth Keepers* by Joan Anderson, with photographs by George Ancona. You might enjoy reading the entire book to find out more about people who have learned from nature by taking a hands-on interest in it.

Bluebird, What Do You Feed On?

by Carl Sandburg

Bluebird, what do you feed on?
It is true you gobble up worms, you
swallow bugs,
And your bill picks up corn, seed,
berries.
This is only part of the answer.
Your feathers have captured a piece of
smooth sky.
Your wings are burnished with
lake-morning blue.
It is not a worm blue nor a bug
blue nor the blue
Of corn or berry you shine with.
Bluebird, we come to you for facts,
for valuable
Information, for secret reports.
Bluebird, tell us, what do you
feed on?

Slender-Billed Parakeet

by Pablo Neruda
translated by Jack Schmidt

The tree had so many leaves
it was toppling with treasure,
from so much green it blinked
and never closed its eyes.

That's no way to sleep.

But the fluttering foliage
went flying off green and alive,
each bud learned to fly,
and the tree was left naked
weeping in the winter rain.

Bee Song

by Carl Sandburg

Bees in the late summer sun
Drone their song
Of yellow moons
Trimming black velvet,
Droning, droning a sleepysong.

Culture of Japanese Gardens

Japanese people love nature and enjoy growing plants and trees. It's no surprise that the gardens they create are beautiful natural places. Each area of a Japanese garden is meant to make people feel closer to natural things.

A Japanese garden can be in a city or in the country. It can be large or small. Either way, a garden gives people a chance to get away from the outside world and to learn from nature.

Lanterns

Some gardens have lanterns that light the way to evening tea ceremonies. In other gardens, lanterns are just for decoration.

Garden Gate

A gate gives clues about the kind of garden inside. A gate such as this one might be on the grounds of a mansion.

Dry Garden
A dry garden is made of rocks and gravel. It is a place for quiet thoughts. The gravel represents a body of water, so people are not to walk on it.
Arched Bridge
Bridges in Japanese gardens are made of natural materials, such as earth, wood, or stone.
Pine Trees
The pine is the most commonly grown tree in Japanese gardens. Age is highly respected in Japan, and the pine tree represents long life.
Water Basin
Visitors to a Japanese garden may wash their hands at a water basin. Washing their hands stands for cleansing their bodies and souls.
Zigzag Bridge
The zigzag design of this bridge makes visitors walk slowly and notice their beautiful surroundings.

Why are all of these flowers
In bloom? Don't they know
This house is for sale?

Snow makes a new land.
One step, two steps. I explore
The way to my school.

Coming home late,
Only my moonlit shadow
Dances on the street.

Haiku

by Kazue Mizumura

Who tossed these golden coins,
The dandelions glittering
On my lawn?

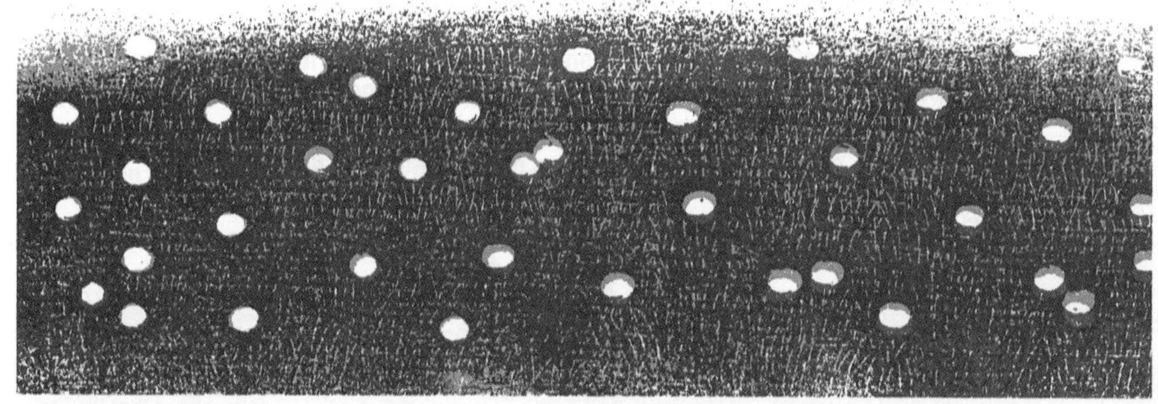

president takes office just to spray anti-starling chemicals along parade routes where important officials will stand.

No wonder so many people hate starlings! But it isn't doing any good. In 1890, there were only 120 of these birds in North America. In 1985, despite the efforts of starling-haters coast to coast, there were *hundreds of millions* in the United States alone.

Starlings, in other words, have come to stay. They have become a part of our lives, and so we must accept that there are two ways to look at them—or at any species of wildlife. We can look at them in a self-centered way. We can ask: Do they harm or help us? Dirty our buildings? Make noise? Eat crops? Or we can let pure curiosity take over. We can look at starlings as scientists would. Then they take on a new identity. They even become respectable—leading members in a small club of organisms that live where few other organisms can: in the heart of the human world.

If this seems easy, then think again. Remember the four basic needs of wildlife: food, water, places to raise young, and space in which to hunt or hide. Now consider what a typical city center provides: hurtling metal monsters . . . sizzling cement. . . . How can the starlings cope? How can rats, gulls, or ginkgo trees? How can any other form of metropolitan life?

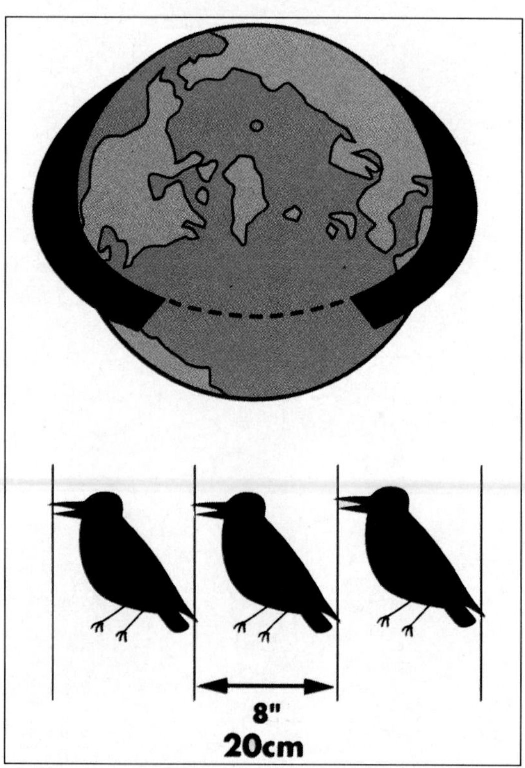

The average starling is only eight inches (20 cm) long. Lined up end to end, however, North America's starlings would stretch three-quarters of the way around the world.

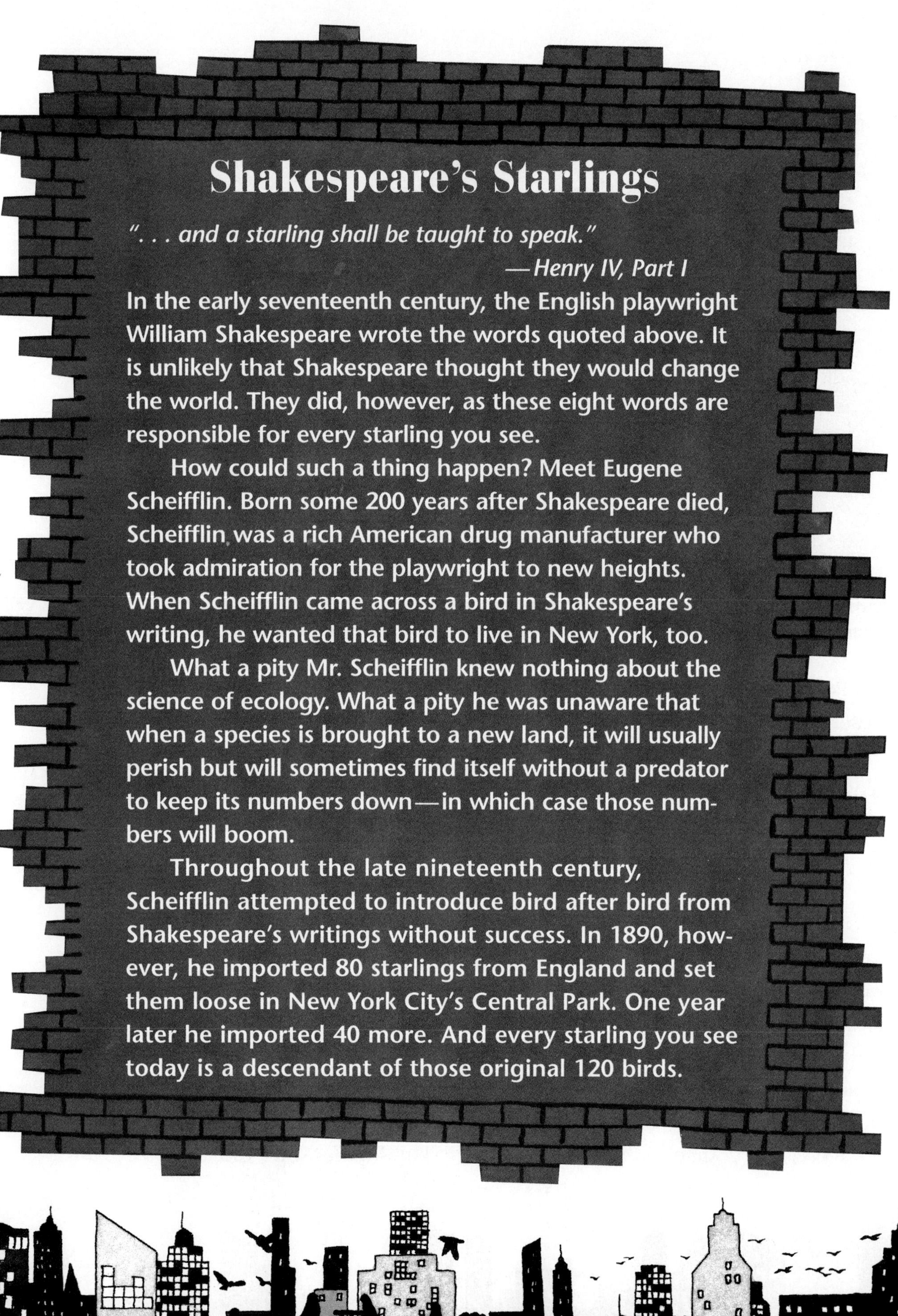

Shakespeare's Starlings

". . . and a starling shall be taught to speak."

—Henry IV, Part I

In the early seventeenth century, the English playwright William Shakespeare wrote the words quoted above. It is unlikely that Shakespeare thought they would change the world. They did, however, as these eight words are responsible for every starling you see.

How could such a thing happen? Meet Eugene Scheifflin. Born some 200 years after Shakespeare died, Scheifflin was a rich American drug manufacturer who took admiration for the playwright to new heights. When Scheifflin came across a bird in Shakespeare's writing, he wanted that bird to live in New York, too.

What a pity Mr. Scheifflin knew nothing about the science of ecology. What a pity he was unaware that when a species is brought to a new land, it will usually perish but will sometimes find itself without a predator to keep its numbers down—in which case those numbers will boom.

Throughout the late nineteenth century, Scheifflin attempted to introduce bird after bird from Shakespeare's writings without success. In 1890, however, he imported 80 starlings from England and set them loose in New York City's Central Park. One year later he imported 40 more. And every starling you see today is a descendant of those original 120 birds.

Starlings gather on everything from telephone lines to rooftops to trees in large communal roosts. They may look black from afar, but in sunshine their feathers reflect many colors of light.

Perhaps you can answer these questions for yourself. Organize an expedition into deepest downtown. Instead of paying attention to the human scene, however, look behind, above, and around the scene. Take the naturalist's approach. Watch the window ledges, the roofs. Look for sources of water. See how the sun shines on cracks in the paving, then check out what lives there. When you do see an animal, don't just watch passively; ask yourself *why*.

Bright Lights, Bug City

You may notice, for example, that the city provides shelter for those who can find it. Many birds would perish without trees to house their roosts and nests. Look up in the city one day, however, and you may see what looks like a tornado of flying cigars spiraling above a rooftop. They are chimney swifts, and fortunately for them, chimney swifts' instincts always told them to roost in a hollow tree, or what seemed like one. The

tornado you see above the city ends as the birds drop one by one into a chimney, where they spend the night clinging to tiny outcroppings on the inside walls.

But perhaps the best way to discover how some city birds (*including* chimney swifts) survive in the center of town is to watch gulls.

If you live in a coastal city like Boston or Los Angeles, you probably see lots of gulls. You won't see any "sea gulls," because "sea gulls" don't exist; but you may well see ring-billed gulls and herring gulls. The herring gulls, with their yellow bills, snowy white chests, and black wing tips (with white spots) are what most people think of when they say, "Look, there's a sea gull." People love to watch herring gulls, especially on hot days, because they glide so beautifully. But wait! Aren't these herring gulls rising without a flap of their wings?

These gulls aren't flying, they're soaring, hitching a ride on a rising elevator of air.

How? Because it's summertime, and in summertime downtowns get hot. "I'm getting out of this city, it's an oven!" This is what people say, isn't it? Well, they have a point. Cement and asphalt store heat, glass and metal reflect it. Together these city substances warm the surrounding air. And hot air, as everybody knows, goes up.

Up goes the air. Up go the gulls. Up go other things, too: insects. Uncountable numbers of flying insects and other small creatures are attracted by the brilliant lights of downtown, where they find themselves aloft and rising in the warm air. There's nothing that something the size of an aphid or a ballooning spider can do about it. On a hot day, they may form an invisible layer of life above the office towers.

Invisible to us, that is. But now you can understand why birds like chimney swifts and nighthawks wheel above the skyscrapers of deepest downtown. They are called aerial filter feeders. They scoop their food out of the air as they fly, and feast on a buzzing banquet the city itself serves up to them.

The Ultimate City Bird

Of all the city birds, however, one stands out. Others you have to look for, this one you can't miss. In its ranks we find war heroes and sports superstars. We find millions of mighty-muscled flying machines that baffle science with their feats (though, these days, they rarely have to fly more than a few feet between bread crumbs). You've seen this bird a million times, but now let's actually meet the pigeon.

Look at that one bobbing its way along the sidewalk, pecking at everything from Chinese food to melted ice-cream cones. Don't just stand there! If there is no traffic nearby, chase it. Try to get near enough to touch it. Isn't this strange? No matter what you try,

Along with millions of others, these pigeons are the descendants of farm birds that flew to town.

that dumb-looking pigeon seems always to stay just out of reach. You get so close you're sure that this time you'll catch it, but then . . . drat!

How does it judge our movements so well? Part of the answer lies with the fact that pigeons know people, and they have had a lot of time to learn. Archaeological records tell us that as long as 6,500 years ago, wild pigeons, called "rock doves," had already found new kinds of "rocks" to live on—namely, the houses and temples of ancient human beings. Soon afterward, humanmade nest holes started appearing in these structures, making it clear that the people wanted the pigeons to stay.

Pigeons were the chickens of those early times, probably the first bird ever raised and tended for its meat. But too bad for the culture that saw no further than plump drumsticks. For at some point—no one knows exactly when—someone realized that pigeons were fanatical homebodies. That is, if you removed a pigeon from its nest, it would fly home

Photos taken thousandths of a second apart show a pigeon rising into the air. Specially bred pigeons may fly at ninety miles per hour (145 km/h) and find their way across 1,500 miles (2,400 km) to their roosts. They can even navigate blind! No one is certain how.

again just as soon as it could, even with a message strapped to its leg. If you mated the best of these speedy "homing" pigeons generation after generation, you ended up with more capable homebodies than ever before—birds capable of navigating across whole continents; birds that changed history by flying home.

Reading this, you may be wondering: Were these homing pigeons really no different from

During World War I, a homing pigeon named Cher Ami flew through enemy fire carrying a message that saved about 500 surrounded U.S. soldiers. Cher Ami died of his wounds soon after, but you can still admire his preserved body (and his medal of honor) at the Smithsonian Institution in Washington, D.C.

those bobbing freeloaders downtown? Well, yes and no. They are the same species of animal. In other words, they are so similar to the downtown birds that they could mate with them and produce young. However, homing pigeons were bred for their homing ability, whereas the ancestors of most street pigeons were bred for the pot. They arrived with the pioneers, lived in farmlands for a time, escaped, and flew to town.

Scientists have tried to find explanations for the pigeon's speed and its remarkable sense of direction, but both remain a mystery. About all they can say is that pigeons—all pigeons—rank among the best fliers in the world. There is at least a partial explanation, however, for the rock dove's extraordinary airborne form.

It might happen anywhere—at a bus stop, in a park. Suddenly you hear a flurry of wingbeats, a scream! The usual scattering of pigeons is making for the air, but it's already too late. A blur has streaked over and away. Now all is quiet, but one less pigeon remains.

If you are really lucky, you will look up onto a nearby billboard or ledge and see the "blur" devouring its feast. Twenty inches (51 cm) long, the peregrine falcon is larger than its prey; yet if you look more closely, you will see that it resembles its pigeon

victim. Both share the same teardrop body, the same pointed wings. In flight, both rely on the same short, quick flaps to carry them so swiftly on their way.

This is not a coincidence. In fact, you could say that falcons and pigeons form a team. Not exactly a friendly team, to be sure, but certainly a long-standing one. Falcons have chased pigeons through the centuries since their ancestors first evolved in the foothills of the Middle East. During some periods, the pigeons had a better wing structure or body shape. Then the falcons were in danger; they would perish without pigeons they could catch. At other times, however, the falcons were better developed. Then, the pigeons' numbers decreased.

Falcons have chased pigeons for millions of years. Through this competition, both predator and prey have evolved into the superb fliers they are today.

Whenever a species was on the losing side, its members would die off until only those strong enough to match the other side remained. In this way, pigeons and falcons *co-evolved* to become the extraordinary fliers they are today.

You didn't think pigeons got to be one-third flying muscle by chasing after potato chips, did you? Then again, we shouldn't knock potato chips. Body types aside, the pigeon owes its survival to its diet.

The Peregrine Returns

Have you begun to wonder why we see so many pigeons around and so few falcons? The answer is simple. It has three letters: DDT.

DDT is a pesticide. It kills insects that eat crops. In the 1950s, it was the American farmer's best friend, a symbol of modern technology. It also proved that you can never be certain what new technology will do.

By the 1970s, when DDT was banned, peregrine falcons in the United States had disappeared everywhere east of the Rocky Mountains. How could this have happened? Peregrines don't eat crops. Nevertheless, they suffered most from the long-lasting pesticide. First, the chemical would land on plants. From there it would enter the bodies of insects. Then, small birds such as starlings would eat the insects. Finally would come the peregrines, which feed on small birds. Eating bird after bird, they would accumulate the greatest and most dangerous quantities of DDT in their bodies.

The DDT didn't usually kill them outright. Its main effect was to weaken their eggs. As shell after shell collapsed under a parent bird's weight, the result was the same as if every soaring falcon had been shot out of the sky.

Then why do we see any peregrines at all? Because, as DDT finally disappears from the environment, people around the continent are trying to bring these awesome hunters back. After hatching chicks in captivity, they

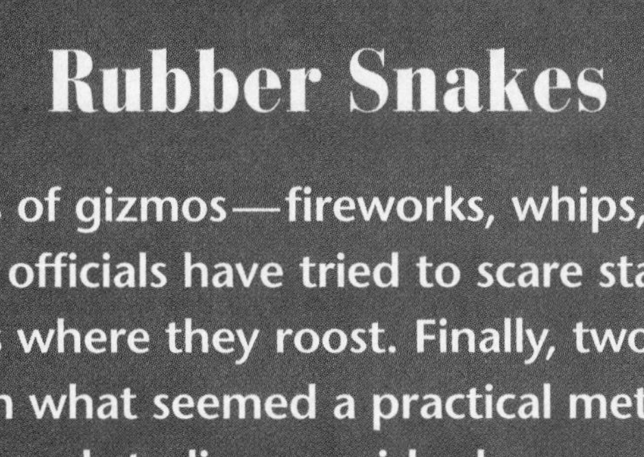

Rubber Snakes

With all sorts of gizmos—fireworks, whips, even rubber snakes—city officials have tried to scare starlings from the buildings where they roost. Finally, two professors came up with what seemed a practical method. By holding captured starlings upside down and then playing recordings of their distressed screams, the professors cleared several buildings of these messy birds.

Other birds usually shared the roosts, however, and the starlings soon noticed that these remained safely at home. Back came the starlings.

Yet the most interesting result was still to come. For as it happened, the professors had sent some of the screaming starling tapes to Denmark. The tapes had no effect there. But when the overseas birds heard new recordings, this time of screaming Danish starlings, they fled.

What did this mean? Aren't starlings in this country European starlings like those in Denmark? Indeed. Yet somehow the sounds they use to communicate have changed, so that now starlings here "speak" differently from their European cousins.

are releasing them into the wild. But what kind of wilds are these? The Rocky Mountains sound all right, but the Canada Life Building in Toronto? The McCormack Post Office Building in Boston? San Francisco's Golden Gate Bridge? Suppose it was your job to save the few remaining babies of a species that was almost gone. Are these the places you would choose?

If they were peregrines, yes! For like pigeons, falcons look on city structures as just another sort of cliff. Ledges and bridge girders make excellent nest sites, skyscraper roofs unequaled lookouts from which to swoop down on unwary city birds below.

Peregrine falcons are making a comeback in North American cities, where skyscraper ledges make as good a site for their nests and lookouts as cliffs do in the wild. The fastest peregrine can swoop down at almost 200 miles per hour (322 km/h) to snatch other birds out of the sky.

IN RESPONSE

Ask the Experts

A local television station is planning a program to teach people about plants and animals in the city. The speakers will be authors Ethan Herberman ("City Birds") and Joan Anderson ("Farming on Avenue B"). You will represent your school on the program. Based on the two articles you read, make a list of questions for these experts about their work.

Appreciate Your Wildlife

What can you do to learn more about the animals and plants in your community? Look back at the article for suggestions or use your own ideas. Then take one of your ideas and plan an activity for your class.

AUTHOR AT WORK

Author Ethan Herberman lives in Massachusetts now, but he grew up in Toronto, Canada. He worked there as a radio columnist for the Canadian Broadcasting Corporation.

Mr. Herberman writes for magazines, including the science magazine *Discover.* He is a columnist for NOVA on the Prodigy computer network and the author of two NOVA books.

Another Book by . . .

Ethan Herberman

The Great Butterfly Hunt
by Ethan Herberman,
Simon and Schuster,
1990

Library Link "City Birds" was taken from *The City Kid's Field Guide* by Ethan Herberman. You might enjoy reading the whole book to learn more about the natural world in your town or city.

Flights of Fancy

We see birds every day, but we may not always notice them. An artist's imagination can make people look at birds differently.

What words would you use to describe a chick? Does this painting fit that description? Why or why not?

Painting by Frida Kahlo (Mexican), *The Chick (El pollito)*, 1947

The artist who painted these birds is famous for creating patterns that trick the eye. What pattern do you see here?

Painting by M.C. Escher (Dutch), *Baarn IV*, 1948

This sculpture also makes use of patterns. Look at the birds' wings and bodies. What do the shapes and patterns remind you of? Explain.

Sculpture by René Magritte (Belgian), *The Natural Graces*, 1967

Painting by John Audubon (United States), *Carolina Parakeet*, 1825

Look at the works of art on these two pages. What is happening in them? How do the birds look in each piece? Now compare the settings. How do they add to your thoughts about each piece?

Sculpture by Joseph Cornell (United States), *Untitled (The Hotel Eden)*, 1945

Express **Yourself**

The characters, authors, and photographers in Learning from Nature enjoyed making discoveries about the natural world. Some even used their knowledge as a survival tool. Others studied the plants and animals around them and then created something to share with friends and neighbors.

An Eye for Photography

Jim Brandenburg ("Wolf Watch"), George Ancona ("Farming on Avenue B"), and Ethan Herberman ("City Birds") took photographs for nonfiction selections in this theme. In a small group, compare the photos in these stories. Which person told the best nature story with his pictures? Give three reasons for your choice. Discuss with your group what you learned about nature from the photos.

Learning *Your* Way

Writers, photographers, and other people in this theme learned about nature in different ways. Some just observed. Others recorded what they saw. Still others used what they had to create something new. Whose example would you follow to study nature in your community? Write a brief description of the example that person set. Why is this choice the best one for you?

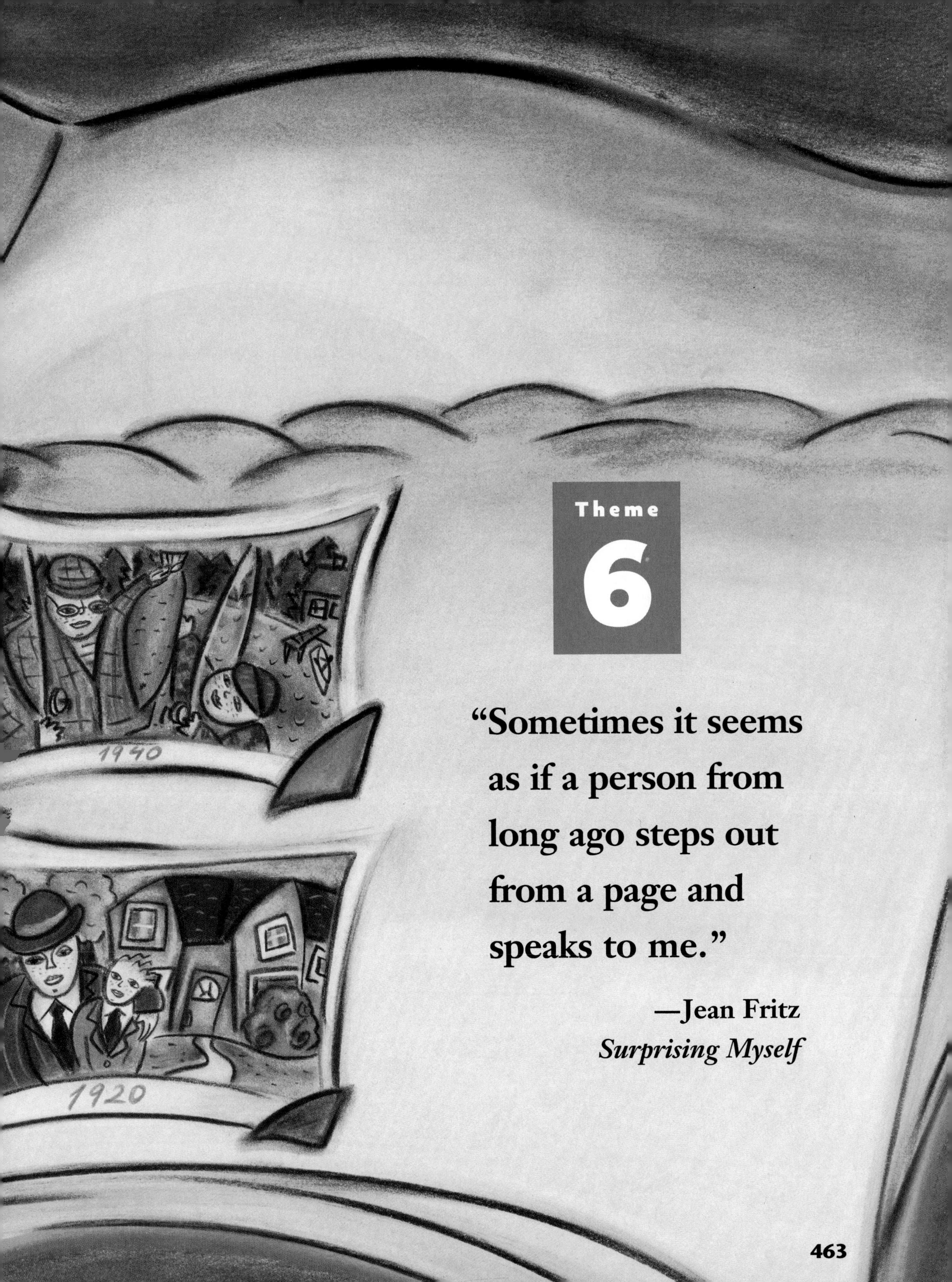

Theme 6

"Sometimes it seems as if a person from long ago steps out from a page and speaks to me."

—Jean Fritz
Surprising Myself

Theme 6

Voices from America's Past

CONTENTS

Theme Trade Books

The Navajos

by Virginia Driving Hawk Sneve
This book traces the history of one of the oldest groups of Native Americans, from the time they were created to the present day.

The Iron Dragon Never Sleeps

by Stephen Krensky
Winnie Tucker spends the summer of 1867 with her father, who works on the first cross-country railroad. She befriends a Chinese boy, but their friendship is tested when Chinese railroad workers go on strike.

Theme Magazine

What was life like for children a hundred years ago? How do you say *hello* in Cherokee? Grab a copy of the Theme Magazine *History Zone* to find the answers.

RICHARD BERLETH
Mary Patten's Voyage
illustrated by BEN OTERO

Richard Berleth

Mary Patten's Voyage

illustrated by Ben Otero

FOREWORD

They were built for speed, not comfort or safety. Full hundred and thirty feet a clipper's masts thrust into the sky to carry more sail higher than any ship had before. The clipper's hull was like a knife, sharp and clean, and her timbers, light and strong, a marvel to behold. Speed was what people wanted then—speed to reach the gold fields of California, speed to bring factory goods from the East to pioneers in the West. The clipper went farther faster, and at less cost, than any ship ever had.

Money was at the root of the matter, as often it is. A penny nail in New York, then, brought a whole dollar in San Francisco. A dollar hammer, twenty-five dollars. A steam engine could be sold in California for the price of an entire ship built in New York's yards. As gold flowed east, the products of America's cities flowed west faster and faster. The first goods to arrive brought the best prices. Ship owners and merchants competed to get their cargoes to San Francisco first.

So were born the clipper ship races: fifteen thousand miles from New York to California over some of the world's stormiest ocean. In 1851, *Flying Cloud* reached San Francisco in only eighty-nine days, nineteen days ahead of her rival, *Challenge*. Not only did *Flying Cloud* sell her cargo at the highest possible prices, but thousands of dollars more went to anyone who bet on her speed.

Clippers had become like race horses. Business had turned to sport as rich men rushed to wager fortunes on sailing time. Of course these gamblers risked their money, but we common seamen, we risked our lives to sail these ships.

Timothy Hare is my name. I have been a mariner all my life. No oceans are there I have not sailed, no continents I have not touched, and many a shipmate I have known snatched by the hungry sea. I have a mind now to tell what I have seen of this world, and of ships long gone. But not just to hear myself speak. For folks who've never seen the terrors of nature I spin this tale; for any ashore who wonder what love and faith and courage can still achieve, I offer this story. It is a true one.

I was a fresh second mate, the tar from the ropes still sticking to my hands like a common seaman, when the first clippers slid down the ways of America's shipyards and changed sailing forever. In Boston, New York, Baltimore, they followed one another fast in those years. Aye, a clipper ship in full sail on a running sea makes the prettiest picture. But clippers were not built just for their beauty; they were creatures of speed and power, and how well I remember the torture of those who served them.

Which brings me now to the voyage of the *Flying Cloud's* sister ship, *Neptune's Car*, and the gravest peril I ever knew at sea.

In 1856, the owners of *Neptune's Car*, *Intrepid*, and *Romance of the Seas* announced that their clippers would leave New York on July first, bound for San Francisco in the first three-way race ever over the gruelling course. This race was all the news of New York's South Street, where captains and merchants met to set odds and talk of ships.

A great sailing ship, everyone knew, was only as good as its master, and Captain Joshua Patten of *Neptune's Car* was thought one of the finest. He had just returned home from around the world with a hold full of China tea. His bride, Mary, eighteen years old, had accompanied him on that long voyage. She had nursed a seaman struck by lightning back to life, rumor said. Here was a good ship's wife who could shoot the sun and set a course as well as her husband.

Now many dollars were bet that *Neptune's Car* was a lucky ship and would glide past the hills of San Francisco before the others. Captain Patten was young and daring and had invested his life's savings in the cargo. With his pregnant wife aboard, he had every reason to bring *Neptune's Car* swiftly and safely to port.

Aye, this is what they guessed at South Street on a pleasant summer day. Yet 'tis one thing to wager on a clipper's speed in a South Street tavern and another to cling to her rigging as she plunges and rears through a terrible blow. I tell you: men may build ships and man them, stake their fortunes on them if they will, but in the end, it's the god of the sea that decides. In that stormiest winter, 1856, Mary Ann Patten had to take charge of her husband's ship, and I chose to stand by her side.

We sailors knew the course. Down the Atlantic we would race to the tip of South America, then up the Pacific past Mexico to foggy San Francisco. Look at

soup made. In a hard blow the galley fires were often snuffed out, and there'd be no food but what was set aside.

The wind began to roar like never before, and riding up on the swell of the waves, the clipper groaned, hesitated, then plunged downhill into the black seas. Down the bow would go, deep into the trough, and each time we'd wait seconds to see if it would rise while our hearts were in our mouths and our stomachs heaved. But up again the bow came, and the sea flooded back along the decks, drowning our hatches and breaking against our masts.

Men in the rigging, a hundred feet up, felt the angry ocean snatch at their feet as *Neptune* heeled over hard and dove between the waves. Then up again they rode with the rise, arcing wildly against the sky. The crew fought to clear ice that fouled the lines. One moment they were there, then suddenly men and masts vanished from sight in driving sheets of snow and sleet.

Mary had come on deck; she clutched a rail to keep her footing.

"How is he?" I shouted.

"Sleeping quietly. How is it here?"

"The worst I've ever seen," I told her truthfully.

This day and the next we stood the worst furies that the Horn could throw and never once saw sign of sun. We had not turned the corner. Without sun, Mary could not fix our position. Without position, we dared not sail north out of the storm. A ship fighting the westerly winds and turning north before the Horn was passed ran through the dark and snow onto the rocks of the shore. The bones of many lay strewn along these coasts.

"We're going backward," Mary said in the chartroom below. "The winds force us back. We can't keep fighting." The great waves boomed on the decks and hatches. *Neptune* was like a drum pounded by an angry giant. "How long can we bear it?" The hatch covers were splintering under the force of the waves. If they broke, the sea would fill the holds. "How long can this crew stand it?" Their hands were blue and raw from ice and cold, their gear torn by the wind.

"We'll try a new tack," she announced. Out of a pile of books she pulled one with a worn spine. "This is Maury's book on navigation," she explained. "He says to go as far south as you can to clear the cape. The winds are less there."

"But that puts us near Antarctica," I groaned. "There's icebergs!"

"Not as many as you would think," she answered, "because the wind turns back upon itself and keeps the icebergs home."

So south we went against blizzard and gale, our stern to the hateful Horn. Then, as the cruel winds changed and shifted, we turned back again, doubling our old course. We were near to going mad with the seeming hopelessness of the task. Almost five weeks we spent stuck like a ship in a spinning bottle. First southwest, then westward, then northwest, *Neptune's Car* battered at the stormy door to the Pacific, each time to be driven back exhausted by contrary winds.

Mary scanned the docks where living vessels were moored. Suddenly she groaned and dropped the glass.

I guessed what met her gaze. The *Romance of the Seas* rode high on the tide, her cargo already unloaded. As I took up the glass and studied the wharfside, I noticed that the *Intrepid* was nowhere to be seen. If we had not won, we had not lost either. But I spotted something else, something wonderful. Gathered where we would soon dock was a crowd of citizens. The pilot had spread the story of *Neptune's Car* throughout San Francisco. All of the city now was coming down to the water to welcome the heroine of the Horn. Mary had won much more than a sea race. She had proven for all time what a woman could achieve against the sea.

Aye, you'll want to know about the time and the money. When we hailed the Golden Gate, we were one hundred thirty-two days out of New York, twelve days ahead of *Intrepid.* We sailors received our pay with bonus, and Mary herself—her fame spreading far and wide—was awarded a thousand dollars by the insurance company for saving *Neptune's Car* from destruction.

You might argue 'twas a stingy amount for all she'd done. Here, smudged and creased, yellowed with the years, is a copy of her reply to the insurance company: "I am embarrassed," she wrote, "by the fear that you may overestimate the value of my services, because I feel that without the services of Mr. Hare, the second officer, a good seaman, and of the hearty cooperation of the crew, the ship would not have arrived safely."

This is all I have left of Mary Patten. I was never to see her again. Yet many times in storms at sea a wild bird has come to me for safety, and I feel that this is she—still daring the winds and sea at my side.

EPILOGUE

Mary Ann Patten's son, Joshua Adams Patten, was born early in 1857. Several months later her husband died of tuberculosis. She never again went to sea. Within months of her husband's death, she, too, was found to be suffering from tuberculosis. Mary died at age twenty-four in Boston of that disease. In memory of the lives she saved, and her care for merchant seamen, the hospital of the U.S. Merchant Marine Academy at King's Point, New York, is named in her honor.

IN RESPONSE

Mary's Diary

Imagine that Mary Patten kept a diary during her daring adventure aboard *Neptune's Car*. Write a diary entry describing one of the stormy days when the clipper was rounding Cape Horn. Consider how Mary probably felt about the men she was traveling with, including First Mate Keeler, Moses, Timothy Hare, and, of course, her husband, Captain Patten. Think about some of her likely concerns about her health and her future.

Ships Without Souls

With a partner, discuss the idea of "ships without souls." Have you ever seen an abandoned boat? How did it make you feel? Why do you think Mary and Timothy Hare, the narrator, feel so sad when they see the deserted ships in San Francisco Bay?

AUTHOR AT WORK

Richard Berleth says he most enjoys researching and writing about historical events that took place close to his home, in Brooklyn, New York. Berleth says he got the idea for *Mary Patten's Voyage* while reading a book about clipper ship voyages.

Because *Neptune's Car* sailed off from New York's South Street seaport, Berleth found a wealth of resources close at hand. Accounts from local newspapers, such as *The New York Times* and *The Herald Tribune*, provided first-hand reports of the launching of the boat. The New York Historical Society, the South Street Seaport, and the New York Merchant Marine Academy offered information about the voyage itself.

The most interesting document, by far, was the eyewitness account written by second mate Timothy Hare. Berleth says that after much research, it became clear that Hare would be the natural choice for the narrator of the story. "The central thrust of the book is in Timothy Hare's story. His experience was typical of the awful conditions that seamen lived under. Sailing these ships was no picnic," says Berleth.

Another Book by . . .

Richard Berleth

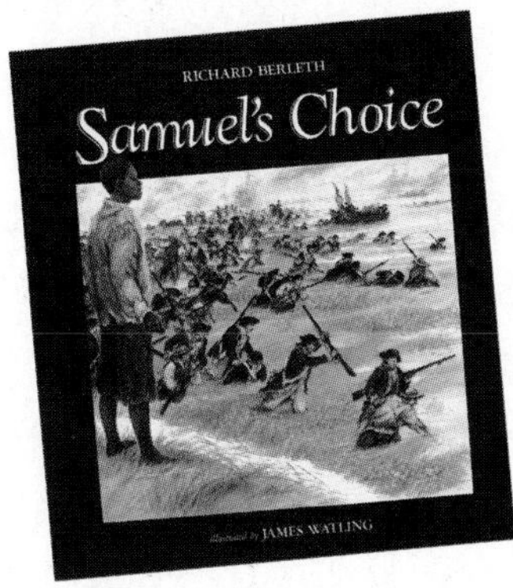

Samuel's Choice
by Richard Berleth
illustrated by
James Watling,
Albert Whitman &
Company, 1990

AWARD WINNER

Carrying the Running-Aways

THE PEOPLE COULD FLY
American Black Folktales
told by VIRGINIA HAMILTON
Illustrated by LEO *and* DIANE DILLON

from *The People Could Fly*
retold by Virginia Hamilton
illustrated by Leo and Diane Dillon

Never had any idea of carryin the runnin-away slaves over the river. Even though I was right there on the plantation, right by that big river, it never got in my mind to do somethin like that. But one night the woman whose house I had gone courtin to said she knew a pretty girl wanted to cross the river and would I take her. Well, I met the girl and she was awful pretty. And soon the woman was tellin me how to get across, how to go, and when to leave.

Well, I had to think about it. But each day, that girl or the woman would come around, ask me would I row

the girl across the river to a place called Ripley. Well, I finally said I would. And one night I went over to the woman's house. My owner trusted me and let me come and go as I pleased, long as I didn't try to read or write anythin. For writin and readin was forbidden to slaves.

Now, I had heard about the other side of the river from the other slaves. But I thought it was just like the side where we lived on the plantation. I thought there were slaves and masters over there, too, and overseers and rawhide whips they used on us. That's why I was so scared. I thought I'd land the girl over there and some overseer didn't know us would beat us for bein out at night. They could do that, you know.

Well, I did it. Oh, it was a long rowin time in the cold, with me worryin. But pretty soon I see a light way up high. Then I remembered the woman told me to watch for a light. Told me to row to the light, which is what I did. And when I got to it, there were two men. They reached down and grabbed the girl. Then one of the men took me by the arm. Said, "You about hungry?" And if he hadn't been holdin me, I would of fell out of that rowboat.

Well, that was my first trip. I was scared for a long time after that. But pretty soon I got over it, as other folks asked me to take them across the river. Two and three at a time, I'd take them. I got used to makin three or four trips every month.

Now it was funny. I never saw my passengers after that first girl. Because I took them on the nights when the moon was not showin, it was cloudy. And I always met them in the open or in a house with no light. So I never saw them, couldn't recognize them, and couldn't describe them. But I would say to them, "What you say?" And they would say the password. Sounded like "Menare." Seemed the word came from the Bible somewhere, but I don't know. And they would have to say that word before I took them across.

Well, there in Ripley was a man named Mr. Rankins, the rest was John, I think. He had a "station" there for escaping slaves. Ohio was a free state, I found out, so once they got across, Mr. Rankins would see to them. We went at night so we could continue back for more and to be sure no slave catchers would follow us there.

Mr. Rankins had a big light about thirty feet high up and it burned all night. It meant freedom for slaves if they could get to that bright flame.

I worked hard and almost got caught. I'd been rowin fugitives for almost four years. It was in 1863 and it was a night I carried twelve runnin-aways across the river to Mr. Rankins'. I stepped out of the boat back in Kentucky and they were after me. Don't know how they found out. But the slave catchers, didn't know them, were on my trail. I ran away from the plantation and all who I knew there. I lived in the fields and in the woods. Even in caves. Sometimes I slept up in the tree branches. Or in a hay pile. I couldn't get across the river now, it was watched so closely.

Finally, I did get across. Late one night me and my wife went. I had gone back to the plantation to get her. Mr. Rankins had him a bell by this time, along with the light. We were rowin and rowin. We could see the light and hear that bell, but it seemed we weren't gettin any closer. It took forever, it seemed. That was because we were so scared and it was so dark and we knew we could get caught and never get gone.

Well, we did get there. We pulled up there and went on to freedom. It was only a few months before all the slaves was freed.

We didn't stay on at Ripley. We went on to Detroit because I wasn't takin any chances. I have children and grandchildren now. Well, you know, the bigger ones don't care so much to hear about those times. But the little ones, well, they never get tired of hearin how their grandpa brought emancipation to loads of slaves he could touch and feel in the dark but never ever see.

"Carrying the Running-Aways" is a reality tale of freedom, a true slave narrative. The former slave who first told the tale was an actual person, Arnold Gragston, a slave in Kentucky. His story of rowing runaways across the Ohio River represents thousands of such stories of escape to freedom.

The abolitionist who helped the runaways once they were across the river was John Rankin, a Presbyterian minister and a southerner who lived in Ripley, Ohio. The town is still there, situated on the great river. A rickety wood staircase leads up Liberty Hill from Ohio River bottom lands to the Underground "station" house of the Rankin family. From 1825 to 1865, more than two thousand slaves were sheltered at the house and guided on by the family. Today, the Rankin house is a State Memorial open to the public from April through October.

Another fugitive, Levi Perry, born a slave, crossed the Ohio River into freedom with his mother about 1854. They were rescued by John Rankin and were taken in and taken care of at the house with the light. Years later, every six months or so, Levi Perry would settle his ten children around him and he would begin: "Now listen, children. I want to tell you about slavery and how my mother and I ran away from it. So you'll know and never let it happen to you." This tale was told to me recently by my mother, Etta Belle Perry Hamilton, who is 92 years old and Levi Perry's oldest daughter.

—Virginia Hamilton

Last Days at RED CLAY

from *The Trail on Which They Wept: The Story of a Cherokee Girl*

by Dorothy and Thomas Hoobler

It was harvest time in the land of the Cherokees. At dawn, from the front porch of her family's house, Sarah Tsaluh[1] Rogers watched blue mist rise above the floor of the valley. She stepped onto the grass, feeling the dew tickle her bare feet. The rising sun gradually lit up the hills in the distance. Every tree was ablaze with gold and crimson leaves.

It was a wonderful sight, but in the back of Sarah's mind was the thought: Will this be the last harvest?

The year had been a good one on the Rogers plantation. The workers had filled wagon after wagon with corn, taking it to the mill to be ground into meal. The corn plants had been gathered into sheaves and left to dry.

The hard work of picking the cotton was finally finished. The plantation had produced nearly a thousand bales, and Sarah's family had sold them for a high price. When the trees lost the last of their leaves and winter came, the big plantation house would be warm, and there would be more than enough food for everyone.

But then the sun went behind a cloud. A chilly

---

1 **Tsaluh** (*JAH lee*)

breeze blew down from the hills. Sarah wrapped her arms around her body, thinking again of the shadow that hung over her people.

The state government of Georgia wanted the Cherokees to leave their land. For years the Cherokees had fought Georgia in the courts. Finally the Supreme Court of the United States had ruled in favor of the Cherokees.

But President Andrew Jackson would not enforce the Supreme Court's order. He wanted the Cherokees to move hundreds of miles west, across the Mississippi River. He said they would be happier there. Of course everyone knew that wasn't true. The Cherokees were happy right here in the land where they had always lived.

It's our land! Sarah thought angrily. We won't leave it!

Many Cherokees felt the same way. Although some had moved west, others refused to go. And, now, perhaps they had reason to hope.

For at the beginning of that year, 1837, President Jackson had retired. The United States had a new president, Martin Van Buren. John Ross, the chief that the Cherokees had elected, had gone to Washington, D.C., to meet President Van Buren. Ross would ask the new president to let the Cherokees stay on their land.

Ross had left two months ago. Sarah and her family, and all the rest of the Cherokees, waited for him to return and tell them what had happened. But so far, they had no word.

Sarah's head buzzed with thoughts and questions. She decided to walk into the hills and visit her grandmother.

Grandmother lived alone in the log lodge that she and her husband had built. Although Grandfather had been a white trapper, the Cherokees had welcomed him. When he and grandmother married, he became a Cherokee too.

That was the Cherokee way. Cherokees also had welcomed Christian missionaries to their land. Over the years, many Cherokees had become Christians, like Sarah's family. That was why so many of them had white names.

But not Grandmother, even though she had married a white man. She was a *ghighau,*[2] a respected old woman who kept the Cherokee traditions alive. When her son, Sarah's father, had built the big plantation house, he asked her to come and live there. But Grandmother refused. "Too much like a *unaka*[3] house," she said. Like the other old people, Grandmother called the whites *unakas.*

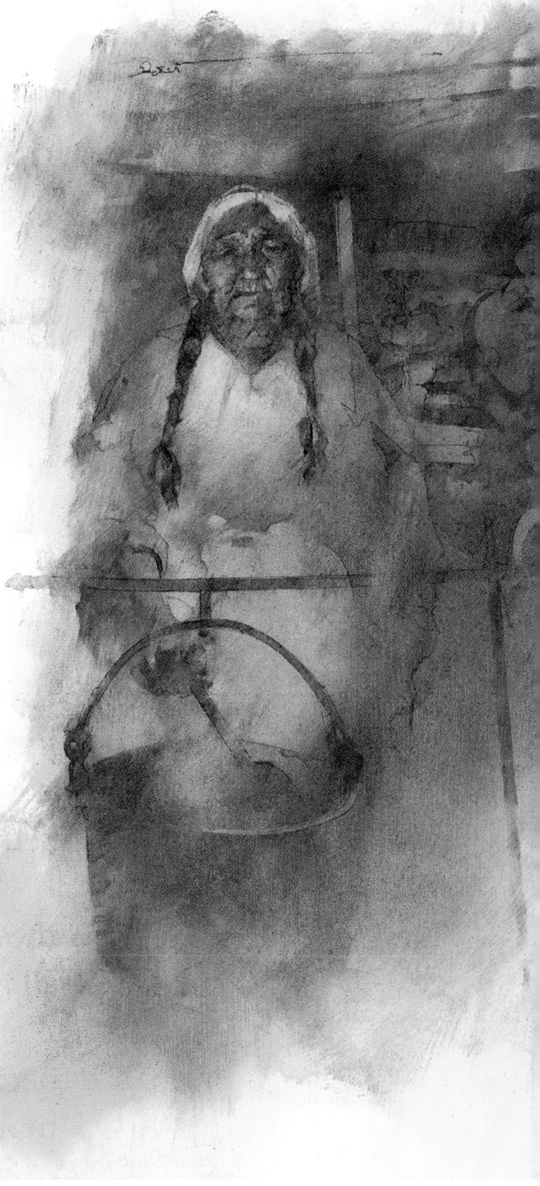

Sarah could smell Grandmother's cooking pot even before she came to the lodge. Grandmother looked up as she stirred the pot over the fire. "Tsaluh," she said. "What have you come to ask me?"

Grandmother always called Sarah by her Cherokee name. And she knew that her grandchild Tsaluh always visited when she had questions.

"What are you cooking today, Grandmother?" Tsaluh asked with a smile.

"Squirrel stew," Grandmother replied. "Nice fat squirrel, full of acorns. But to make it taste good, you have to find other things. Onions, chestnuts, good-tasting roots—I told you this before. Has that Christian schoolteacher made you forget all the Cherokee ways?"

---

2 ghighau (*jih GAY yoo*)
3 unaka (*oo NAY gah*)

Tsaluh shivered. The Raven Mockers were the spirits that came after your soul when you died. If you didn't have someone to watch you die, the Raven Mockers would take it.

"He'll come back," Grandmother said firmly. "And we must be here to send his soul back to the stars where the first Cherokees came from. If Sequoyah dies in the west, in the Darkening Land, the Raven Mockers will take his soul."

In school Sarah had learned that the sun really doesn't sink into the Darkening Land at night. It vanishes because the Earth turns. But she had never seen that for herself. Tsaluh, the Cherokee part of her, still believed that maybe the sun really went west to the Darkening Land each day and died. Who was right? Sarah? Or Tsaluh?

The sound of hoofbeats broke into her thoughts. She ran and looked down the path. It was Sam, her younger brother, looking as if he were fleeing from the Raven Mockers himself.

"Sarah!" he called, reining in the horse. "Father sent me to find you. Is Grandmother here?"

"Of course she is. What's the matter?"

"Some people from Georgia have come, and they brought soldiers. They want us to get out of our house! They say they own it now!"

Sarah rode back on the horse with Sam. Grandmother wouldn't come with them. She said she wasn't afraid, because even the *unakas* wouldn't bother an old woman.

When they arrived home, they saw a crowd of people in front of the house. Some of their neighbors had arrived carrying hoes and hatchets. The soldiers were looking around nervously, for even though they had guns, there were only five of them.

Father was standing on the front porch, arguing with a big man with a red face. Both of them were shouting. Another soldier, wearing a sword at his belt, kept trying to push them apart.

The big man kept saying, "I won it. Fair and square." He was waving a paper at Father.

Mother stepped out of the crowd when Sarah and Sam came up. She said, "Can you imagine? He says he won our land in a lottery."

"That's not fair!" Sarah said. "How could anyone think that was right?"

Mother shook her head. "I don't know, Sarah," she said. "I don't know what will happen."

The soldier on the porch held up his hands and faced the crowd. "There's no need for trouble," he shouted. "Everybody, listen to me. My orders are to carry out the relocation peacefully."

An angry murmur passed through the crowd. *Relocation*—that was the word Andrew Jackson had used to describe his plan to move the Cherokees. Sarah hated the sound of it, and so did everyone else.

Father took the soldier's arm and said, "When John Ross gets back, he'll tell you to change your orders."

The crowd cheered. "John Ross!" some of the people yelled. "Wait for Chief John Ross!"

"He's come back," the soldier shouted at them. "And he'll tell you all what you have to do." A silence followed. People in the crowd looked at each other. Could it be true?

The soldier turned to the big man who said he had won the Rogers' land. "As for you, it won't hurt to wait a couple of days to let these people prepare to leave. Get back in your carriage and follow us."

The man protested, but Sarah could see he was too afraid to stay without the soldiers. He did as he was told. The crowd moved aside to let him pass.

Before the soldiers rode off, Sarah's father spoke a few more words with them. "They say John Ross will be at the town of Red Clay this evening," Father told his neighbors. "If he is, we'll hear what he has to say."

He motioned to Sarah and Sam, and they followed him and Mother into the house. Father sat down in a chair. He looked worried. "I fear that what the soldiers say may be true."

"But John Ross couldn't agree to leave," Sarah said. "He's always told us not to give up hope."

Father shook his head. "We'll see. We'll see."

For the rest of the day, Sarah's family acted as if someone had died. Mother walked through the rooms, looking at the furniture, the pictures on the walls, the vases of flowers that she always kept full from her garden. She touched each object as if she knew she would soon be leaving it behind.

We can't just give up like this, Sarah thought. Somebody has got to do something. "Should I tell Grandmother?" she asked Father.

He shook his head. "I'd better go see her myself. Maybe she'll come with us to hear John Ross. I know this will be very hard on her."

Late in the afternoon he returned, bringing Grandmother with him. She was sitting in the buggy when the rest of the family came out. Sarah sat next to her and reached for Grandmother's hand. But she just shook her head. She was still working on the medicine belt. Father snapped the reins, and they headed for Red Clay.

The town had once been a busy place, especially on Saturdays when most people came to shop. All the

stores had been owned by Cherokees. But now many had boards nailed over the windows. Their owners had accepted cash payments from the state of Georgia and moved west.

Tonight, Red Clay came alive one last time. Carriages and wagons were arriving from all over the countryside. The people in them wore their best clothes, as if they were coming to church. They wore woolen suits and cotton dresses, and looked very much like people in Boston, Philadelphia, or anywhere else in the United States. But there was one difference. They were Cherokees.

"Look at them," Grandmother said loudly enough so that others turned their heads. "They wanted to be like the *unakas*. But a Cherokee can't ever be an *unaka*. An *unaka* can become a Cherokee, but not the other way around. It will always be that way."

They helped her out of the buggy and went inside. Sarah and Sam went up to the balcony where the rest of the children were. They looked down and saw Grandmother seated in front with the other old people. The room was already so crowded that people were standing in the back and along the walls.

The crowd hushed, and John Ross stood up. He was a short man, but when he spoke his voice was deep and powerful. "I am sorry it has taken me so long to return," he said. "When the other chiefs and I arrived in Washington, the President would not see us. He sent others to talk in his place. But I said I was the chief of the Cherokee Nation. I would speak only with the chief of the United States."

Sarah saw people's heads nodding in approval. They had voted for John Ross as chief because of his great dignity. He was as great a man as the President of the United States, and they knew it.

"Finally," John Ross continued, "President Van Buren invited me to the White House—alone. He would not let the other chiefs come, though many of his own assistants were there. Perhaps," he said with a smile, "he was afraid of me."

John Ross tapped his chest. "I was not afraid of him." Laughter rang out, but it was a nervous sound. What did the President say? Sarah thought.

"Van Buren told me he was a generous man. He knew that George Washington had promised we could live here forever. But Van Buren said that other Cherokees had agreed to move west."

The crowd murmured in anger. It was true that some Cherokees had taken money for their land. But most had refused. Grandmother had said, "They will spend the money, and soon it will be gone. But land cannot be spent or sold. It is the gift of the Great Spirit."

Ross raised his hand. "Van Buren made me an offer. He said he would pay five million dollars if all the Cherokees would move west."

Sarah's head spun. Five million dollars? How much was that? Father said that all the cotton they had grown that year sold for seven hundred dollars. And he thought that was a lot.

"Five million dollars." Ross said again. "But I had to agree right away. He would not let me come back and ask the people to decide. So I ask you now: What should I have said?"

A moment passed. Then one of the old men near Grandmother shouted, "No!" And the rest of the hall took it up. "No! No!" they all shouted.

Ross nodded, and waved for quiet. "I told Van Buren no. I asked what price he would take for the city

of Washington. How much money would he take for the graves of his parents and the house where he was born?" People clapped and shouted.

"But he wouldn't listen," said Ross. "The President has hardened his heart against us."

"Fight him!" shouted an old woman. Sarah could not tell if it was Grandmother. "Yes!" other voices agreed. "We will fight."

But Ross shook his head, and Sarah felt her heart drop. She knew what he was about to say.

"The soldiers are already here. They have guns, and we do not. They are many, and we are few. Let me tell you what they have already done to clear one of our towns. They rounded up all the children and put them into camps. Their parents had to follow or they would never see their children again."

Angry shouts echoed through the hall. "They won't do that here!" someone said.

"They will do that, and worse," said John Ross. "Van Buren has given the order to drive us out. They will stop at nothing." He looked up to the balcony and pointed right at Sarah. Her spine tingled.

"Our children are our future," said John Ross. "We cannot risk their lives. We cannot keep the Americans from taking our land. We must find another."

People began to weep and shout. John Ross hung his head and listened to all they had to say. But he would not change his decision. Sarah's eyes filled with tears. All she could think was, It isn't right. It isn't right.

The next few days were a blur of activity to Sarah. Each family could take only what they could carry. Sarah's family was lucky—they had enough horses to pull two wagons. But even so, they would have to leave a lot behind.

Mother gave Sarah a box and told her to fill it with clothes for the journey. The box seemed to grow smaller as Sarah tried to make her choices. She picked out her best dress, a pink organdy frock decorated with little ribbons. She had worn it only once, when her parents had given a big party last year.

Sarah folded the dress carefully, but it still took up more than half the space in the box. The petticoat that Sarah had worn under the dress was almost as large. Sarah added a straw hat that she wore when the sun was hot.

The box was nearly full. Sarah added some other underthings and an extra blouse. Around the plantation, she nearly always went barefoot, but she thought she might need a pair of shoes. After they went in, there was no room for anything else.

When Mother came to look at the box, she shook her head. She sat down with Sarah on the bed. "Dear, I know you don't quite understand what is happening," Mother said.

"I do understand," Sarah said. "But I don't think it's fair."

Mother sighed. "It isn't fair," she said. "But we have to make the best of it. It's going to be colder in the new land than it is here. And there won't be any parties. We're going to have to do a lot of work. We must start a new life." Mother turned her head away, and Sarah realized she was crying.

Sarah hugged her mother. "I'm sorry," she said. She wasn't sure just what she had done wrong, but she didn't want Mother to cry.

Mother emptied the box. "Take the shoes," she said. "And your coat."

"I almost never wear my coat," Sarah said.

"You will need it where we're going," Mother insisted. "And take your plain dresses that you wear in the fields. Anything that will last a long time."

Sarah did what she was told. But when Mother was gone, she tried on the party dress one last time. She looked in the mirror. Would she ever have a pretty dress like this one again? She closed her eyes and tried to see the future, like Grandmother said she could.

But nothing happened. It is because of the dress, she thought. This is Sarah's dress. Sarah, the *unaka.* When I take this dress off, I will be Tsaluh, true Cherokee.

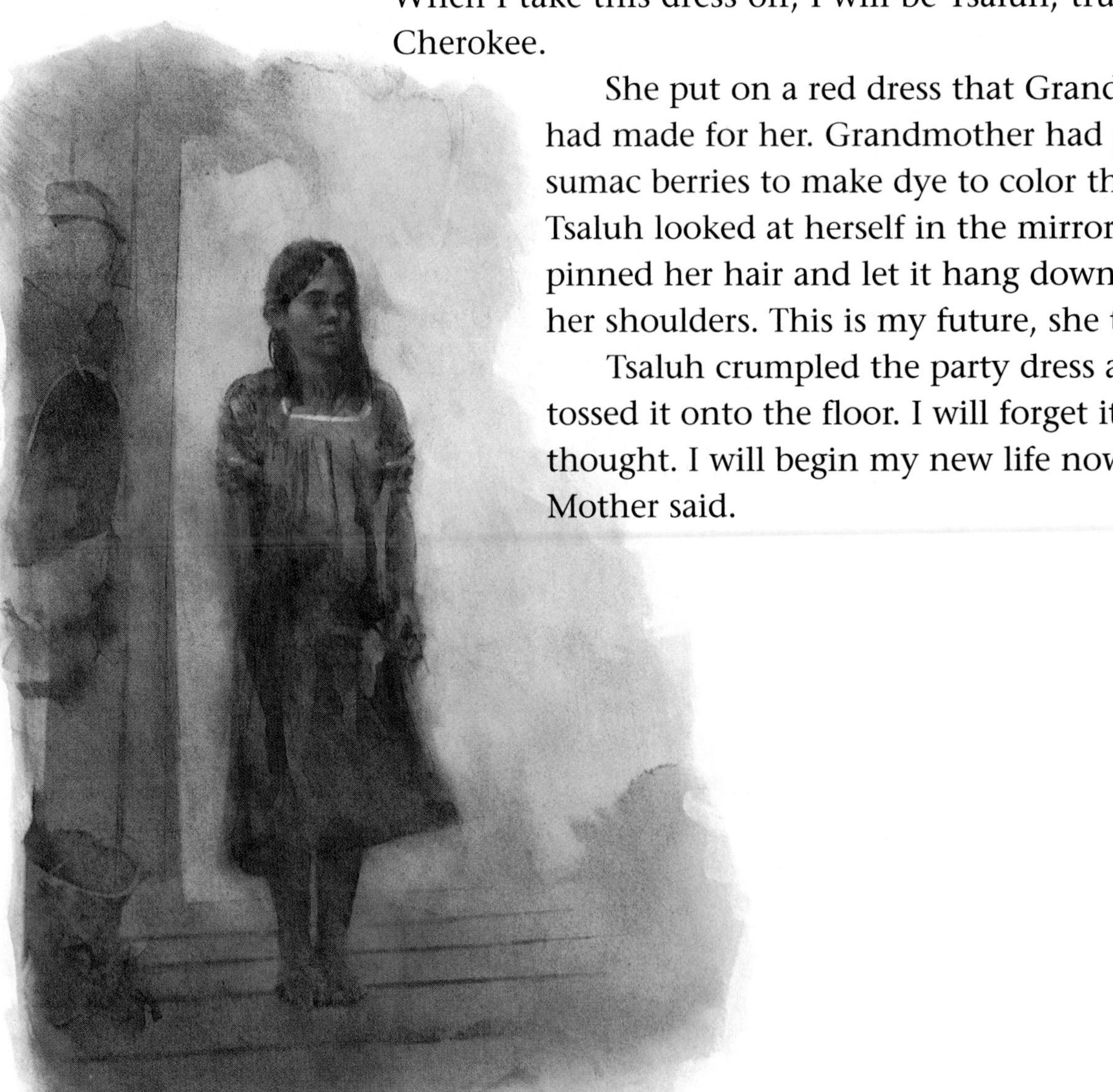

She put on a red dress that Grandmother had made for her. Grandmother had picked sumac berries to make dye to color the cloth. Tsaluh looked at herself in the mirror. She unpinned her hair and let it hang down around her shoulders. This is my future, she thought.

Tsaluh crumpled the party dress and tossed it onto the floor. I will forget it, she thought. I will begin my new life now, like Mother said.

IN RESPONSE

Remember This . . .

Sarah will have a lot on her mind as she begins her new life out West. Pretend you are her grandmother. What important things would you tell Sarah to remember as she leaves home? Think about the values her grandmother has tried to teach her. Write your thoughts in a paragraph.

Two Names, Two Worlds

Sarah has an *unaka* name and a Cherokee name. In what ways is she a Cherokee? An *unaka*? Look through the story for examples of things she does and objects she uses. How do you think Sarah feels about being a part of these two worlds? Explain.

A Few Choice Words

Sarah and Mary Patten are brave as they face great challenges. What other words describe both characters? In a small group, think of at least three words or phrases for each character. Which descriptions apply to just Sarah? Mary? Which words or phrases describe both characters?

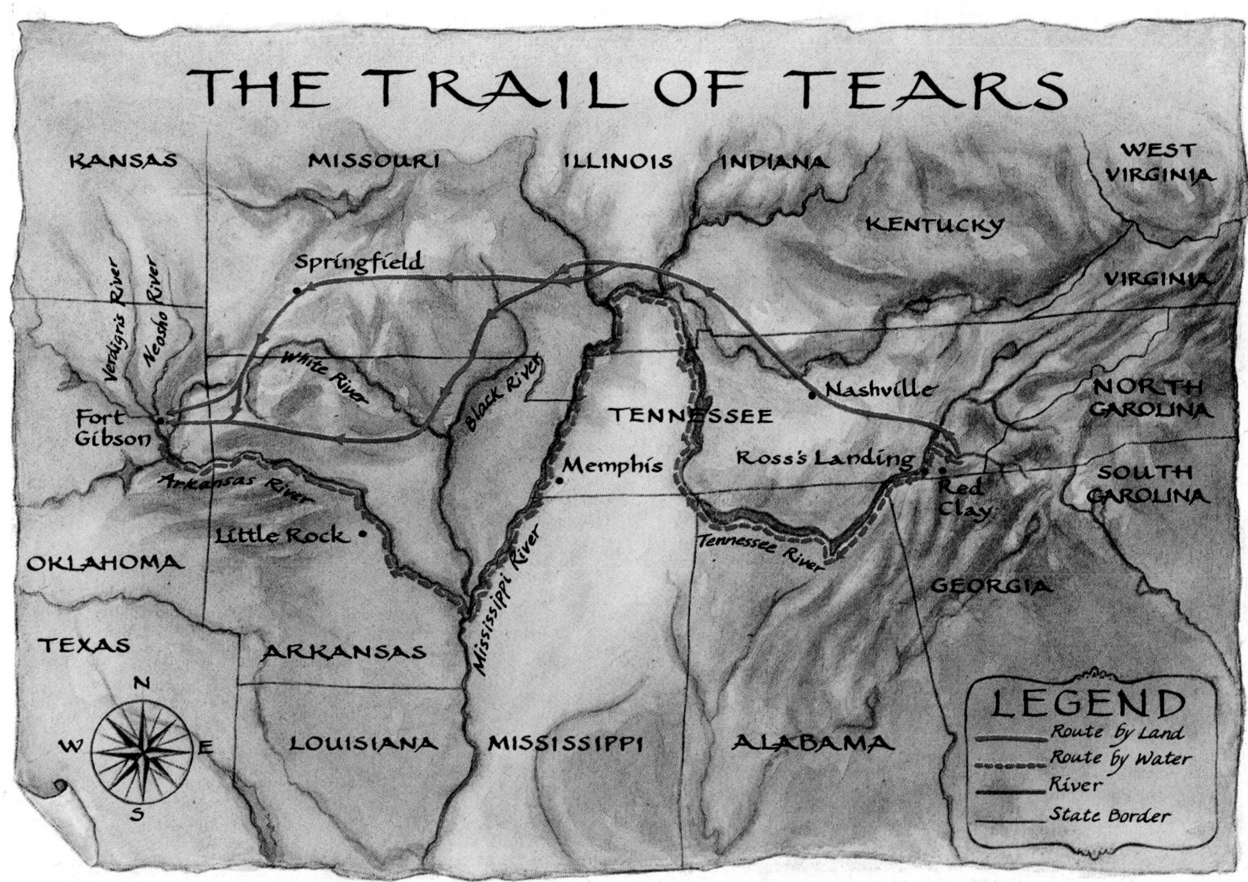

This map shows the routes taken by the Cherokees when they were forced to leave their land. Present-day names and boundaries are used.

Dorothy and Thomas Hoobler

Dorothy Hoobler reads up on a subject for one of her books.

Dorothy and Thomas Hoobler, a husband-and-wife writing team, have been writing books for young readers for more than twenty years.

The couple works in a New York apartment that is piled high with pads of paper, pens, and books. "We probably own about ten thousand books, mostly on history," says Mr. Hoobler. "We use encyclopedias, too—*World Book* and *Encyclopaedia Britannica*," Mr. Hoobler adds, "but we usually start our research with our own books."

The Hooblers take turns at the word processor. "I'm the night person," says Mr. Hoobler. "I started working at night when our daughter was a baby."

Reference books, note cards, and computer printouts fill the Hooblers' work space.

Thomas Hoobler works at a computer in his home.

Not only do the Hooblers work at different times, they often do different jobs on a single book. "Tom's the better writer," says Mrs. Hoobler. "Dorothy knows a lot more about research," her husband replies.

Sometimes one of the Hooblers will write a first draft, then the other will edit it. "The writing goes back and forth like a Ping-Pong® ball," says Mr. Hoobler.

The Hooblers wrote *The Trail on Which They Wept* as part of a fictional series on girls at different times in American history. Other books in the series include *A Promise at the Alamo: The Story of a Texas Girl* and *The Sign Painter's Secret: The Story of a Revolutionary Girl.*

Other Books by . . .

Dorothy and Thomas Hoobler

The Summer of Dreams: The Story of a World's Fair Girl by Dorothy and Thomas Hoobler, illustrated by Rénee Graef, Silver Burdett Press, 1993

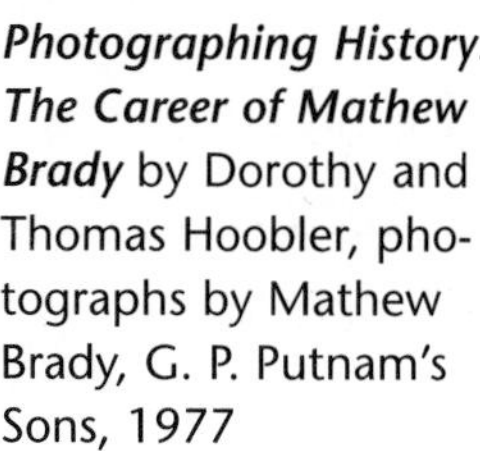

Photographing History: The Career of Mathew Brady by Dorothy and Thomas Hoobler, photographs by Mathew Brady, G. P. Putnam's Sons, 1977

Library Link "Last Days at Red Clay" was taken from *The Trail on Which They Wept* by Dorothy and Thomas Hoobler. You might want to read the entire book to find out about Sarah's journey on the Trail of Tears.

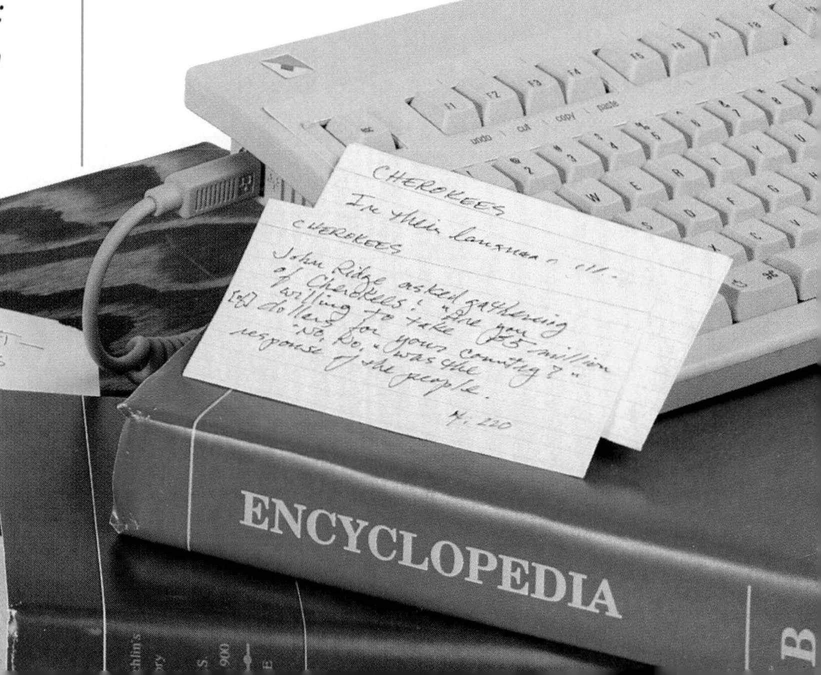

The Youngest Buffalo Hunter

from *My Indian Boyhood*
by Luther Standing Bear

Ota K'te[1] was excited. The Sioux scouts had found a large herd of buffalo nearby. This morning the men of the village were riding out to hunt the buffalo, and Ota K'te was going with them. It would be his first buffalo hunt.

The buffalo were reported to be about five or six miles away as we should count distance now. At that time we did not measure distance in miles. One camping distance was about ten miles, and these buffalo were said to be about one half camping distance away.

Some of the horses were to be left at a stopping-place just before the herd was reached. These horses were pack-animals which were taken along to carry extra blankets or weapons.

---

1 **Ota K'te** (*OH tah guh TEE*)

They were trained to remain there until the hunters came for them. Though they were neither hobbled nor tied, they stood still during the shooting and noise of the chase.

My pony was a black one and a good runner. I felt very important as I rode along with the hunters and my father, the chief. I kept as close to him as I could.

Two men had been chosen to scout or to lead the party. These two men were in a sense policemen whose work it was to keep order. They carried large sticks of ash wood, something like a policeman's billy, though longer. They rode ahead of the party while the rest of us kept in a group close together. The leaders went ahead until they sighted the herd of grazing buffalo. Then they stopped and waited for the rest of us to ride up. We all rode slowly toward the herd, which on sight of us had come together, although they had been scattered here and there over the plain. When they saw us, they all ran close together as if at the command of a leader. We continued riding slowly toward the herd until one of the leaders shouted,

"Ho-ka-he!"[2] which means, "Ready, Go!" At that command every man started for the herd. I had been listening, too, and the minute the hunters started, I started also.

Away I went, my little pony putting all he had into the race. It was not long before I lost sight of father, but I kept going just the same. I threw my blanket back and the chill of the autumn morning struck my body, but I did not mind. On I went. It was wonderful to race over the ground with all these horsemen about me. There was no shouting, no noise of any kind except the pounding of the horses' feet. The herd was now running and had raised a cloud of dust. I felt no fear until we had entered this cloud of dust and I could see nothing about me—only hear the sound of feet. Where was father? Where was I going? On I rode through the cloud, for I knew I must keep going.

Then all at once I realized that I was in the midst of the buffalo, their dark bodies rushing all about me and their great heads moving up and down to the sound of their hoofs beating upon the earth. Then it was that fear overcame me and I leaned close down upon my little pony's body and clutched him tightly. I can never tell you how I felt toward my pony at that moment. All thought of shooting had left my mind.

2 **Ho-ka-he** (*HOH kah HAY*)

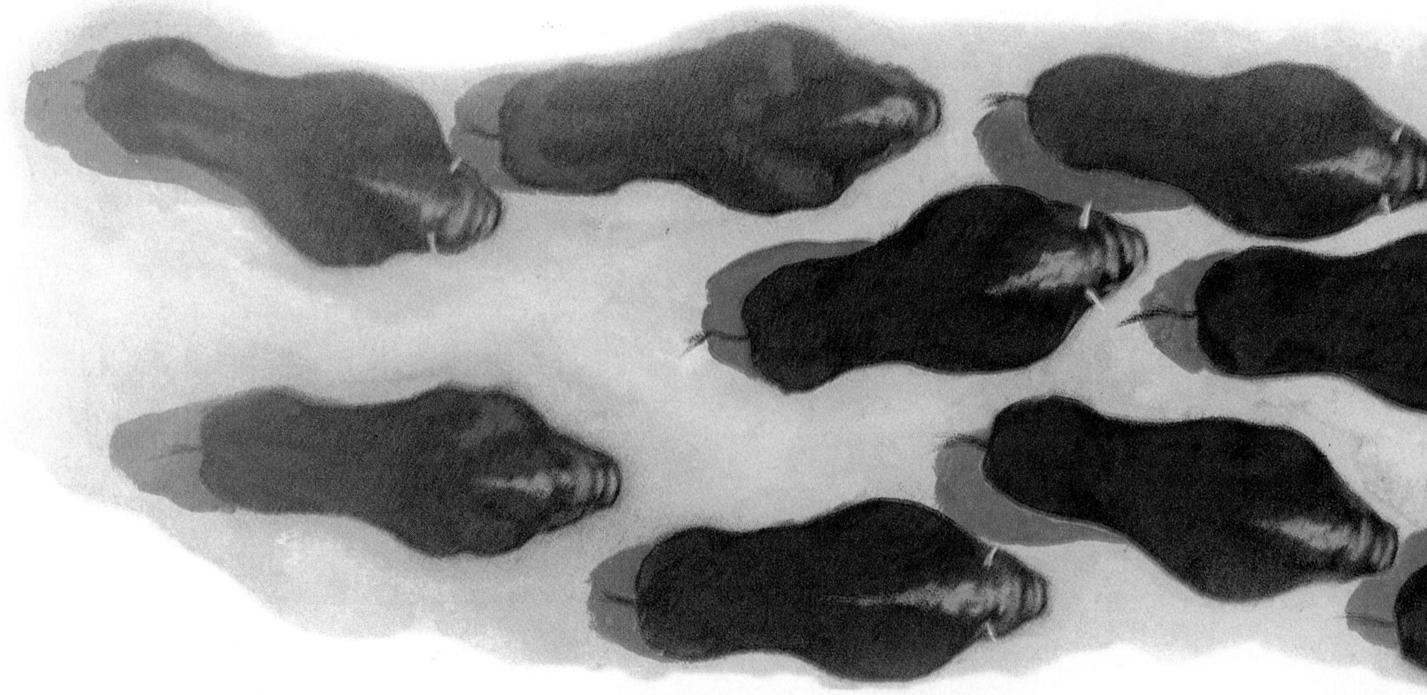

I was seized by blank fear. In a moment or so, however, my senses became clearer, and I could distinguish other sounds beside the clatter of feet. I could hear a shot now and then and I could see the buffalo beginning to break up into small bunches. I could not see father nor any of my companions yet, but my fear was vanishing and I was safe. I let my pony run. The buffalo looked too large for me to tackle, anyway, so I just kept going. The buffalo became more and more scattered. Pretty soon I saw a young calf that looked about my size. I remembered now what father had told me the night before as we sat about the fire. Those instructions were important for me now to follow.

I was still back of the calf, being unable to get alongside of him. I was anxious to get a shot, yet afraid to try, as I was still very nervous. While my pony was making all speed to come alongside, I chanced a shot and to my surprise my arrow landed. My second arrow glanced along the back of the animal and sped on between the horns, making only a slight wound. My third arrow hit a spot that made the running beast slow up in his gait. I shot a fourth arrow, and though it, too, landed it was not a fatal wound. It seemed to me that it was taking a lot of shots, and I was not proud of my

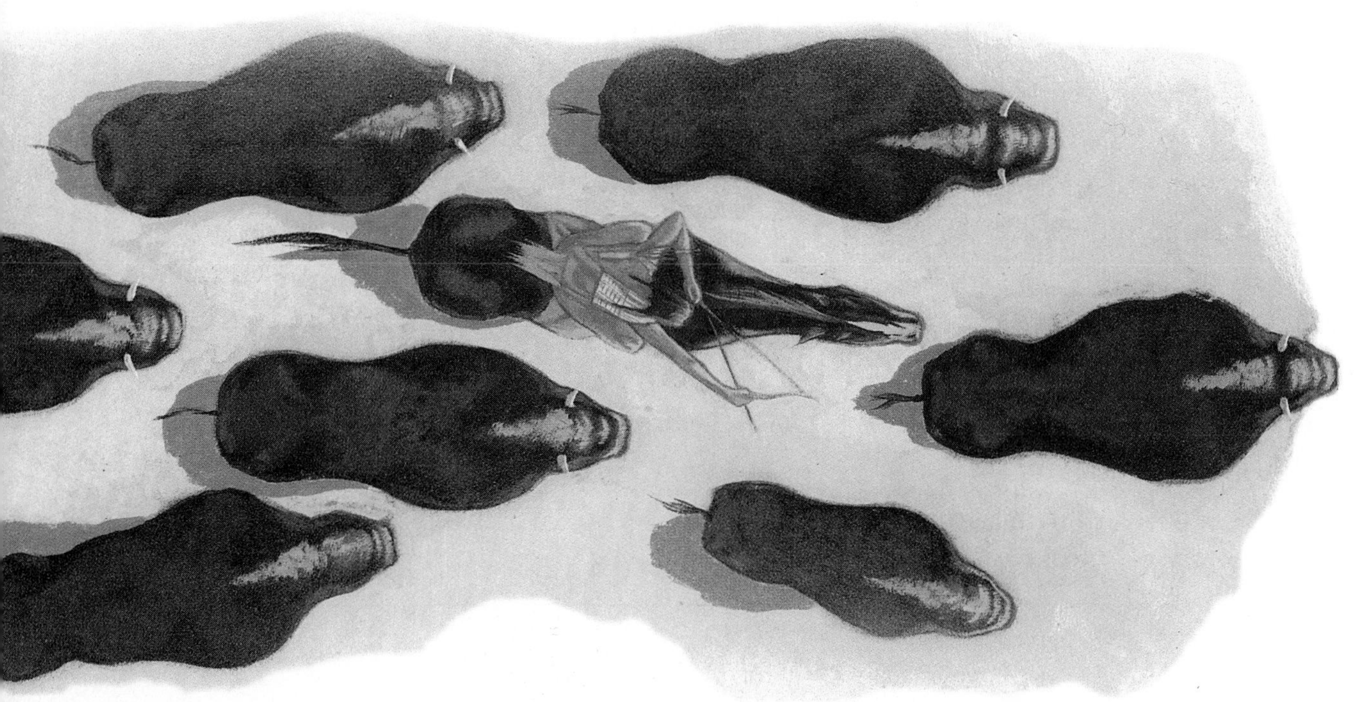

marksmanship. I was glad, however, to see the animal going slower and I knew that one more shot would make me a hunter. My horse seemed to know his own importance. His two ears stood straight forward and it was not necessary for me to urge him to get closer to the buffalo. I was soon by the side of the buffalo and one more shot brought the chase to a close. I jumped from my pony, and as I stood by my fallen game, I looked all around wishing that the world could see. But I was alone. In my determination to stay by until I had won my buffalo, I had not noticed that I was far from every one else. No admiring friends were about, and as far as I could see I was on the plain alone. The herd of buffalo had completely disappeared. And as for father, much as I wished for him, he was out of sight and I had no idea where he was.

I stood and looked at the animal on the ground. I was happy. Every one must know that I, Ota K'te, had killed a buffalo. But it looked as if no one knew where I was, so no one was coming my way. I must then take something from this animal to show that I had killed it. I took all the arrows one by one from the body. As I took them out, it occurred to me that I had used five arrows. If I had been a skillful hunter, one arrow would have been sufficient, but I had used five. Here it was that temptation came to me. Why could I not take out two of the arrows and throw them away? No one would know, and then I should be more greatly admired and praised as a hunter. As it was, I knew that I should be praised by father and mother, but I wanted more. And so I was tempted to lie.

I was planning this as I took out my skinning knife that father had sharpened for me the night before. I skinned one side of the animal, but when it came to turning it over, I was too small. I was wondering what to do when I heard my father's voice calling, "To-ki-i-la-la-hu-wo,"[3] "Where are you?" I quickly jumped on my pony and rode to the top of a little hill near by. Father saw me and came to me at once. He was so pleased to see me and glad to know that I was safe. I knew that

3 **To-ki-i-la-la-hu-wo** (*tah GEEEE lah lah hoo WOH*)

I could never lie to my father. He was too fond of me and I too proud of him. He had always told me to tell the truth. He wanted me to be an honest man, so I resolved then to tell the truth even if it took from me a little glory. He rode up to me with a glad expression on his face, expecting me to go back with him to his kill. As he came up, I said as calmly as I could, "Father, I have killed a buffalo." His smile changed to surprise and he asked me where my buffalo was. I pointed to it and we rode over to where it lay, partly skinned.

Father set to work to skin it for me. I had watched him do this many times and knew perfectly well how to do it myself, but I could not turn the animal over. There was a way to turn the head of the animal so that the body would be balanced on the back while being skinned. Father did this for me, while I helped all I could. When the hide was off, father put it on the pony's back with the hair side next to the pony. On this he arranged the meat so it would balance. Then he covered the meat carefully with the rest of the hide, so no dust would

reach it while we traveled home. I rode home on top of the load.

I showed my father the arrows that I had used and just where the animal had been hit. He was very pleased and praised me over and over again. I felt more glad than ever that I had told the truth and I have never regretted it. I am more proud now that I told the truth than I am of killing the buffalo.

We then rode to where my father had killed a buffalo. There we stopped and prepared it for taking home. It was late afternoon when we got back to camp. No king ever rode in state who was more proud than I that day as I came into the village sitting high up on my load of buffalo meat. Mother had now two hunters in the family and I knew how she was going to make over me. It is not customary for Indian men to brag about their exploits and I had been taught that bragging was not nice. So I was very quiet, although I was bursting with pride. Always when arriving home I would run out to play, for I loved to be with the other boys, but this day I lingered about close to the tipi so I could hear the nice things that were said about me. It was soon all over camp that Ota K'te had killed a buffalo.

My father was so proud that he gave away a fine horse. He called an old man to our tipi to cry out the news to the rest of the people in camp. The old man stood at the door of our tipi and sang a song of praise to my father. The horse had been led up and I stood holding it by a rope. The old man who was doing the singing called the other old man who was to receive the horse as a present. He accepted the horse by coming up to me, holding out his hands to me, and saying, "Ha-ye," which means "Thank you." The old man went away very grateful for the horse.

That ended my first and last buffalo hunt. It lives only in my memory, for the days of the buffalo are over.

IN RESPONSE

A Song for Ota K'te

After Ota K'te kills the buffalo, an old man sings a song of praise. What words might he have sung? Write them down. The words don't need to rhyme. Just be sure the song explains what Ota K'te experienced during the hunt and why his feat is worth singing about.

Facing a Challenge

Ota K'te and Mary ("Mary Patten's Voyage") both faced dangerous situations. What thoughts did Ota K'te have when he was alone with the buffalo? What was on Mary's mind as she steered *Neptune* around the tip of Cape Horn? With a partner, talk about the answers. Then discuss how their experiences changed Ota K'te and Mary Patten.

The Whole Truth

Ota K'te is tempted to lie about the number of arrows he used to kill the buffalo. Why? What does he finally decide to do? What do you think Ota K'te's decision says about him? Write a brief paragraph describing what you've learned about Ota K'te.

AUTHOR AT WORK

Luther Standing Bear lived from about 1868 to 1939. He had a career in show business, first in Buffalo Bill's famous *Wild West Show* and then as an actor in Hollywood. He also worked as a teacher, rancher, storekeeper, and minister.

Mr. Standing Bear worried about how little the white people he met knew about the Sioux and other Native Americans. To teach others about Sioux customs, he wrote *My Indian Boyhood* and three other books. "Of my old life I have much to remember with pride," he wrote. Mr. Standing Bear dedicated *My Indian Boyhood* to "the boys and girls of America."

Library Link "The Youngest Buffalo Hunter" is one of the stories in *My Indian Boyhood* by Luther Standing Bear. You may want to read the entire book to learn more about Sioux hunting, fishing, and games.

Other Books About . . .

The Sioux

The Sioux
by Barbara Brooks, illustrated by Luciano Lazzarino, Rourke Publications, 1989

The Sioux
by Elaine Landau, Franklin Watts, 1989

The Sioux: A First Americans Book
by Virginia Driving Hawk Sneve, illustrated by Ronald Himler, Holiday House, 1993

As I Walk Along the Hillside

by Misty Stands in Timber

As I walk along the hillside,
I think about who my ancestors were
and how they lived.

I see tepees, and smoke
rising from them; the dry-meat poles
are filled,

buffalo hides being tanned,
children laughing, playing,
old men telling stories,
and young men become
warriors.
I hear the sound of drums beating

and people singing, dancing, eating.
I see horses grazing
on green grass in the meadow,
and as I walk along the hillside
I feel all these things inside me,
helping me to be who I am.

Tales From Tucson

from *Images and Conversations*
by Patricia Preciado Martin
photographs by
Louis Carlos Bernal

In 1776, as part of its territory in the Americas, Spain founded a military post at what is now Tucson, Arizona. It remained a Spanish city until the United States bought it and the surrounding territory in 1853. Tucson never lost its Hispanic flavor. That heritage lives on in the memories of Mexican Americans who grew up in the city during the early 1900's.

Margarita Martínez

Ms. Martínez was born in Tucson in 1889.

My grandmother was here when the first train arrived. She used to wash for the families of the men who worked for the railroad—laying the track. Those families were poor, but not as poor as the rest of us, because they had regular paying jobs. After the day's work was done, my grandmother would say to me, *"Vámonos, mijita.*[1] *Vamos a llevar la ropa."*[2] "Come on, my little daughter. We shall go and deliver the clothes." And she would tie up the day's wash in a bundle and we would take the bundle with the clean clothing and deliver it to the families. On the way, we would pass the flour mill. The flour mill had doors above and a scale below. That's where they would put the sacks of wheat to weigh them. They grew wheat along the river in those days. Some people would buy large amounts, and some people would buy small amounts. We would always buy a little sack of wheat for the hens and the little chicks. We always had fresh eggs, and I was used to that. But then the Americans came, and I guess they don't like chickens because they always buy their eggs in a box.

1 **Vámonos, mijita** *(BAH moh nohs mee HEE tah)*
2 **Vamos a llevar la ropa** *(BAH mohs ah yeh BAHR lah ROH pah)*

Alberto Urías

When Mr. Urías was born in 1904, his was one of many Mexican families that farmed land along the Santa Cruz River.

When I was a child, there was a tribe of Apache Indians that lived in an encampment right at the foot of "A" Mountain. It's where the Holiday Inn is now. There used to be a well right here where we live now, and the Indians used to come and get water from the well. It was sweet water. We had a little table outside, like we do now, and they always used to leave a little token on the table—a bowl of pinole, beef jerky, corn tortillas. They never spoke, except to my grandmother, because she could speak the Apache language.

The Santa Cruz had water all year round. The water ran clear, about eighteen to twenty inches deep. All along the river there were groves of willows and huge cottonwoods. The trees were so lush that they arched over the river. People would go and hunt and fish along the river—there was everything aplenty. There were ducks and quail and doves and rabbits—and even fish. There were large rocks along the river and the women would go down to wash and gossip along the river. It was a sight to behold. They would make soap from a plant named *amole*.[3] They would crush the fibers of the plant with a rock. When they finished washing, they would spread the clothes to dry over the bushes along the river—the clothes looked like flowers on all the bushes. Then they would wash their long, beautiful hair.

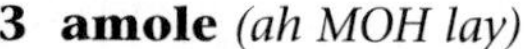

3 amole *(ah MOH lay)*

Elína Laos Sayre

Ms. Sayre, born in 1889, has many happy childhood memories of picnics by the river.

The Chinese people had farms all along the Santa Cruz River. That's where they raised their vegetables and where we had picnics. It was very beautiful—there was lots of water and many trees. We would lay our picnic out right along the banks of the river. We would play the guitar and sing. My mother used to play the guitar beautifully and she had a beautiful soprano voice. We knew the owner of the farm and he would come and have dinner with us and he would bring us a big sweet watermelon. Oh, we used to have so much fun! We had a picnic of one kind or another almost every Sunday.

Henry García

Mr. García, born in 1921, has watched his neighborhood change with time.

Our house was at 218 El Paso Street—there is still a little piece left of El Paso Street, but where our house used to be is now part of the parking lot of the Community Center. Urban Renewal also tore down our old store on South Meyer—it has been gone for some time now. My brother has continued in the drycleaning business, however; it's called García's Cleaners and it is now located

on 22nd Street and 5th Avenue. He has a lovely place of business, but as for me, I got out of the business. I work for the state now.

Now that I remember, the life in those old barrios was a full and rich one. We all lived together—there was a mixture of people—Jews, Syrians, naturally many Mexicans, Chinese, Lebanese—and everyone spoke Spanish.

You know, when I think about my memories as a boy, the life of a child today seems sterile in comparison. *Sin chiste*[4]—without flavor. Everything children of today know, they get from the TV. It seems to me that they know very little of real life. It's sad, because everything is so spread out and disconnected now—there's no sense of community. People stay inside their houses. They don't seem to want to live close to anyone. It's as if people hate one another. Everyone wants to live on an acre—no one wants to have neighbors.

Anyway, as I have said, in those days we all lived close together—one house was right next to the other and women visited over the fence. A boy could have a lot of adventures. I saw a lot of things and learned a lot.

4 sin chiste *(seen CHEES tay)*

Antonio Córdova

Mr. Córdova grew up on a ranch just outside Tucson. His father was a cowboy. Life was simpler then, Mr. Córdova remembers.

In 1915 we built a house and a well. The house was made of adobe—it had three rooms as was the style of those days—a room for sleeping, a *sala*[5] (living room) and a kitchen.

We had a few cattle, but mostly we farmed. We planted barley, chile, squash, watermelon, corn, tomatoes, beans, and even a little wheat. After the harvest, my father would come into town and sell the vegetables that we grew on our ranchito. My father had a wagon and a mule for coming into town. And what a mule that was! I remember that we used to have to hold the mule until my father was seated in the wagon—and then the mule would take off, and I don't think he would stop until he got into town! With the money that he made selling vegetables, my father would buy provisions. He would buy salt, sugar, wooden buckets of lard, flour, rice, kerosene, and bolts of cloth. We used the kerosene for our lamps. He would go to town about every six months, and when he returned he wouldn't think about town until the next harvest. It was an interesting life because it was very rustic, and we were so independent.

5 **sala** *(SAH lah)*

Images of the Past

Looking at art can tell you a lot about America's past. Art helps you see through another person's eyes into another time and place.

Notice the landscape and the people in this painting. What might the people be doing? What does this scene show you about the past?

Painting by Thomas Moran (United States), ***Cliffs of the Upper Colorado River, Wyoming Territory,*** **1882**

The Sioux painted colorful images of daily life on buffalo hides. Why do you think they painted on hides? What feeling do you get from the colors on this hide?

Painting on Buffalo Hide **(Sioux), late 1800's**

Courtesy Morning Star Gallery, Santa Fe, N. M., Photo Addison Doty

What details can you find in the photograph that tell you about these pioneers? Why do they look so serious? What do you notice about their house?

Photograph by Solomon D. Butcher (United States)
The Gardner family, Custer County, Nebraska, 1888

Look at the words and the lines on this quilt. What does the quilt represent? What information about the past does it give you? Explain.

Detail from a quilt by Harriet Angelia Deuel (United States), *Untitled*, 1887

A Gift for Athens

from *Jim-Dandy* by Hadley Irwin

Thirteen-year-old Caleb lives with his stepfather, Webb Cotter, on a Kansas homestead shortly after the Civil War. He hears rumors of trouble coming from Cheyenne warriors but is too lonely to worry. He misses his mother, who died a few months earlier. Before she died, Caleb's mother began to paint a scene from a picture she had once seen. She painted directly on a shingle left over from the roof of their sod house. Caleb cherishes this memento and keeps it under his straw mattress.

Eventually, Caleb finds comfort in a young horse named Dandy. Then he meets someone who shares his interest in Dandy.

No "Indian trouble" came that spring or in the summer that followed, at least not as far as anyone bothering us. Once when Webb returned from a trip up to Fort Hays to get seed and supplies, he said there'd been a big meeting between a lot of the tribes and some general, and it looked like maybe there'd be room for Indians and settlers and railroads in Kansas after all.

By the next spring, Dandy was two years old, I was thirteen, and Webb Cotter had used the money from last year's crops to buy another forty acres of land. I couldn't see the point in it myself. It never made sense exactly who he was buying it *from*. So far as I knew, we were the only ones around between Fort Larned to the south and Fort Hays to the north, which was probably why whatever else the Cheyennes were doing, they sure never bothered us.

That spring, when the rains washed out the frost locked deep in the fall plowing, the creek filled and roared, making a swamp of the land around it. Then the sky, rinsed clean of clouds, blued, and the sun burned through the June days. Wheat sprouted, broke through dry, cracked soil, and withered right back to where it came from.

That's when I learned Webb wasn't the only crazy homesteader in western Kansas. There was at least one other, and he showed up one morning and leaned against the fence. His name was Mason. He and his family had settled just a few miles away.

"Good-looking horse you got there." The man watched Dandy gallop the length of the lot and skitter sideways until he danced up next to where I was standing.

"Yep." Webb gave the man a quick once-over glance. "Ain't the ugliest I ever seen . . . quite."

"He'll be a stubborn one to break," the man went on.

"I'll break him," Webb muttered, watching Dandy without turning his head, just moving his eyes.

My stomach knotted when he said "break," crunching off the word like the sound of bones snapping.

"He'll be tough as a pine knot." Mason pushed back the brim of his hat. "Don't know where you got the stud, but some critters are born skittish and nothing a fellow can do about it."

"Anything can be broke. It just takes a strong, gentle hand." Webb fingered the corner of his mustache and turned toward me. "Thought I told you to fetch some water."

I took my time about moving.

"Your boy?" Mason asked.

"My wife's." Webb didn't bother to look at me. "Died two years ago." He wiped his forehead with the back of his hand and stared at the sky. "If we don't get rain soon, can't hope for much wheat."

If the water I was supposed to fetch was for Webb instead of the horses, I would have let him thirst to death. As it was, I grabbed a pail and went on to the creek. Even in the drought, there was a gush of cold water from the underground spring that pumped out enough for both us and the horses. Anybody else would have fenced the lot so the stream flowed through it. Not Webb. Guess he liked to see me busy carrying buckets.

What did they mean? Stubborn! Tough! Skittish! They didn't understand Dandy. Couldn't they see he wasn't ugly? The rest of him'd catch up with his legs someday. He'd fill out so his neck wouldn't look so gangly. And he wasn't skittish! He just didn't like to have all four hooves on the ground at the same time. When I got back Webb and Mason were walking down toward the field where winter wheat showed a few straggly green shoots—Webb a full foot taller and a good foot skinnier than the new neighbor.

It was July when Webb turned out the hobbled horses into the fields to grub what green they could find. The dwarfed shoots must have tasted brittle and bitter to Dandy, whose coat looked as dry as the wheat. The only thing he had enough of was water that I fetched.

Then one morning Webb announced, "I'm lending Mason the mare for his keeping an eye on you. Signed up for work on the Santa Fe Trail so I'll be gone for a spell."

He'd been gone a couple of times when money was short before Ma died, but that was only for whatever job he could pick up down at Larned for a week or so. Even I knew a trip to Santa Fe would take him over a month, and I wondered why he'd waited so long. We'd been needing cash ever since he bought that extra land.

"You need anything, you scoot over to Mason, you hear?" He got on the cow pony, the mare's lead rope in one hand. He looked like he was making up his mind to say something else, but instead rode away leading the mare.

A day later Mason showed up and with him came the dog.

"You can have him. He's the throwaway of the litter," he told me. "Don't worry about feeding him. He can fend for himself. Thin as a splinter—that's his name—Splinter. Part collie, part coyote and the runningest critter I ever seen. He grew up chasing tumbleweeds."

Splinter wasn't the only thing Mason brought that day when he drove up in a buckboard pulled by our mare.

I'd been so busy watching the pup race around in circles, I didn't notice the scraggy, straw-headed kid tagging along behind until Mason said, "And this here's Athens."

Blue eyes stared straight at me from underneath eyebrows bleached the same color as the hair.

I stared back. I'd never met any boys since we began homesteading, but this one looked to be about my age, thirteen. I couldn't think of anything to say back that didn't sound dumb, so I just nodded and stuck my hands in my pants pockets like I'd seen Webb do when he didn't want to talk.

Mason watched me as he went right on, his words coming out as easy as if he was used to people listening. Webb never looked at me except when he was giving orders.

"Told Athens about you and the colt." He nodded toward Dandy, who'd come sidling up to the fence. "It's pretty lonesome out here and I thought you could use some company. I've got to go down to Larned and pick up some supplies. Maybe you two can get acquainted while I'm gone. What do you say, Caleb?"

"When do you figure to be back?" I'd planned on trying to get Dandy to settle into a slow walk as we made our daily round of the lot, but now I had two new things to put up with—a dog named Splinter, who still hadn't stopped running, and a boy who was frowning at me and looking mad before we even got to know each other.

"Should be back by sunset," Mason said.

By the time Mason got back in the wagon and drove off, I'd sneaked another look at the boy, his hands lost in shirt sleeves that were too long and wearing a pair of britches that looked like castoffs from his pa.

"What are you staring at?"

My face got hot and when I tried to swallow, I didn't have any spit to swallow with. "You're a girl!" I finally managed to say.

She watched me like I was as dumb as Splinter. "Of course I'm a girl. What else could I be with a name like Athens?"

"I never heard a name like that before."

"It's for the town where I was born, Athens, Ohio. Then we moved on west to Indiana. My sister Terry Haute was born there."

"You're both named after towns?" I wondered if Webb Cotter knew what kind of person was supposed to be keeping an eye on me.

"Sure. That way we all remember where we lived and when. We moved to Illinois next and—"

"You mean there's more of you?"

"Yep. That's where Normal was born. Normal, Illinois. We just stayed long enough for that to happen before we left for Iowa."

"And then . . . ?"

"My sister Pella."

"A whole family of girls?"

There was something about her that wouldn't let me get a whole sentence out of my mouth.

"What's wrong with that? Pa says the hands that rock the cradles rule the world. I've seen enough cradles, but I like the idea of ruling." She looked up at the sky. "Think of sitting up there and ruling everything from Ohio clear through Kansas."

Just then Splinter squatted down, front legs flat in front of him, hind legs bunched up, nose sticking in the air like a howling coyote, and Dandy trotted over, stretching his neck and sniffing like he'd found something that might taste good if he took a nibble. They stayed still until Splinter flipped around fast as a jackrabbit and raced down the fence line, Dandy right behind. They tore around the lot and then switched directions so the dog was chasing Dandy.

"So that's your colt?" the girl asked.

"Sure is," I bragged. "His name's Dandy and I was just fixing to teach him to let me ride him."

"He hops around like a grasshopper in a heat wave." She rolled up the too-long sleeves. "Well, let's get started. What do you want to do first?"

First was easy, especially since Dandy stood still for once, catching his breath. It didn't take long to fetch the rope I had hidden and loop it around his neck. I made a big thing of leading him up and down trying to make it look like I didn't think he'd take off running any second.

Maybe it was because of Athens that Dandy was showing off as much as me, but he danced beside me as if we'd been practicing for months instead of weeks. After about five trips past her, I brought him up to the fence. I hoped he wouldn't take one close look and bolt away with me trying to haul him back. A good thing that Splinter got bored with the whole business right about then. He found a spot in the shade of the barn, flopped down flat on his side and, from the looks of his paws, was chasing rabbits in his sleep.

"What next?" Athens asked like she already knew the answer to her own question. "Have you tried sacking him out yet?"

I didn't want to let on that I didn't understand what the heck she was talking about, so I shrugged and said, "No, but now's as good a time as any."

She was already headed for the barn and called back over her shoulder, "I'll look for a gunnysack. Where do you keep them?"

We had a few left from the seed Webb bought last spring, so I yelled back. "Inside the door on the right." I wondered what she was going to do with one.

She was back so quick I decided even if she was a girl, she could run as fast as me.

"I don't see a snubbing post." She looked around the lot and shook her head. "Maybe you mean to gentle him instead of sacking?"

Dandy watched her, ears forward, ready for another game of tag.

"That's been my plan," I told her as if I'd been thinking of it for months.

"Then we'd best start out easy." She snaked through the fence and walked right up to Dandy's head, the sack dragging on the ground. He blew through his nose, moved his feet, and didn't shy from her like I expected.

"Guess we could use a fence post, but maybe you'd better hold him instead. It won't seem so strange to him that way. I'll just put this on his back and see what happens."

I could have told her what would happen, but there wasn't time. The second he felt that gunnysack across his withers, Dandy was gone like a whistle in the wind. Good thing for me I wasn't holding tight to the rope.

"What'd you go and do a fool thing like that for?" It was my turn to be mad, and the rope burn across my hand didn't help my feelings.

She was trying to keep her mouth straight, I could tell, and that didn't make things better. In a minute she said, "You never did see a horse sacked, did you?" Before I could lie, she went right on. "See, you tie him up tight to a post, so tight he can't jerk loose or throw himself on the ground, and then you flap the bejeezus out of him with the sack until he either learns to stand still or drops dead."

It sounded like something Webb would come up with when he said "break." That made me even madder. "We were going to gentle him. You said so yourself."

She didn't apologize. She bent down and picked up the sack. "We better try again. You fetch him and we'll start over."

It took a lot of coaxing and molasses and rope burns till he finally gave in and let us lay the gunnysack on him for more than a blink of his eyes. By that time we were tired and hot, so after watering Dandy we walked back to the shade of the sod house. Athens chose a bare spot and sat, her legs spread, and with both hands she smoothed a patch of dirt in front of her and drew a circle in the dust with her finger.

Then she tugged at a leather thong hanging around her neck and untied a jackknife, a bone-handled knife with ends tipped in silver and slots for four blades, except all the blades but one were broken off.

She snapped open the lone blade, a long, thin, pointed, ugly blade, and balancing the handle up against her chin, asked, "Ever play mumblety-peg?" Without waiting for an answer, she gave the knife a flip. It arced through the air and came down with a quiver, sticking upright in the dirt, exactly in the center of the circle.

I didn't know any games except the ones I made up myself and if I'd had a knife, I wouldn't have wasted it that way.

Then she laid the knife on her closed fist and at a quick turn of her wrist, the knife flew through the air again and landed almost in the same place as the first time.

"That was the right hand. Now the left."

She did it again, the knife, like magic, sticking in the same spot.

"How'd you learn to do that?" I was beginning to think there wasn't anything Athens couldn't do and what was worse there wasn't anything I could do that she didn't already know how to do.

"Pa taught me. I can do it better with the other knife I have at home."

"You got two knives!" I didn't even have one. If I'd had anything worth trading, I would have offered it then and there.

"Sure." She handed me the knife. "Here. Try it, then we'll play one game and see how it goes."

I took the knife. It was cold and hard against my palm and fit like it was meant to be mine. After about a dozen tries I finally got the blade to stay long enough for Athens to call it a "sticker," even if it was clear out on the edge of the circle.

"Now this is the way we play." Athens smoothed out the dirt and redrew the circle. Reaching into a pocket, she pulled out a wooden peg, sharpened at one end and, using the handle of the knife, pounded the peg in the middle of the circle. "See, we take turns trying to hit nearest the peg."

"But you'll win. You've had practice." No matter how hard I tried, I couldn't keep the knife inside the circle let alone make it stay stuck.

"That's all right. The loser gets the peg."

"What do I do with a peg?" I was not liking the game. I wasn't too sure I was liking her either.

"You'll see. Come on. You start first." She sat back, arms folded, and watched as I flipped the knife and saw it skitter off beyond the circle.

"You're not doing it right." She took the knife, placed it on top of her head and gave it a flip. It nudged right up to the peg. "See? That's the way you do it."

"I see," I grumbled, carefully aiming my right-hand-closed-fist throw. The knife stayed in the circle, but it was what Athens called a "leaner."

"Almost a 'sticker,' though," she added. "You're catching on real fast."

It might have been a game to Athens, but I was not having fun. No matter how she flipped the knife, it sailed right in next to the peg. She missed only once when she tried to do it with her eyes shut.

I finally got one to stick inside the circle.

"Game's over!" she announced. "I won, but you get the peg."

"I don't want the old peg. You can have it."

"You're not playing fair. The loser *has* to take the peg." She snapped the knife shut and strung it back on the leather thong. "The loser has to pull the peg out," she smiled a nasty smile, "with his teeth!"

I felt like punching her right then and there and wiping the silly grin off her face, until I remembered what Ma used to tell me when I got mad and clenched up inside. "He who is slow to wrath is of great understanding." I hadn't known who Wrath was, but I knew now. Its name was Athens. I waited, but no understanding came. I finally got down on my belly, stuck my face in the dirt, and pulled out the peg. I handed it to her, spit out a mouthful of dust, wiped my face on my sleeve, and started for the barn.

"My pa's coming!" she shouted after me.

I looked off at the horizon and sure enough, I spied a cloud of dust that meant Mason was back from Larned. I thought real fast. It didn't take any great understanding for me to know that I didn't want her telling him about trying to teach Dandy and then have him tell Webb Cotter. It was face up to him or her.

I faced her. "Breaking Dandy is a big surprise for Webb, so it's a secret between you and me. We won't even tell your pa. What do you think?" I smiled, but it wasn't a nice smile.

She looked at me as if she didn't believe a word I was saying. All the same she nodded, spit on her palm, and held it out to me. "I won't tell if you won't tell."

I spit on my own hand and we shook on it.

As it turned out, being alone on the homestead wasn't much different from when Webb was around except I felt better. I was free of having Webb always asking where I'd been or ordering me to quit lolling around and get busy doing something. The best part of being alone was I could do things I wanted to do without having to sneak around to do them.

A few days later I was sitting on the porch, my feet propped against the railing Webb had made for Ma after she took sick, when I saw three of the Masons coming across the field, Athens herding two little ones like she was a sheepdog.

"Pa thought you might like to come with us."

I couldn't forget what it felt like when she made me get down and stick my face in the dirt just because I'd lost a game. "I'm busy," I said, squinting into the sun like I was deciding what time it was.

"Doing what?"

"Thinking."

"I thought you said you were busy." She sat on the bottom step. "This here's my sister Pella and the little one's Topeka."

Pella, a miniature Athens, held the hand of a pudgy ball of a girl with a face full of fist who sucked on a thumb and looked up at me with eyes like a cat's through a maze of copper hair.

"Topeka?" I repeated.

Topeka moved the thumb to one side of her mouth and jabbered.

"What'd she say?" I looked down at Athens.

"I don't know. Ask Pella. She's the only one who can understand what she says."

Pella didn't wait to be asked. "She said she was born in Topeka."

"That's in Kansas," Athens added.

"I know," I answered, frowning.

"Well, I bet I know something you *don't* know."

"What?" I didn't really care, but somehow she made me ask anyway.

"I bet you don't know who can take a hundred people up to Fort Hays in one wagon."

"A hundred people in one wagon? Nobody can."

"Can too."

"There's not a wagon big enough."

"You're wrong. Anybody can." She stood up eyes level with mine. "Anybody who makes enough trips!" She laughed.

I didn't laugh.

"Don't you get it?"

"Of course I do. It's not very funny, though." I liked her less and less.

"It's a riddle. Don't you know riddles? Like—what's taller sitting down than standing up?"

I didn't answer. She wasn't going to get me to ask "what" again.

I didn't get a chance. She laughed so hard she could hardly talk. "Out there by the fence—Splinter."

"You mean a dog?" I couldn't help laughing this time. "Tell you what I can do." I tried to make it sound important.

It worked because she asked, "What?"

"I can throw up any time I want to."

"Let's see you do it then." She waited, hands on her hips.

I stood up, looked around, and finally shrugged one shoulder and said, "I don't want to." I laughed at *her* this time.

She looked at me for a minute, and, not bothering with spit, stuck out her hand. We shook. I figured we were even.

"Where'd you say you were going?" I asked.

"Checking our trap lines."

"What're you trapping?"

"Rabbits."

"Are they coming with us?" Topeka wasn't much bigger than a rabbit herself.

"Pella has to take care of Topeka and explain what she says. Besides, if you don't watch her she'll eat anything that doesn't eat her first. And I have to take Pella with me because she's the only one who can stand to kill the rabbit when we catch one."

I looked again at Powerful Pella. She smiled like she'd received a medal for bravery.

"Well, let's go," I said. "Where'd you set your snares?"

"Over by the river."

We started out, Athens leading the way, Pella tugging Topeka along by the hand not stuck in her mouth, me bringing up the rear, with Splinter already racing far ahead of us.

"You see," Athens said as we slid down the riverbank, "if we catch enough rabbits for stew, we get to have Christmas tomorrow."

"Tomorrow? But this is July!"

Athens didn't hear me. She was crawling up to the base of a big cottonwood tree. "Get your stick ready, Pella," she shouted.

Nobody said anything. Topeka stopped sucking her thumb. All I could hear was the rustle of the wind stirring the leaves. Athens pulled gently on the twine of the snare. "Empty!" she muttered. "Thunderation! We got to catch a rabbit or we can't have Christmas."

"Why are you having Christmas now?"

She sat up, her back against the tree. "Because we missed it last winter. Pa just sold some wolfskins and got enough money to get us all presents so we're going to celebrate tomorrow. We *always* have rabbit stew for Christmas dinner."

It made some sort of sense, I guessed, and when the next snare held a big jackrabbit, the noose tight around his neck, I was just as tickled as everybody else, except the rabbit, of course. I shut my eyes, though, when Pella finished him off and was glad Athens didn't notice.

"Hocomheeshuies," mumbled Topeka around her fist.

"What'd she say," I asked automatically.

Pella looked at me and grinned. "She said how come you shut your eyes when I whopped the rabbit."

I glanced down at it, its legs twitching as if it was trying to run. "I guess I don't take kindly to killing." I sounded just like Webb Cotter.

"We're not killing for fun," Athens snapped. "Pa says it's killing each other that's hurtful."

"Are you Quakers too?" Ma and Webb were the only ones I knew of.

Athens knelt down in the grass, slipped the knife from around her neck, cut the snare, and picked up the rabbit. "Nope. Pa says we're Mormons who took a different trail." She turned to face me. "I forgot the other day," she began and then started over. "I meant to tell you that if the loser does pull out the peg with his teeth, he gets the winner's knife to keep." She tossed the knife to me.

I caught it in midair. I figured she'd made up that rule along with all the rest, but I wanted a knife bad enough that I didn't care. I slipped the thong over my head and tucked it inside my shirt.

"Now that we have the rabbit, I'm supposed to ask you to come over and eat with us tomorrow." She didn't wait for an answer. She had all the answers as it was.

After we got back to the soddy and the three of them had left, I sat on the porch trying to think what I could take as a present for their July Christmas. Splinter was playing tag with Dandy until he got tuckered out and curled up in a ball next to the fence. He didn't even raise his head when I brought a pail of water up from the creek. Dandy nickered to me and came dancing as fresh as ever. Before he stuck his nose in for a drink, he leaned over and nuzzled my neck like he used to do his mare. Maybe he liked the way I smelled. I smoothed his forelock, rubbed his neck, and started thinking that if I was going over to the Masons' for Christmas stew, I'd better take me a bath.

It took a while to find the last of the lye soap Ma had tucked away and then no time at all to get back to the creek, strip down, and give myself a good scrubbing up to and including behind my ears. The water was cold, but the evening was warm so I dried myself with my shirt, wadded everything into a bundle, and started back to the cabin.

Dandy trotted across the lot and edged up to the fence like a dark shadow in the twilight. It was magic—him standing so still, for once, his head turned toward me, his feet not moving.

I dropped my clothes on the ground, climbed up on the fence, took hold of his mane, and slid on to his back as quiet as a tadpole moving in the creek. Then we were flying. I couldn't tell where my skin stopped and his began, but I felt the flow of his muscles and the pounding of his heart as we raced the length of the lot until I went one way and he went the other. Somehow, my trip to the ground seemed to take longer than the ride. It didn't matter because for halfway around the lot, my face against his neck, I had ridden Dandy.

Getting up off the ground hurt for a minute, but by the time I'd crawled through the fence and picked up my clothes, I figured that nothing was broken. Dandy was in the far corner and didn't look like he planned on coming back in my direction. Splinter had waked up and was licking at my legs, and I wasn't sure but what I'd dreamed the whole thing.

Inside the house, I lit a candle, looked at my arm and leg scrubbed raw from the fall, and knew our ride had been real.

In the morning I rummaged through the trunk that held what few clothes I owned till I came up with a pair of britches Ma had made me just before she got sick and a shirt that had belonged to my real father. She'd been saving that for me until I grew, but I figured that even if it was too big at least it wasn't ripped.

I went out and sat down on the porch step. I still didn't have anything to take for a present. The hot wind blew whirligigs of dust across the burned wheat field, and I thought that if I'd been a wheat seed, I wouldn't have sprouted either. The only thing that grew no matter what the weather was the buffalo grass that covered the plains. I wondered what it was that made

Webb Cotter so stubborn in picking the worst place in all of Kansas to set up a homestead. Out of the whole one hundred twenty acres, he had only one little field of dead wheat to show for all the work and the money.

Thinking of him made me think of Ma again. I knew as sure as if she whispered in my ear what to take as a present. "The greatest gift is giving freely to someone else what you love." That thing I loved most, next to Dandy, was the only thing I had to give. I hustled back inside the soddy, and pulled Ma's picture out from under my mattress and ran out across the homestead toward the Masons'.

I saw Athens coming to meet me when she was nothing but a speck in the distance. For once, she was by herself. I held the painting behind my back as she got close.

"I was afraid you forgot," she said. She sounded different. Maybe it was because she was wearing a dress.

"I wouldn't forget." The words sounded funny. Athens was easier to talk to when she had on her pa's cast-off britches. "Here," I said, holding out the painted shingle. "It's a present."

She took the shingle, looked at one side, and turned it over.

"It's a picture," I tried to explain.

"Oh! Sure."

"You're holding it upside down," I said, thinking it really wasn't the right gift for Athens after all.

"Oh, now I see." She turned the shingle right side up. "That crazy boy! Look. He's got his arm wrapped around that big old lion!"

"It's called 'Peaceable Kingdom.'" I tried to explain more.

"Poor little kid." Athens shook her head. "Wearing

nothing but a sheet out in that jungle. Skeeters'll eat him alive."

"What it says . . ." I went on, even if I didn't think she was hearing me.

She wasn't. "Lions have awful big teeth and so do wolves even if their mouths are shut. Sheep won't hurt him, though."

I kept on trying. "See, those fierce animals are all kneeling with the steer, and the lamb's with this boy in the middle because if lions would quit eating sheep then you could walk through a jungle wearing a sheet and nothing would hurt you."

I'd never put the idea into words before, but I liked how they sounded.

"So," I continued, "if things didn't kill each other, nobody would have to be afraid." Then I felt guilty. "I don't think it means rabbits, though."

I looked down the road, and coming toward us was a stairstep of little straw-haired kids with Topeka's carrottop tagging along last. Together we walked back to their dugout, Athens holding the shingle against her chest. I hoped Ma's homemade paint wouldn't rub off on her dress.

Pella kept busy trying to stop Topeka from eating the blue flowers of the bull thistles. Terry Haute and Normal hung onto each other, looking at me and giggling.

The rabbit stew was mighty thin and there wasn't much meat, but what with my new knife, it was the best Christmas I ever had.

"Peaceable Kingdom," the painting that Caleb's mother was working on before she died, was originally painted by Edward Hicks (1780–1849). The idea for the painting was taken from a biblical passage in which the prophet Isaiah predicted that the wild animals would lie down with a lamb and a calf, "and a little child shall lead them."

The scene in the background shows William Penn signing his famous treaty with the Native Americans. This detail is further proof of Hicks's belief in peace between opposing forces.

Hicks painted more than sixty versions of this particular scene. In addition to creating works of art, Hicks was a sign painter, a farmer, and an evangelist.

IN RESPONSE

Forming a Friendship

Caleb doesn't feel friendly toward Athens at first. When does he feel that they have become friends? Sketch the scene. Write a caption that explains how the two children become friends at that moment.

Growing Up Is Hard to Do

Caleb remembers advice his mother once gave him. Sarah ("Last Days at Red Clay") and Ota K'te ("The Youngest Buffalo Hunter") have role models in their families who help them grow up. How do the three characters' relatives help them handle the challenges of growing up? With a partner, look back at the stories. Which character do you think handles his or her challenges best? Explain why.

Compare the Times

"A Gift for Athens" describes a frontier boy's life after the Civil War. In the story, what things does young Caleb think about and do that children still do today? In a small group, make a list. Use examples from the story and your own life. What things do you do that aren't mentioned in Caleb's story? Make another list. What do you think is the biggest similarity between your life and Caleb's? the biggest difference?

AUTHORS AT WORK

Lee Hadley and Ann Irwin wrote several books together under the pen name Hadley Irwin. Ms. Irwin is a retired English instructor at Iowa State University. The late Ms. Hadley also taught English at Iowa State University.

The duo had an unusual style of writing. One would sit at the typewriter and they would "talk the words of the novel onto the page." Sometimes one would start a sentence and the other would finish it.

Both woman wanted their books to show that young people have the same emotions as adults. Ms. Irwin says many of her ideas come from her experiences as a mother of four children while Ms. Hadley said that she drew upon her own childhood memories.

Library Link "A Gift for Athens" was taken from *Jim-Dandy* by Hadley Irwin. You may want to read the entire book to follow Caleb and Dandy on their adventures.

★ Award-winning Authors

Other Books by . . .

Hadley Irwin

The Original Freddie Ackerman by Hadley Irwin, Macmillan, 1992

Kim/Kimi by Hadley Irwin, Puffin Books, 1987

THEME WRAP-UP

Express **Yourself**

In Voices from America's Past, you met characters growing up in the late 1700's and the 1800's. Many of them dealt with challenging or dangerous situations. You also read about some people from the present who remember what life was like many years ago. Their voices are part of our country's diverse history. Yours can be, too.

Tough Choices

Mary ("Mary Patten's Voyage") and Ota K'te ("The Youngest Buffalo Hunter") both made important choices. What were they? Look back at the stories to find them. Have you made choices similar to theirs? Write a paragraph that compares a choice you've made with either Mary's or Ota K'te's decision. How were they alike and different?

Characters Worth Remembering

Several of the characters you have read about in this theme were talented, hard workers. Think about two characters whose talent you admire. Describe the courageous acts and personal qualities that make these characters memorable. Discuss how you might like to model your own behavior after one or both of the characters you have written about.

Remembering the Past

"I think about who my ancestors were/and how they lived," writes Misty Stands in Timber ("As I Walk Along the Hillside"). Suppose a modern-day relative of Ota K'te's and a relative of Sarah's ("Last Days at Red Clay") meet to discuss their ancestors' past. Based on the stories, what might the relatives say? With a partner, role-play a talk between them.

A Word of Advice

Caleb ("A Gift for Athens") relies on his mother's teachings to help him make decisions. What is the advice? Write your answer in a paragraph. Then think about your own life. What is some good advice that you have received when making an important choice?

Interview About the Past

The people in "Tales From Tucson" describe life long ago. You can learn more about the past by interviewing an older relative or another senior citizen. List some questions to ask about the person's everyday life as a child. Ask about chores, games, clothes, studies, and family traditions. Look back at the selections for more ideas. Take notes so that you can write up the interview to share with your class.

More Books for You to Enjoy

The Great American Gold Rush

by Rhoda Blumberg, Bradbury Press, 1989

"Gold-rush fever" sent thousands of Americans to California in 1848 to hunt for gold that supposedly was as "common as clay." Some found riches and others only disappointment, but their move westward changed America. Old photos and drawings explain how people traveled, ate, and lived.

The Battle of Lexington and Concord

by Neil Johnson, Four Winds Press, 1992

Vivid photographs transport readers to the first confrontation between red-coated British soldiers and American colonists. The photographs are from a modern-day reenactment of the battle that began the Revolutionary War with "the shot heard round the world."

Going to School in 1776

by John J. Loeper, Atheneum, 1973

Even during the Revolutionary War, children went to school. The schools were very different then. What and how you learned depended on who you were and where you lived. Stories about children in 1776 explain different types of schooling.

Tales from Gold Mountain: Stories of the Chinese in the New World

by Paul Yee with paintings by Simon Ng, Macmillan, 1989

These eight stories tell of the adventures of Chinese immigrants who journeyed to the Old West to seek their fortunes on Gold Mountain. The collection includes stories of the gold rush and the building of the transcontinental railroad.

Grasshopper Summer

by Ann Turner, Macmillan, 1989

Twelve-year-old Sam White isn't happy at all about leaving his comfortable Kentucky home for the harsh Dakota Territory. Living in a sod house is the most miserable experience of all—until the grasshoppers come.

Glossary

The pronunciation of each word is shown just after the word, in this way: **abbreviate** [ə·brē′vē·āt′]. The letters and signs used are pronounced as in the words in the chart at right. The mark ′ is placed after a syllable with a primary, or heavy, accent, as in the example above. The mark ′ after a syllable shows a secondary, or lighter, accent, as in the following example: **abbreviation** [ə·brē′vē·ā′shən].

Pronunciation Key

Symbol	Key Words	Symbol	Key Words
a	cat	b	bed
ā	ape	d	dog
ä	cot, car	f	fall
e	ten, berry	g	get
ē	me	h	help
i	fit, here	j	jump
ī	ice, fire	k	kiss, call
ō	go	l	leg
ô	fall, for	m	meat
oi	oil	n	nose
oo	look, pull	p	put
o͞o	tool, rule	r	red
ou	out, crowd	s	see
u	up	t	top
ʉ	fur, shirt	v	vat
ə	a in ago	w	wish
	e in agent	y	yard
	i in pencil	z	zebra
	o in atom	ch	chin, arch
	u in circus	n̂g	ring, drink
		sh	she, push
		th	thin, truth
		th	then, father
		zh	measure

ablaze

anchor

ablaze [ə·blāz′] adj. on fire; brightly colored, as if on fire.

abnormality [ab′nôr·mal′ə·tē] n. a defect or other flaw.

absorbed [ab·sôrbd′] adj. paying close attention. syn. preoccupied.

abstract [ab′strakt] adj. not resembling reality: Ted didn't enjoy the exhibit of abstract portraits because he likes people to look like people.

accessible [ak·ses′ə·bəl] adj. readily obtained or reached.

acrid [ak′rid] adj. sharp; bitter.

aerial [er′ē·əl] adj. high up in the air.

agony [ag′ə·nē] n. a strong pain or suffering.

allergic [ə·lur′jik] adj. having a negative physical reaction to something: People who are allergic to shrimp sometimes break out in hives after eating them.

aloft [ə·lôft′] adj. in the air.

alpha [al′fə] adj. chief or most dominant.

altitude [al′tə·to͞od] n. height.

anchor [ang′kər] n. a heavily weighted object that, when lowered overboard, holds a ship in place in the water.

ancient [ān′chənt] adj. extremely old.

archaeologist or **archeologist** [är′kē·äl′ə·jist] n. one who studies earlier civilizations through items taken from the earth.

arduous [är′jo͞o·əs] adj. difficult to accomplish; requiring much energy or effort.

arrangement [ə·rānj′mənt] n. a plan agreed upon in advance: Shelly made an arrangement with her teachers to come in early and make up missed work.

assembly line [ə·sem′blē līn] n. a process used in making many kinds of products that involves repeating a sequence of steps.

astonished [ə·stän′ishd] adj. amazed and filled with wonder: When the little boy climbed out of the wreckage without a scratch, his astonished parents fell to their knees in relief.

autumn [ôt′əm] n. the season immediately after summer and before winter. syn. fall: During autumn, the leaves turn beautiful colors and eventually fall from the trees.

bale [bāl] n. a large bundle, often of a standard size or weight, as in harvested cotton.

baleful [bāl′fəl] adj. harmful or predicting evil.

bamboo [bam·bo͞o′] n. a tropical grass that resembles a tree, with tall, hollow, jointed stalks.

barbarian [bär·ber′ē·ən] n. an uncivilized person.

bean sprout [bēn sprout] n. the sprout of a soybean or other bean, used in salads and other dishes and especially in Chinese cooking: Laura was a picky eater and would not taste even a single bean sprout at the China Palace.

bellow [bel′ō] n. a loud voice or powerful sound.

billy [bil′ē] n. a club that a police officer uses as a weapon or as a device to keep order.

blur [blûr] n. something that is indistinct to the memory or senses.

boarding school [bôrd′ing sko͞ol] n. a place of learning that provides living space and meals for students: While his parents did archaeological work in Peru, Dominic spent his freshman year at a boarding school in Ohio.

boast [bōst] v. to brag or speak with excessive pride: It's not polite to boast about our delicious dinner when some people have nothing to eat.

boll weevil [bōl wē′vəl] n. an insect that, when hatched in a cotton plant, destroys the cotton.

bolt¹ [bōlt] v. to suddenly run away. syn. dart.

bolt² [bōlt] n. a sliding bar that locks a door, gate, or the like.

bolt³ [bōlt] v. to eat or drink quickly: "I know you're in a hurry, Rachel," said Mom, "but it's impolite to bolt your dinner and run."

boom [bo͞om] v. to increase greatly.

bore [bôr] v. carried or brought forth (past tense of *bear).*

bow [bou] n. the front part of a boat: When our speedboat bumped headfirst into the pier, Louie leapt out to examine the bow for damage.

brackish [brak′ish] adj. salty tasting.

break¹ [brāk] v. to tame a horse.

break² [brāk] n. a rest period: After working all morning on his term paper, Brad took a break and drank some juice.

bridge [brij] n. the raised front area of a ship from which the ship is operated: From the bridge, the captain could see a small, sinking vessel in the distance.

brigade [bri·gād′] n. a group of people organized for a specific activity: The neighborhood bucket brigade helped put out fires long ago.

buckboard [buk′bôrd] n. a horse-drawn wagon with a seat in the front and a flat area in the back.

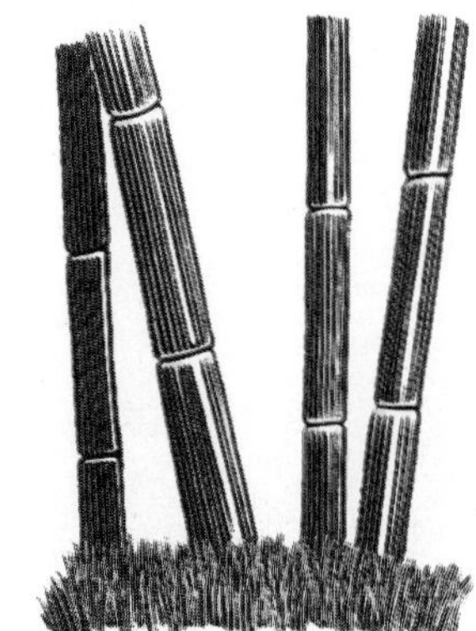

bamboo

boll weevil on cotton

a cat	ô fall, for	ə = a *in* ago
ā ape	oi oil	e *in* agent
ä cot, car	oo look, pull	i *in* pencil
e ten, berry	o͞o tool, rule	o *in* atom
ē me	ou out, crowd	u *in* circus
i fit, here	u up	
ī ice, fire	ûr fur	
ō go		

canyon

carp

C

cable [kā′bəl] n. a strong, heavy cord, usually made of wire.

calf [kaf] n. young offspring of certain large animals, such as cattle, buffalo, and the like.

canyon [kan′yən] n. a long, narrow valley with steep sides: Hiking down into the deserted canyon was risky, but we were careful.

capsule [kap′səl] n. a small enclosed area, often part of a craft that is engaged in space or sea exploration.

carne asada [kär′nā ä·sä′dä] n. Mexican marinated round steak.

carp [kärp] n. a type of large, edible freshwater fish.

cartographer [kär·täg′rə·fər] n. one who draws maps: After earning his college degree in geography, Uncle Bruce went to work making maps for a famous cartographer.

castoff [kast′ôf′] n. a hand-me-down or other discarded item: The pink party dress may have been a castoff from my cousin Lois, but it still looked brand-new to me.

Cherokee [cher′ə·kē′] n. a Native American group that originally lived in the Allegheny Mountains of southern Appalachia.

cinnamon [sin′ə·mən] n. a reddish-brown spice made from the inner bark of certain trees or shrubs: When Mom bakes, she always uses lots of cinnamon.

clamor [klam′ər] n. noise or disturbance.

clench [klench] v. to tighten up one's jaws or fists.

coastal [kōs′təl] adj. close to the sea: Some of Florida's coastal birds feed along the shore but nest inland.

coffin [kôf′in] n. a box in which a dead person or animal is enclosed for burial.

cofounder [kō′foun·dər] n. one who establishes or creates something with one or more partners: Sally told the class that her great-grandmother was a cofounder of the League of Women Voters.

coincidence [kō·in′sə·dəns] n. an accidental occurrence of facts or events at the same time: That Mom and Dad ran into each other at the grocery store was pure coincidence.

collected [kə·lek′təd] adj. in command of one's wits; calm. syn. composed.

commercial [kə·mur′shəl] n. an advertisement aired on television or radio.

commitment [kə·mit′mənt] n. a calling or dedication to a person, job, or cause.

committed [kə·mit′id] adj. determined to behave in a certain way.

communal [kə·myōōn′əl] adj. shared by an entire group.

commune [kä′myōōn] n. a small group of people who live together and share chores, income, and the like.

Communist [käm′yōō·nist] n. a member of a political group that supports the idea of a society without classes and an economy under government control: The breakup of the Soviet Union signaled the beginning of the end of Communist control in many countries.

composition [käm′pə·zish′ən] n. a piece of writing.

conciliatory [kən·sil′ē·ə·tôr′ē] adj. tending to be apologetic. When Sylvia called to say she was sorry for forgetting my party, she sounded conciliatory.

congested [kən·jest′id] adj. overcrowded; too full.

consequence [kän′si·kwens′] n. the result of a behavior or action. syn. outcome.

convince [kən·vins′] v. to persuade or win over: How can I convince Mom and Dad that I can handle a part-time job?

copper [käp′ər] adj. bright orange or reddish-brown; the color of copper.

countermand [koun′ tər·mand′] v. to cancel or revoke an order or command.

cow [kou] n. the adult female of some mammal species, such as an elephant seal or a moose.

craggy [krag′ē] adj. rugged.

crawfish [krô′fish] n. a type of edible freshwater animal that resembles a small lobster: We found crawfish in the water when we were playing by the creek.

crevice [krev′is] n. a narrow crack or opening.

cringe [krinj] v. to draw back from fear or pain.

crucial [kro͞o′shəl] adj. of critical importance: Mariana studied hard for her last math test; she knew a high score would be crucial to improving her final grade.

cue [kyo͞o] n. a suggestion or signal.

cultivate [kul′tə·vāt′] v. to break up soil to prepare it for planting. syn. till.

dachshund [däks′hoont′] n. a breed of small dog with a long body, short legs, and drooping ears.

daft [daft] adj. insane; crazy.

debut [dā·byo͞o′] n. a first performance or beginning in one's chosen field.

dejectedly [dē·jek′tid·lē] adv. sadly or in a depressed manner: When he saw the team lineup, Jack thought dejectedly, "I'll never get to play."

dense [dens] adj. slow to understand.

depression [dē·presh′ən] n. an economic period marked by joblessness and widespread poverty.

descendant [dē·sen′dənt] n. one who is an offspring of a certain line, family, or the like: While no one in our class claimed to be the direct descendant of a famous person, Stephanie reported that her aunt was married to a movie star.

copper wire

cow, or female, elephant seals

long-haired dachshund

a	cat	ô	fall, for	ə = a *in* ago
ā	ape	oi	oil	e *in* agent
ä	cot, car	oo	look, pull	i *in* pencil
e	ten, berry	o͞o	tool, rule	o *in* atom
ē	me	ou	out, crowd	u *in* circus
i	fit, here	u	up	
ī	ice, fire	ur	fur	
ō	go			

descent

descent [dē·sent′] n. downward movement or journey: After checking all the controls, the captain of the submarine began to make a slow descent.

desolate [des′ə·lit] adj. deserted; lonely. syn. isolated.

desperately [des′pər·it·lē] adv. with little hope of a solution: On the way to school, Anna realized that she hadn't done her homework; she desperately tried to complete it as the school bus rumbled along.

destination [des′tə·nā′shən] n. a goal or expected ending place: When Mrs. Alvarez left her house for a morning walk, she had no destination in mind.

detach [dē·tach′] v. to unfasten or separate one thing from another: José detached the house key from his key chain and gave it to his mother.

detain [dē·tān′] v. to stop or halt someone's progress: The police wanted to detain the two suspects for questioning.

determined [dē·tur′mənd] adj. having one's mind made up; resolved. syn. firm.

dignified [dig′nə·fīd′] adj. having self-respect and commanding the respect of others. syn. honored.

dignity [dig′nə·tē] n. worthiness and self-respect.

dimension [də·men′shən] n. size.

disconsolately [dis·kän′sə·lət·lē] adv. in a sad or a very disappointed way. syn. cheerlessly.

distinguish [dis·ting′gwish] v. to recognize one from another.

distracted [di·strak′təd] adj. unable to concentrate. syn. confused: Telling a story to young children is sometimes a challenge because young children are very easily distracted.

diversity [də·vur′sə·tē] n. variety or wide assortment.

document [däk′yo͞o·mənt] v. to verify or establish as true.

documentary [däk′yo͞o·ment′ə·rē] adj. recording reality, without any fictional additions.

doldrums [dōl′drəmz] n. a gloomy, moping feeling; ocean regions, near the equator, noted for calms and light winds.

dome [dōm] n. a hemisphere, often of glass or other transparent material, used as a cover.

Astrodome, Houston, Texas

dominant [däm′ə·nənt] adj. showing authority or importance.

dormant [dôr′mənt] adj. resting. syn. inactive.

dramatic [drə·mat′ik] adj. having great effect; bringing out a lot of emotion.

drought [drout] n. a period of little or no rainfall.

ecology [ē·käl′ə·jē] n. the study of the relationship between living things and their environment.

effusive [e·fyo͞o′siv] adj. overly enthusiastic. syn. gushing.

Ellesmere Island [elz′mir′ ī′lənd] n. an island in the Northwest Territories, Canada.

elusive [ē·lo͞o′siv] adj. difficult to capture or retain.

embroider

embroider [em·broi′dər] v. to stitch a design onto cloth or a garment, often with brightly colored threads: After I finish sewing the vest, I'll embroider a moon and stars on the back.

emerge [ē·murj′] v. to come out: When you emerge from the dark movie theater, you may squint in the bright sunlight.

emigrate [em′i·grāt′] v. to leave one's native country with the intention of resettling in another place.

emperor [em′pər·ər] n. a supreme ruler: As emperor of China, he was feared by his people.

encounter [en·koun′tər] v. to come upon or meet unexpectedly: Bob was surprised to encounter an opossum when he took out the garbage.

encroach [en·krōch′] v. to come so close as to invade another's space. syn. intrude: I wish my sister would not encroach on my space by leaving her clothes on my bed.

enforce [en·fôrs′] v. to require obedience to, as a law.

evaporate [ē·vap′ə·rāt′] v. to move from a liquid to a gaseous state: In the desert heat, ice cubes can melt and even evaporate in a matter of minutes.

exhaust [eg·zôst′] n. the fumes released from an automobile or other machine: After breathing the bus's exhaust for two blocks, Ned regretted jogging so closely behind it.

exotic [eg·zät′ik] adj. strangely fascinating: The health food store sold many kinds of tea and coffee as well as exotic herbs and spices.

exhaust

a cat	ô fall, for	ə = a *in* ago
ā ape	oi oil	e *in* agent
ä cot, car	oo look, pull	i *in* pencil
e ten, berry	o͞o tool, rule	o *in* atom
ē me	ou out, crowd	u *in* circus
i fit, here	u up	
ī ice, fire	ur fur	
ō go		

expectation [ek´spek·tā´shən] n. something that one thinks will happen based on other evidence: Mr. Armstrong told his fifth-grade class, "Everyone passed the test, so it's my expectation that all of you will be in the sixth grade next fall."

experiment [ek·sper´ə·ment] v. to test or try many different approaches.

exploit [eks´ploit´] n. a bold or daring act.

express [eks·pres´] v. to communicate or describe: Jed could not express the love he felt for his grandmother.

fancy up [fan´sē up] v. to decorate or exaggerate.

feathery [fe*th*´·ər·ē] adj. airy and delicate looking, often soft.

fend [fend] v. to take care of or get along.

fiber [fī´bər] n. any material that can be separated into threads for making cloth.

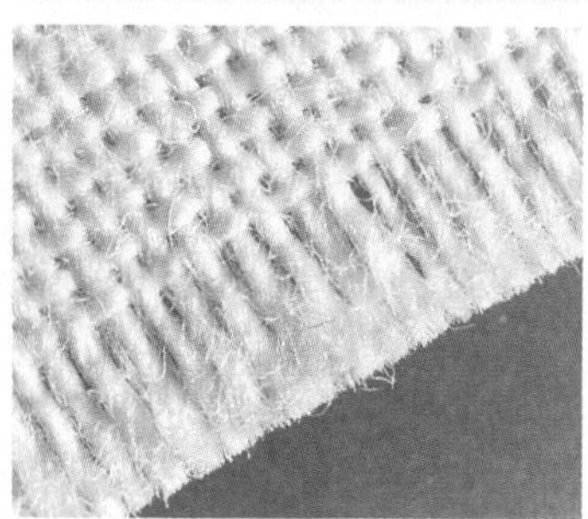
fiber

fidget [fij´it] v. to move restlessly: Small children can't sit still for very long, so don't be surprised if they fidget during the concert.

financial aid [fī·nan´shəl ād] n. money that is given to needy students to pay for school, usually at the college level.

flatland [flat´land] n. a wide stretch of land, such as a desert.

flaunt [flônt] v. to show off, especially in a bold way.

flustered [flus´tərd] adj. confused and upset: When the teacher called on her, Alicia became too flustered to answer the question.

fond [fänd] adj. caring deeply about someone or something. syn. loving.

foreign [fôr´in] adj. from a different country or place.

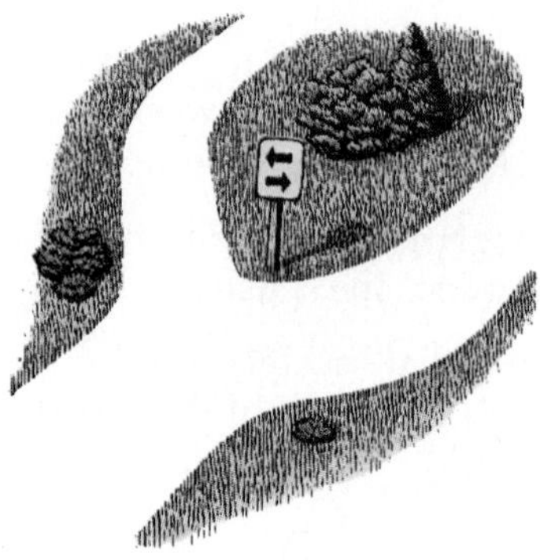

fork [fôrk] n. a point at which a road, path, or river divides into two or more branches.

fragment [frag´mənt] n. a piece or part of a whole: Although we had cleaned up the broken glass carefully, Jerry found a fragment under the table this morning.

fragrance [frā´grəns] n. a pleasant scent. syn. perfume.

frantically [frant´ik·lē] adv. furiously and anxiously.

freeloader [frē´lōd´ər] n. someone who takes advantage of others' generosity but contributes little or nothing in return.

frijoles [frē·hō´les´] n. Mexican beans, often boiled and then mashed into a paste.

frizzy [friz′ē] adj. extremely curly: Joy was disappointed with the results of her permanent—a head full of frizzy hair.

frock [fräk] n. a dress.

furiously[1] [fyoor′ē·əs·lē] adv. quickly and with great energy.

furiously[2] [fyoor′ē·əs·lē] adv. angrily: "How could you forget the package? It was sitting right on your desk!" Melissa shouted furiously.

gait [gāt] n. pace or movement.

game [gām] n. wild birds or animals hunted for sport or for food: Deer and pheasants are two of the most popular game animals hunted in the United States.

gaze [gāz] n. a steady look: The noisy children could not escape the librarian's disapproving gaze.

generation [jen′ər·ā′shən] n. all those born and living around the same time: In my parents' generation, most teens did not have their own phone.

genius [jēn′yəs] n. a person of exceptional intelligence.

ghostly [gōst′lē] adj. like a supernatural being. syn. spooky.

gifted [gift′əd] adj. possessing special skill or talent.

ginkgo tree [gin′kō trē] n. a tree, originally from Asia, that has fan-shaped leaves and bad-smelling yellow fruit: The gingko tree is said to be one of the oldest plants still in existence.

glance [glans] v. to hit and bounce off at an angle.

glimpse [glimps] n. a brief, quick view: Juan caught only a glimpse of the suspect, so he could not identify her in a lineup.

gospel [gäs′pəl] n. a type of music that uses vigorous rhythm and is sung in many African American churches.

granny glasses [gran′ē glas′iz] n. glasses with wire rims and small, round lenses (so named because they were once worn by many elderly people).

graze [grāz] v. to feed in a pasture or other expanse of land: Our cow Maizie likes to graze in the pasture behind the barn.

grove [grōv] n. a group of trees: We ate our picnic lunch on the grass by a grove of maple trees.

gunnysack [gun′ē·sak′] n. a storage bag made of a rough fiber similar to burlap.

handbill [hand′bil] n. a small poster or notice.

harvest [här′vist] n. the gathering in of a mature crop.

haughty [hôt′ē] adj. proud, especially in a scornful way; snobbish: Marcy swept into the rehearsal in a haughty manner, looking down her nose at the others in the cast.

headland [hed′lənd] n. a stretch of land that reaches out into water. syn. cape.

heart [härt] n. the central or main idea.

ginkgo trees

harvesting corn

a cat	ô fall, for	ə = a *in* ago
ā ape	oi oil	e *in* agent
ä cot, car	oo look, pull	i *in* pencil
e ten, berry	o͞o tool, rule	o *in* atom
ē me	ou out, crowd	u *in* circus
i fit, here	u up	
ī ice, fire	ur fur	
ō go		

hull

herbicide [hur′bə·sīd′] n. a chemical that is put on plants, particularly weeds, to kill them or to control their growth.

hierarchy [hī′ər·är′kē] n. a group of things ranked by importance.

hobble [häb′əl] v. to limit the movement of an animal, such as a horse, by tying two of its feet together.

homebody [hōm′bäd′ē] n. someone who prefers to stay close to where he or she lives: When Ruth suggested spending our family vacation in the backyard, Dad joked, "What? One of my children, a homebody?"

homesteader [hōm′sted′ər] n. someone who settles on land with the government's permission, planning to live there permanently.

honorable mention [än′ər·ə·bəl men′shən] n. in a competition, an award given to a contestant who performs well but does not earn one of the top honors.

horizon [hə·rī′zən] n. a distant line at which the sky appears to meet the earth.

horse latitudes [hôrs lat′ ə·to͞odz] n. either of two belts over the oceans at c. 30° – 35° N. and S. latitude, characterized by calms, light winds, and high barometric pressure.

hull [hul] n. the outer shell of a boat.

humbow [hum′bō] n. a Chinese roll stuffed with barbequed pork.

horizon

identity [ī·den′tə·tē] n. who one is; one's idea of self: The hospital workers searched the patient's wallet for some clue to his identity.

idly [īd′lē] adv. in a slow, lazy, or casual manner.

illumination [i·lo͞o′mə·nā′shən] n. light.

illusion [i·lo͞o′zhən] n. a false idea or picture: By acting calm when she felt nervous, Ellie created the illusion that she was feeling fine.

imagine [i·maj′in] v. to create a mental picture of something.

immature [im·mə·to͞or′] adj. not having reached full growth or adulthood: Although considered adults, most college students are still immature in their thinking.

impede [im·pēd′] v. to make difficult or get in the way.

impress [im·pres′] v. to persuade; to have a big impact.

improvise [im′prə·vīz] v. to make a substitute plan.

incredulous [in·krej′oo·ləs] adj. unable to believe. syn. doubtful.

industrial [in·dus′trē·əl] adj. related to producing something.

insolence [in′sə·lens] n. disrespectful speech and behavior.

instinct [in′stingkt′] n. an inborn tendency to act in a certain way.

insubordination [in′sə·bôr′d'nā·shən] n. an act of disobedience to authority.

internal [in·tur′nəl] adj. inside. syn. inner.

interpreter [in·tur′prə·tər] n. a person who translates from one language into another.

intersperse [in′tər·spurs′] v. to mix or scatter randomly.

Jackson, Andrew [jak′sən an′drōō′] n. an American general and seventh president of the United States (1829–1837).

jerky [jurk′ē] n. dried meat.

journal [jur′nəl] n. a book, similar to a diary, in which a person writes thoughts and feelings.

joystick [joi′stik′] n. a manually operated device that controls the movement of something else, such as a computer.

Kampuchea [kam′pōō·chē′ə] n. a country in Southeast Asia, usually known as Cambodia.

kelp [kelp] n. a type of seaweed: Sea otters wrap themselves in kelp to keep from drifting away while they sleep.

kennel [ken′əl] n. a place where dogs are boarded while their owners cannot care for them.

kingpin [king′pin′] n. the head of an organization.

kinship [kin′ship′] n. a close relationship or connection: We felt a kinship with the other families of cancer patients.

knot[1] [nät] n. a hard lump left on a tree after a branch grows out, often leading to an imperfect spot in lumber.

knot[2] [nät] n. a fastening made by looping or drawing two ends of a string or rope around each other: Kevin learned the figure-eight knot when earning his Scout badge, and he showed us all how to tie it.

laden [lād′n] adj. weighed down, as if by bundles or packages: Mom opened the door to find two tired shoppers, heavily laden from a day at the mall.

lair [ler] n. a place where a wild animal lives. syn. den.

kelp

lair

a	cat	ô	fall, for	ə =	a *in* ago
ā	ape	oi	oil		e *in* agent
ä	cot, car	oo	look, pull		i *in* pencil
e	ten, berry	ōō	tool, rule		o *in* atom
ē	me	ou	out, crowd		u *in* circus
i	fit, here	u	up		
ī	ice, fire	ur	fur		
ō	go				

landscape [land′skāp] n. a picture of nature on land, such as a forest, meadow, or prairie: My favorite landscape, a field of poppies, hangs in Mr. Samuelson's office.

league [lēg] n. a unit used to measure distance, about three miles.

lease [lēs] v. to pay for the privilege of using. syn. rent.

lifeboat [līf′bōt′] n. on a ship, a small rowboat that is lowered into the water during an emergency and takes passengers to safety.

lifeboat

lodge [läj] n. the home of some Native Americans: The museum's exhibit of a Pawnee lodge shows where people ate and slept.

loiter [loit′ər] v. to hang around without any obvious purpose: Now that the high school sponsors the teen drop-in center, few of us loiter in the shopping mall.

loll [läl] v. to lounge around doing nothing.

lone [lōn] adj. single; only.

longshoreman [läng′shôr′mən] n. one who loads and unloads a ship's cargo.

loom [lo͞om] v. to rise up or appear suddenly.

lottery [lät′ər·ē] n. a game in which numbered tickets are distributed, with winning numbers drawn at random.

macho [mä′chō] adj. showing exaggerated masculine traits.

makeshift [māk′shift′] adj. substitute or temporary.

marinated [mar′ə·nāt′əd] adj. soaked in a sauce.

mariner [mar′ə·nər] n. a sailor; seaman.

marker [märk′ər] n. one of a group of items that indicate a trail or path.

mast [mast] n. a tall vertical beam that rises from the deck of a ship and supports the operation of sails, radar equipment, and the like.

meal [mēl] n. coarsely ground grain used in cooking.

meditate [med′ə·tāt′] v. to pause and reflect.

menace [men′əs] n. an enemy or threat to survival. syn. danger: The dog who bit four boys was a menace to our neighborhood.

mend [mend] v. to repair or fix: Dad promised, "When Grandpa visits, I'll ask him to help me mend the hole in the fence."

mesa [mā′sə] n. a high, flat piece of land with steep sides: When we climbed to the top of the mesa, we looked around at the vast flatland.

mesa at Monument Valley, Utah

metropolitan [me′trō·päl′i·tən] adj. belonging to a central city and surrounding areas.

migrant worker [mī′grənt wʉrk′ər] n. a farm worker who moves from place to place and harvests seasonal crops: Luisa traced her strong work ethic to her father, a migrant worker who traveled up and down the coast of California.

migration [mī·grā′shən] n. the large-scale movement of people or things from one place to another.

mimic [mim′ik] v. to imitate another, usually in a mocking way.

mission [mish′ən] n. a trip or activity with specific goals.

missionary [mish′ən·er′ē] n. one who is sent, usually to another country or region, by a religious group to spread its religion.

misstep [mis′step′] n. a wrong move or mistake: In his first mountain-climbing class, Rey learned that one misstep could cost him his life.

modern dance [mäd′ərn dans′] n. a form of dance as a performing art, begun in the 1900's and using movements less formal than ballet.

moldering [mōl′dər·ing] adj. decaying; wasting away.

monotonous [mə·nät′n·əs] adj. having little or no change.

Mozart, Wolfgang Amadeus [mō′tsärt′ vôlf′gäng̑k′ ä′mä·dā′o͞os] n. a noted Austrian composer (1756–1791): To open her recital, Anna played a movement of *Eine Kleine Nachtmusik*, by Wolfgang Amadeus Mozart.

mural [myo͞or′əl] n. a picture painted on a wall or ceiling.

mutiny [myo͞ot′'n·ē] n. a revolt against authority, especially of sailors or soldiers against their superiors.

mystery [mis′tə·rē] n. a puzzling event or a situation: Not until months after Christmas did we solve the mystery of the vanished toy: Grandma found it inside the piano.

naturalist [nach′ər·əl·ist] n. one who studies nature by observing plants and animals: Was Luther Burbank the famous naturalist who developed the peanut?

navigate [nav′ə·gāt′] v. to find one's way or get around.

navigator [nav′ə·gāt′ər] n. one who helps chart the direction of a craft.

nervously [nʉr′vəs·lē] adv. tensely or anxiously. syn. apprehensively.

oasis [o·ā′sis] n. a lush, welcome spot in an otherwise empty area: Finding a bench to rest on after our long walk was almost like finding an oasis in the desert.

objective [əb·jek′tiv] adj. dealing only with facts and not emotions.

occupant [äk′yo͞o·pənt] n. one who lives or works in a space.

occur [ə·kʉr′] v. to become known: Why didn't it occur to me that Adam needed a ride to school this morning?

Wolfgang Amadeus Mozart

a	cat	ô	fall, for	ə =	a *in* ago
ā	ape	oi	oil		e *in* agent
ä	cot, car	oo	look, pull		i *in* pencil
e	ten, berry	o͞o	tool, rule		o *in* atom
ē	me	ou	out, crowd		u *in* circus
i	fit, here	u	up		
ī	ice, fire	ʉr	fur		
ō	go				

a mother goose and her offspring

offspring [ôf′spriṅg] n. any child or children of parents: As the sun set, the young father collected his tired offspring and left the playground.

omen [ō′mən] n. a sign of something to come.

ordeal [ôr·dēl′] n. a very difficult undertaking.

orderly [ôr′dər·lē] n. an assistant to a military leader.

ordinance [ôrd′n·əns] n. a government rule, especially of city government: Businesses in this community must obey a complicated sign ordinance.

outcropping [out′kräp·iṅg] n. a ledge of rock or other material that sticks out.

overwinter [ō′vər·wint′ər] v. to spend the cold season: Regina's parents leave Ohio in November and overwinter in Florida.

peer [pir] v. to look closely: Because the shop was closed, we could only peer through the windows at the lovely merchandise.

perceptive [pər·sep′tiv] adj. having keen insight or understanding. syn. sensitive.

peril [per′il] n. exposure to harm or injury; danger.

perish [per′ish] v. to die.

pessimistic [pes′ə·mis′tik] adj. expecting the worst. syn. negative.

an early phonograph

petroglyph [pe′trō·glif′] n. a rock carving, especially from prehistoric times.

phantom [fan′təm] n. a ghost or ghostly being.

phenomenon [fə·näm′ə·nən] n. occurrence or happening.

phonograph [fō′nə·graf′] n. a machine that reproduces sound that has been recorded on audio records. syn. record player; turntable: In 1877 Thomas Edison played back a recording of "Mary Had a Little Lamb" on the first practical phonograph.

pitch[1] [pich] n. a black, sticky substance.

pitch[2] [pich] n. the tone of a spoken sound: For a child, Jeremy's voice has a remarkably low pitch.

pitch[3] [pich] v. to raise or erect, as a tent: "After we unpack the equipment and pitch the tents," said Mom, "let's explore the park a bit."

pitiful [pit′i·fəl] adj. sad to see; worthy of sympathy. syn. pathetic.

plaque [plak] n. a board on which a message is printed, usually to call attention to a special event or achievement.

plateau [pla·tō´] n. a flat stretch of land.

pleadingly [plēd´ing·lē] adv. in a begging manner.

Pollock, Jackson [päl´ək jak´sən] n. an American artist known for his abstract paintings (1912–1956).

porthole [pôrt´hōl] n. a small, usually round, window in a sailing vessel.

precautionary [prē·kô´shən·er´ē] adj. having the goal of avoiding danger or preventing accidents or mistakes: As a precautionary measure, the tour guide asked the visitors not to touch any of the museum's paintings.

predator [pred´ə·tər] n. an animal that kills other animals for food: Humans and other animals consider the shark a dangerous predator in the sea.

previous [prē´vē·əs] adj. former or occurring before. syn. earlier.

principal [prin´sə·pəl] adj. main or chief: Cornmeal, milk, and eggs are the principal ingredients in cornbread.

principle [prin´sə·pəl] n. a strongly held belief or value.

procrastinate [prō·kras´tə·nāt´] v. to put off doing something until a later time.

produce [prä´dōōs´] n. fruits and vegetables: When I was a little girl, my father worked nights setting up the produce in our local supermarket.

proprietor [prō·prī´ə·tər] n. the owner of a business: Mrs. Smith enjoyed her new career as the proprietor of a bookstore.

protest [prō´test´] n. a public display of disagreement with a policy or practice.

pup [pup] n. a young fox, wolf, dog, seal, or whale: The mother wolf groomed each pup in turn.

quiver¹ [kwiv´ər] n. a wiggling back and forth.

quiver² [kwiv´ər] v. to wiggle back and forth: "You're not going to tell Dad, are you?" little Ted sobbed, and then he began to quiver.

quiver³ [kwiv´ər] n. in archery, a storage case for arrows.

ravine [rə·vēn´] n. a large, deep hollow in the earth. syn. gorge.

recite [ri·sīt´] v. to repeat aloud from memory.

reflection [ri·flek´shən] n. the throwing back of sound, light, or heat from a surface: The water-skier saw his reflection in the water.

plaque

wolf pups

reflection

a	cat	ô	fall, for	ə =	a *in* ago
ā	ape	oi	oil		e *in* agent
ä	cot, car	oo	look, pull		i *in* pencil
e	ten, berry	ōō	tool, rule		o *in* atom
ē	me	ou	out, crowd		u *in* circus
i	fit, here	u	up		
ī	ice, fire	ur	fur		
ō	go				

refugee [ref′yo͞o·jē′] n. a person who leaves his or her native land to seek protection in another country: Mr. Fernandez, a Cuban refugee, fled his homeland in a tiny boat.

regenerate [ri·jen′ə·rāt′] v. to restore to an earlier level of quality or being.

regret [ri·gret′] v. to feel sorry.

relieve [ri·lēv′] v. to ease or reduce pain or anxiety.

relocation [rē′lō·kā′shən] n. the moving of someone or something from one place to another.

remains [ri·mānz′] n. the body or body parts of a dead person or animal.

remnant [rem′nənt] n. a scrap or piece left over. syn. trace.

repel [ri·pel′] v. to cause distaste or to hold back.

reservoir [rez′ər·vwär′] n. a place where something is stored or collected: Excess water from the lake flowed into a nearby reservoir.

resolve [ri·zälv′] v. to decide; make up one's mind: I resolve to tell the truth from now on.

respect [ri·spekt′] n. a feeling of honor and high regard. syn. approval.

revelation [rev′ə·lā′shən] n. understanding or awareness.

revelry [rev′əl·rē] n. wild merrymaking.

reward [ri·wôrd′] v. to give something in exchange for good behavior. syn. pay.

rhapsody [rap′sə·dē] n. a piece of music made up of irregular parts.

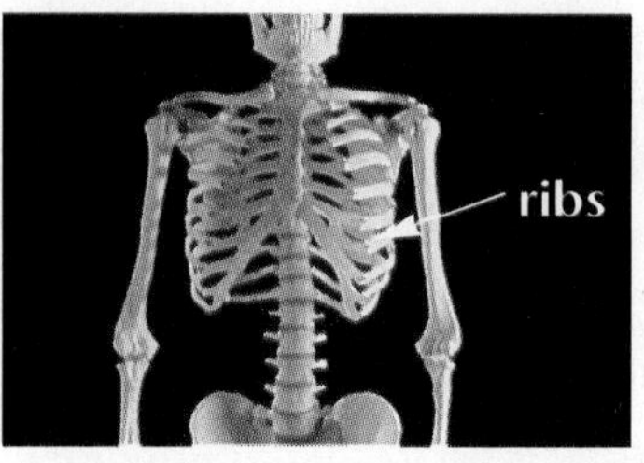

rib [rib] n. one of many curved bones that form the chest cavity: Sara broke a rib sliding into third base.

rigorous [rig′ər·əs] adj. very strict; thorough.

rockslide [rok′slīd] n. a sudden, rapid rush of rocks and earth down a mountainside.

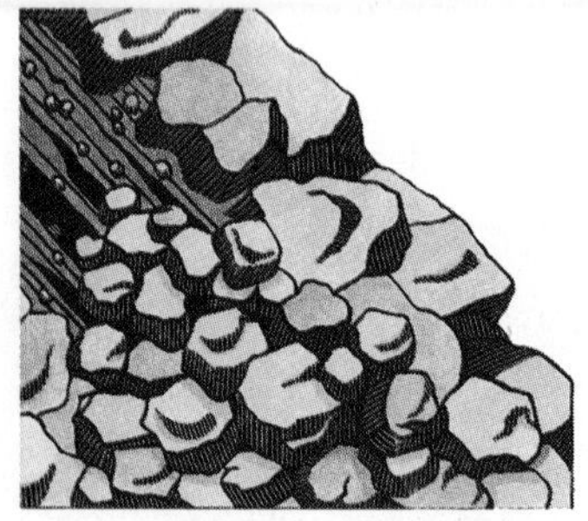

rockslide

route [rout] n. a path: No matter which route you take to school, you will need to cross at least one busy street.

rural [roor′əl] adj. of or like a farm: When Sam was old enough to leave his rural surroundings, he moved to the city.

sabotage [sab′ə·täzh′] v. to ruin by intentionally destroying materials.

sanctuary [saŋgk′cho͞o·er′ē] n. a sheltering place: Trailside Museum serves as a sanctuary for injured wildlife found in our community.

sandspit [sand′spit] n. a bar of sand rising from a body of water.

sanity [san′ə·tē] n. mental health.

scarce [skers] adj. in short supply; rare: When sugar was scarce, people learned to make sugarless cakes.

scavenge [skav′inj] v. to search around for usable goods.

scout [skout] v. to lead a group so as to avoid danger and problems.

scraggly [skrag′lē] adj. messy; irregular; syn. ragged.

scrub[1] [skrub] n. an irregularly shaped bush often found in places with little rainfall.

scrub[2] [skrub] v. to wash with great energy: Surgeons scrub their arms to the elbow before they operate.

sculpture [skulp′chər] n. the art of carving wood, welding metal, chiseling stone, or the like, to form three-dimensional objects.

secluded [si·klo͞od′id] adj. shut off or kept apart from others. syn. isolated.

secret [sē′krit] n. something known by one or more persons and intentionally kept from others.

segregation [seg′rə·gā′shən] n. the act of keeping a person or group apart from the group as a whole: In the 1950's in the United States, the public schools practiced racial segregation.

self-conscious [self·kän′shəs] adj. overly aware of oneself and uncomfortable around others.

sermon [sʉr′mən] n. a speech given as instruction in religious worship: I learned a lot from yesterday's sermon on forgiveness.

serpent [sʉr′pənt] n. a snake, especially a large, poisonous one: Jan jumped back when she saw the hissing serpent hanging from the tree, ready to strike.

sheaves [shēvz] n. bunches of cut grain or other plants, bound into bundles.

shellfish [shel′fish] n. any variety of sea animal with a hard outer covering: Of all the types of shellfish I've tried, I like lobster the best.

shipwrecked [ship′rekt] adj. to be aboard a boat that is destroyed or ruined.

shortage [shôrt′ij] n. a limited amount; not enough of something: With a half gallon of milk and ten thirsty children, we had a serious milk shortage.

shrouds [shroudz] n. ropes used to help keep the mast in position.

sidle [sīd′l] v. to walk sideways, as if shy or secretive: Norman told himself, "Don't back out now! Just sidle up to the new girl and say *hi*!"

Sierra Madre Mountains [sē·er′ə mä′drā moun′t'nz] n. a mountain range in Mexico: Mexico's silver mines are tucked deep within the Sierra Madre Mountains.

serpent

scallops and clams, examples of shellfish

a	cat	ô	fall, for	ə =	a *in* ago
ā	ape	oi	oil		e *in* agent
ä	cot, car	oo	look, pull		i *in* pencil
e	ten, berry	o͞o	tool, rule		o *in* atom
ē	me	ou	out, crowd		u *in* circus
i	fit, here	u	up		
ī	ice, fire	ʉr	fur		
ō	go				

spigots

starling

sighting [sīt′ing] n. the act of observing or spotting, especially something seen rarely.

skeletal [skel′ə·təl] adj. made up of bones or like the bones of a once-living thing.

skirt [skûrt] v. to pass around or avoid: Anthony managed to skirt the issue of who broke the vase.

skittish [skit′ish] adj. excitable or undependable: Hannah's pony was skittish and wouldn't stay on the narrow path.

slavery [slā′vər·ē] n. the owning or keeping of servants as property: During the 1700's and the 1800's, many Africans were brought to the Americas and forced into slavery.

slender [slen′dər] adj. slim or thin: James loved to watch his mother's slender wrists rise and fall as she played the piano.

snare [snar] n. a trap.

somberly [säm′bər·lē] adv. in a serious way, especially with a trace of sadness. syn. grimly.

sonar [sō′när′] n. a device that uses sound waves to detect the presence of other objects, such as submarines.

spatter [spat′ər] v. to scatter in droplets.

species [spē′shēz] n. a group of animals that share certain characteristics.

spherical [sfer′i·kəl] adj. ball-shaped, as a globe: The laboratory hoped to introduce an orange that was not spherical but pear shaped.

spicy [spī′sē] adj. lively and daring. syn. spirited.

spigot [spig′ət] n. a faucet.

spiral [spī′rəl] v. to spin in a circle around a central point or area.

spit[1] [spit] n. saliva.

spit[2] [spit] v. to eject from the mouth forcefully: "If you find a bone in this fish," Auntie Faye cautioned, "don't swallow it; spit it out in your napkin."

spit[3] [spit] n. a thin, pointed rod on which food is speared and cooked, while revolving, over an open fire.

sponsored [spän′sərd] v. took responsibility for another person.

stalactite [stə·lak′tīt] n. a mineral deposit, shaped like an icicle, that hangs from the roof of a cave and is formed when dripping water evaporates.

stall [stôl] n. a small enclosed space, usually large enough for one person: For a voting booth, the tiny town used a beat-up shower stall that someone had thrown out.

staple [stā′pəl] n. a basic food or other item: Milk is a staple in many refrigerators.

starboard [stär′bərd] n. the right-hand side of a ship, facing forward.

starling [stär′liŋ] n. a songbird with glossy black feathers.

statistic [stə·tis′tik] n. a fact in number form.

status [stat′əs] n. position or rank.

Stella, Frank [stel′ə frāŋk′] n. American artist (born 1936).

stereotype [ster′·ē·ə·tīp′] n. a general belief or image about someone or something that does not consider individual differences: Kim questioned the stereotype that all teenagers love rock music.

stern [stûrn] n. the rear part of a ship.

stipulation [stip·yo͞o·lā′shən] n. a rule or condition in an agreement: Kevin agreed to his new work hours, with the stipulation that he could change the schedule after one year.

stoop[1] [sto͞op] n. a small porch or step at the front door of a house.

stoop[2] [sto͞op] v. to lower oneself to ground level by bending the upper body and knees.

strenuous [stren′yo͞o·əs] adj. requiring much effort or energy. syn. laborious.

Styrofoam [stī′rə·fōm′] n. brand name for a type of lightweight plastic that has a variety of uses, such as cups, plates, and insulation.

subject [sub′jekt] n. one who is being photographed.

sublime [sə·blīm′] adj. perfectly wonderful. syn. splendid.

submissive [sub·mis′iv] adj. willing to give in to someone else: All of the dogs bullied Gus, a submissive puppy and the runt of the litter.

sumac [so͞o′mak′] n. a kind of plant whose powdered leaves and red berries can be used for dyeing.

summit [sum′it] n. the highest point of a hill or mountain.

surmise [sər·mīz′] v. to suppose or speculate. syn. guess.

swarm [swôrm] n. a group of animals, such as bees or wasps.

tableland [tā′bəl·land′] n. a high, broad, flat stretch of land. syn. plateau.

tackle [tak′əl] v. to knock down or otherwise keep from moving.

temptation [temp·tā′shən] n. the act of tempting or enticing: A pan of freshly baked brownies is a huge temptation for me.

terrace [ter′əs] n. one of a series of long, flat platforms of land, often rising one above the other on a steep hill.

bag of recyclable Styrofoam

swarm

a	cat	ô	fall, for	ə =	a *in* ago
ā	ape	oi	oil		e *in* agent
ä	cot, car	oo	look, pull		i *in* pencil
e	ten, berry	o͞o	tool, rule		o *in* atom
ē	me	ou	out, crowd		u *in* circus
i	fit, here	u	up		
ī	ice, fire	ûr	fur		
o	go				

trek

thong [thôn̂g] n. a narrow strip or string of leather.

time machine [tīm′ mə·shēn′] n. a make-believe device used to go backward and forward in time.

tinge [tinj] n. a slight trace. syn. hint.

tingle [tin̂g′gəl] v. to have a prickling or stinging sensation.

tinker [tin̂gk′ər] v. to work with, in order to repair or adjust: Carl continued to tinker with his ham radio long after his bedtime.

Titanic [tī·tan′ik] n. a major passenger ship that sank in 1912, on its first voyage, after hitting an iceberg in the Atlantic Ocean.

tolerant [täl′ər·ənt] adj. respectful of others who may have different behavior or beliefs.

tract [trakt] n. an expanse of land.

tradition [trə·dish′ən] n. a people's customs, stories, or beliefs handed down over generations.

tragedy [traj′ə·dē] n. a terrible event. syn. disaster.

transform [trans·fôrm′] v. to change completely: During the time George spent in boot camp, Mom was able to transform his bedroom into a sewing room.

treacherous [trech′ər·əs] adj. dangerous.

trek [trek] v. to travel on foot, often slowly and with difficulty: Before you trek through the Himalayas, you must study the land and pack plenty of supplies.

turbulence [tûr′byo͞o·ləns] n. unrest. syn. disturbance.

turnpike [tûrn′pīk′] n. a highway: Driving to New York from Iowa, Ed marveled at the mountains along the Pennsylvania Turnpike.

undigested [un·dī·jes′təd] adj. not broken down into its basic parts.

undistinguished [un·di·stin̂g′gwisht] adj. lacking features or qualities that seem worthy of special notice or honor: Because Hester failed to study, her performance on the test was undistinguished.

unemployed [un·em·ploid′] adj. without a paying job: Dave's mother, though unemployed, has worked as a full-time mom and school volunteer for many years.

unlawful [un·lô′fəl] adj. against the law. syn. illegal: It is unlawful not to make a complete stop at a stop sign.

vacant [vā′kənt] adj. empty: Three of our guest rooms are vacant, so we have room for up to six more people.

vanish [van′ish] v. to disappear: When I say the words "Be gone!" you will vanish from sight.

vantage [van′tij] n. perspective or position.

veer [vir] v. to change direction sharply or suddenly: We narrowly avoided an accident when we noticed the car in the next lane suddenly veer in front of us.

vegetarian [vej′ə·ter′ē·ən] n. one who does not eat meat: Tyrone, who is a vegetarian, likes to eat rice and beans for dinner.

vivid [viv′id] adj. bright; colorful. syn. brilliant: My sister likes to wear clothing in vivid shades of red or pink.

voyage [voi′ij] n. a journey, especially over water: As the ship began its voyage, passengers gathered on deck and released balloons.

wardroom [wôrd′ro͞om] n. the living quarters of a ship's officers, except for the captain.

wash [wôsh] n. a thin, watery coating. Benjamin painted a sunrise with a peach-colored wash in the background.

weep [wēp] v. to cry: I always weep when I see a sad movie or television program.

welfare [wel′fer′] n. well-being: Our parents do their best to look out for our welfare.

worship [wûr′ship] v. to show adoration or reverence, especially to a supreme being: On Sundays my family likes to worship at our neighborhood church.

wrath [rath] n. great anger. syn. fury.

zucchini [zo͞o·kē′nē] n. a type of summer squash, long and thin with a yellow or dark green skin: Mom made our favorite dish, zucchini with green peppers, tomatoes, and onions.

zucchini

a	cat	ô	fall, for	ə =	a *in* ago
ā	ape	oi	oil		e *in* agent
ä	cot, car	oo	look, pull		i *in* pencil
e	ten, berry	o͞o	tool, rule		o *in* atom
ē	me	ou	out, crowd		u *in* circus
i	fit, here	u	up		
ī	ice, fire	ûr	fur		
ō	go				

ACKNOWLEDGMENTS

Grateful acknowledgment is made to the following publishers, authors, and agents for their permission to reprint copyrighted material. Every effort has been made to locate all copyright proprietors; any errors or omissions in copyright notice are inadvertent and will be corrected in future printings as they are discovered.

"ABOUT NOTEBOOKS" from *Hey World, Here I Am!* by Jean Little. Text copyright © 1986 by Jean Little. Reprinted by permission of the American publisher, HarperCollins Publishers and of the British publisher, Kids Can Press Ltd., Toronto.

"ALI BABA AND THE MISSING GLASS SLIPPER" from *Ali Baba Bernstein, Lost and Found* by Johanna Hurwitz. Text copyright © 1992 by Johanna Hurwitz. By permission of Morrow Junior Books, a division of William Morrow & Company, Inc.

"THE ALLIGATOR AND THE HUNTER" from *Keepers of the Animals: Native American Stories and Wildlife Activities for Children* by Michael J. Caduto and Joseph Bruchac. Copyright © 1992 by Joseph Bruchac. Reprinted by permission of Fulcrum Publishing, Golden, Colorado; 1-800-992-2908.

ALVIN AILEY by Andrea Davis Pinkney, illustrated by Brian Pinkney. Text copyright © 1993 by Andrea Davis Pinkney. Illustrations copyright © 1993 by Brian Pinkney. Reprinted by arrangement with Hyperion Books for Children.

"AS I WALK ALONG THE HILLSIDE" by Misty Stands in Timber from the 1987-1988 Lane Deer School Poetry Calendar. Copyright © 1987 by Misty Stands in Timber. Reprinted by permission of the author.

"BEE SONG" from *Wind Song* by Carl Sandburg. Copyright 1936 by Curtis Brown. Reprinted by permission of Harcourt Brace & Company.

"THE BIRTH OF A STONE" by Kwang-kyu Kim, translated by Brother Anthony, from *Faint Shadows of Love.* Copyright © 1991 by Kwang-kyu Kim. Reprinted by permission of the author.

"BLUEBIRD, WHAT DO YOU FEED ON?" from *Wind Song* by Carl Sandburg. Copyright © 1960 by Carl Sandburg and renewed 1988 by Margaret Sandburg, Janet Sandburg, and Helga Sandburg Crile. Reprinted by permission of Harcourt Brace & Company.

"CARRYING THE RUNNING-AWAYS" from *The People Could Fly* by Virginia Hamilton. Illustrated by Leo and Diane Dillon. Text copyright © 1985 by Virginia Hamilton. Illustrations copyright © 1985 by Leo and Diane Dillon. Used by permission of Alfred A. Knopf, Inc.

"A CHALLENGE FOR CELINDA" from *Kinaaldá: A Navajo Girl Grows Up* by Monty Roessel. Copyright © 1993 by Lerner Publications Company. Used by permission of the publisher. All rights reserved.

"CITY BIRDS" from *The City Kid's Field Guide* by Ethan Herberman. Copyright © 1989 by Ethan Herberman and WGBH Educational Foundation. Reprinted with permission of Simon & Schuster Books for Young Readers, Simon & Schuster Children's Publishing Division.

"COMING OVER" from *Immigrant Kids* by Russell Freedman. Copyright © 1980 by Russell Freedman. Used by permission of Dutton Children's Books, a division of Penguin Books USA Inc. Excerpt from *In the Shadow of Liberty: The Chronicle of Ellis Island* by Edward Corsi. Copyright © 1935 by the Macmillan Company.

"COPYCAT" from *Heads or Tails* by Jack Gantos. Copyright © 1994 by Jack Gantos. Reprinted by permission of Farrar, Straus & Giroux, Inc.

"THE DEER THIEF" from *Cuentos: Tales from the Hispanic Southwest* selected by and adapted in Spanish by Jose Griego y Maestas, retold in English by Rudolfo A. Anaya. Copyright © 1980 by the Museum of New Mexico Press. Reprinted by permission of the publisher.

"DESERT TORTOISE" from *Desert Voices* by Byrd Baylor. Copyright © 1981 by Byrd Baylor. Reprinted with permission of Atheneum Books for Young Readers, an imprint of Simon & Schuster Children's Publishing Division.

"THE DOLPHINS LED ME HOME" from *Island of the Blue Dolphins* by Scott O'Dell. Copyright © 1960, renewed 1988 by Scott O'Dell. Reprinted by permission of the American publisher, Houghton Mifflin Co., and of the British publisher, McIntosh and Otis, Inc. All rights reserved.

"DREAMS" from *The Dream Keeper and Other Poems* by Langston Hughes. Copyright © 1932 by Alfred A. Knopf, Inc. and renewed 1960 by Langston Hughes. Used by permission of the American publisher, Alfred A. Knopf, Inc., and of the British publisher, Harold Ober Associates Incorporated.

"EMPTY HEAD" by Malick Fall from *French African Verse* edited by John Reed and Clive Wake (Heinemann African Writers Series). Reprinted by permission of John Reed and Clive Wake.

"AN EYE FOR REALITY" from *Dorothea Lange: Life Through the Camera* by Milton Meltzer. Copyright © 1985 by Milton Meltzer. Used by permission of Viking Penguin, a division of Penguin Books USA Inc.

"FARMING ON AVENUE B" from *Earth Keepers* by Joan Anderson and George Ancona. Text copyright © 1993 by Joan Anderson. Photographs copyright © 1993, 1990 by George Ancona. Reprinted by permission of the American publisher, Harcourt Brace & Company, and of the British publisher, Writers House Inc.

"FIRST MANNED FLIGHT TO VENUS" by Jan Minter from *Plays, the Drama Magazine for Young People.* Copyright © 1980 by Plays, Inc. Reprinted by permission of the publisher.

"FOR YOUR EYES ONLY: FRIDAY NOVEMBER 4" from *The Journal of Beatrix Potter,* transcribed from her code writings by Leslie Linder. Copyright © 1966, 1989 by Frederick Warne & Co. Beatrix Potter's original illustrations copyright © by Frederick Warne & Co., 1955, 1966, 1968, 1971, 1972, 1975, 1987, 1989. Reproduced by permission of Frederick Warne & Co.

"FOR YOUR EYES ONLY: I DO NOT REMEMBER EVERYTHING..." from *My Sister and I: The Diary of a Dutch Boy Refugee* by Dirk van der Heide, translated by Mrs. Antoon Deventer. Copyright, 1941, by Harcourt Brace & Company, Inc.

"FOR YOUR EYES ONLY: SEPTEMBER 5, SUNDAY" from *Growing Pains: Diaries and Drawings for the Years 1908-1917* by Wanda Gág. Copyright 1940 by Wanda Gág, © renewed 1967 by Robert Janssen. Reprinted by permission of Coward-McCann, Inc.

"FOR YOUR EYES ONLY: SEPTEMBER 30, 1990" from *The Diary of Latoya Hunter: My First Year in Junior High* by Latoya Hunter. Copyright © 1992 by Latoya Hunter. Reprinted by permission of Crown Publishers, Inc.

"FOUR HAIKU" from *Flower Moon Snow: A Book of Haiku* by Kazue Mizumura. Copyright © 1977 by Kazue Mizumura. Reprinted by permission of HarperCollins Publishers.

"A GIFT FOR ATHENS" from *Jim-Dandy* by Hadley Irwin. Copyright © 1994 by Hadley Irwin. Reprinted with the permission of Margaret K. McElderry Books, an imprint of Simon & Schuster Children's Publishing Division.

THE GREAT MIGRATION by Jacob Lawrence. Copyright © 1993 by The Museum of Modern Art, New York, and The Phillips Collection. Reprinted by permission of HarperCollins Publishers.

"IMAGES" from *A Short Walk Around the Pyramids & Through the World of Art* by Philip M. Isaacson. Copyright © 1993 by Philip M. Isaacson. Used by permission of Alfred A. Knopf, Inc.

"IT STARTED WITH MISS IBBOTSON" from *Little By Little* by Jean Little. Copyright © Jean Little, 1987. Reprinted by permission of Penguin Books Canada Limited.

ACKNOWLEDGMENTS

"LAFFF" by Lensey Namioka from *Within Reach,* edited by Donald R. Gallo. © 1993 by Lensey Namioka. Reprinted by permission of the author's agent, Ruth Cohen, Inc.

"LAST DAYS AT RED CLAY" from *The Trail on Which They Wept* by Dorothy and Thomas Hoobler and Carey-Greenberg Associates. Copyright © 1992 by Carey-Greenberg Associates. Reprinted by permission of Silver Burdett Press, Inc. All rights reserved.

MARY PATTEN'S VOYAGE by Richard J. Berleth, illustrated by Ben Otero. Text copyright © 1994 by Richard J. Berleth. Illustrations © 1994 by Ben Otero. Reprinted by permission of Albert Whitman & Company.

"MI CANCIÓN/MY SONG" from *Mi Canción es un pedazo de jade/My Song Is a Piece of Jade* by Toni de Gerez. Illustration by Andrea Arroya from *My Song Is Beautiful* by Mary Ann Hoberman. Text copyright © 1981 by Organización Editorial Novaro, S.A. English translation copyright © 1984 by Organización Editorial Novaro, S.A. Illustrations copyright © 1994 by Little, Brown and Company. Illustrations reprinted by permission of Little, Brown and Company.

"MIGRATION" by Walter Dean Myers. Copyright © 1993 by Walter Dean Myers. Reprinted by permission of HarperCollins Publishers.

"MILO'S MYSTERIOUS GIFT" from *The Phantom Tollbooth* by Norton Juster. Copyright © 1961 and renewed 1989 by Norton Juster. Reprinted by permission of the American publisher, Random House, Inc., and of the British publisher, HarperCollins Publishers Limited.

"MISSING MAIZON" from *Last Summer with Maizon* by Jacqueline Woodson. Copyright © 1990 by Jacqueline Woodson. Used by permission of Bantam Doubleday Dell Books for Young Readers.

"NACHO LOCO" from *Local News* by Gary Soto. Copyright © 1993 by Gary Soto. Reprinted by permission of Harcourt Brace & Company.

"THE NAVAJO LEGEND OF KINAALDÁ" from *Kinaaldá: A Navajo Girl Grows Up* by Monty Roessel. Copyright © 1993 by Lerner Publications Company. Used by permission of the publisher. All rights reserved.

"OLD TRADITIONS, NEW BEGINNINGS" from *Hoang Anh: A Vietnamese-American Boy* by Diane Hoyt-Goldsmith with photographs by Lawrence Migdale. Text copyright © 1992 by Diane Hoyt-Goldsmith. Photographs copyright © 1992 by Lawrence Migdale. Reprinted by permission of Holiday House, Inc.

PEACH BLOSSOM SPRING by Fergus M. Bordewich, illustrated by Yang Ming-Yi. Text copyright © 1994 by Fergus M. Bordewich. Illustrations copyright © 1994 by Yang Ming-Yi. Reprinted with permission of Simon & Schuster Books for Young Readers, Simon & Schuster Children's Publishing Division.

Phonetic respelling system from *The World Book Encyclopedia.* © 1995 World Book, Inc. By permission of the publisher.

"PORTRAITS OF PEOPLE ON THE MOVE" from *Children of the Wild West* by Russell Freedman. Copyright © 1983 by Russell Freedman. Reprinted by permission of Clarion Books/Houghton Mifflin Co. All rights reserved.

"RETURN TO THE TITANIC" from *Exploring the Titanic* by Robert D. Ballard, illustrations of the Titanic by Ken Marschall. Text © copyright Ballard & Family 1988. Design and compilation © copyright Madison Publishing Inc. 1988. Reprinted by permission of the publisher, Madison Publishing Inc. All rights reserved.

"THE SECRET AMONG THE STONES" by Ardath Mayhar from *Within Reach* edited by Donald R. Gallo. Copyright © 1993 by Ardath Mayhar. Reprinted by permission of HarperCollins Publishers.

"SINCE HANNA MOVED AWAY" from *If I Were In Charge of the World and Other Worries* by Judith Viorst. Copyright © 1981 by Judith Viorst. Reprinted by permission of the American publisher, Atheneum Books for Young Readers, an imprint of Simon & Schuster Children's Publishing Division, of the Australian publisher, AM Heath & Company Ltd., and of the author's agent, Lescher & Lescher, Ltd.

"SLENDER-BILLED PARAKEET" from *The Art of Birds* by Pablo Neruda, translated by Jack Schmidt. Copyright © 1985 by Herederos de Pablo Neruda. Reprinted by permission of the University of Texas Press.

"SLOWER THAN THE REST" from *Every Living Thing* by Cynthia Rylant. Copyright © 1985 by Cynthia Rylant. Reprinted with permission of Macmillan Books for Young Readers, an imprint of Simon & Schuster Children's Publishing Division.

"SOLIDARITY/SOLIDARIDAD" by Amado Nervo from *Cool Salsa,* translated into English by Lori M. Carlson. Copyright © 1994 by Lori M. Carlson. Reprinted by permission of the American publisher, Henry Holt and Co., Inc., and of the British publisher, McIntosh and Otis, Inc.

"THE SOUND OF MUSIC" by Richard Rodgers and Oscar Hammerstein II. Copyright © 1959 by Richard Rodgers and Oscar Hammerstein II. Copyright renewed. Williamson Music owner of publication and allied rights throughout the world. International copyright secured. Used by permission. All rights reserved.

"TALES FROM TUCSON" from *Images and Conversations: Mexican Americans Recall a Southwestern Past* by Patricia Preciado Martin. Copyright © 1983 by The Arizona Board of Regents. Reprinted by permission of the publisher, the University of Arizona Press. All rights reserved.

"THIS DAY IS OVER" by Calvin O'John from *The Whispering Wind* edited by Terry Allen. Copyright © 1972 by the Institute of American Indian Arts. Used by permission of Doubleday, a division of Bantam Doubleday Dell Publishing Group, Inc.

"TRACKING THE MONARCH BUTTERFLIES" from *Monarch Butterflies: Mysterious Travelers* by Bianca Lavies. Copyright © 1992 by Bianca Lavies. Used by permission of Dutton Children's Books, a division of Penguin Books USA Inc.

"WHAT DO ANIMALS KNOW?" from *What Does the Crow Know?: The Mysteries of Animal Intelligence* by Margery Facklam. Text copyright © 1994 by Margery Facklam. Reprinted by arrangement with Sierra Club Books for Children and with Lucas-Evans Books Inc.

"WHO LEADS THE WOLF PACK?" from *Wolves* by R. D. Lawrence. Text copyright © 1990 by R.D. Lawrence. Reprinted by permission of the American publisher, Little, Brown and Company, and of the British publisher, Key Porter Books Ltd.

"WOLF WATCH" from *To the Top of the World: Adventures with Arctic Wolves* by Jim Brandenburg. Copyright © by Jim Brandenburg. Reprinted with permission from Walker and Company, 435 Hudson Street, New York, New York 10014, 1-800-289-2553. All rights reserved.

"THE YOUNGEST BUFFALO HUNTER" from *My Indian Boyhood* by Chief Luther Standing Bear. Copyright 1931 by Luther Standing Bear, copyright © renewed 1959 by May Jones. Reprinted by permission of Houghton Mifflin Co. All rights reserved.

COVER: Cover photography © 1996 by Jade Albert Studio. Cover illustration © 1996 by Linda DeVito Soltis. Cover design, art direction and production by Design Five.

ILLUSTRATION: **6–7** Theresa Smith (t.); **8–9** John Martin (t.); **10** Tom Voss; **10–11** Tim Spransy (t.); **14** Leo and Diane Dillon; **14–15** Tatjana Krizmanic (t.); **20–39** Jack Davis; **42–43** Laura Tarrish; **44–57** Karen Watson; **84–85** Gerardo Suzan; **86–91** Leland Burke; **108–111** Theresa Smith; **112–124** Gabriel Picart; **130–149** Tyrone Geeter; **150–151** Judy Pederson; **180** Eliza Schulte (t.); **181** Eliza Schulte (t.l.); **190–191** Eliza Schulte (c.); **192–195** Theresa Smith; **196–199** John Martin; **200–215** Nancy Nash; **219–222** John Burgoyne; **238–239** Andrea Arroyo; **240–251** Lars Hokanson; **282–285** John Martin; **286–289** Tim Spransy; **290–306** Tom Voss; **326–333** Don Margolis; **350–365** Tim McClure; **366–367** Rodney Pate; **368–371** Tim Spransy; **376–391** Shonto Begay; **392–393** Jim Dryden; **412–413** Walter Stuart; **414–417** Red Owl; **418–419** Fabricio Vanden Broeck; **434–435** Lois Schlowsky; **436–437** Oki Han; **440–453** Yan Nascimbene; **462–465** Tatjana Krizmanic; **486–491** Tyrone Geeter; **492–508** Bob Crofut; **509** Hrana Janto; **512–520** Leonard Jenkins; **522–523** Shonto Begay; **536–563** Chris Wiltse; **564–567** Tatjana Krizmanic; **468** Walter Stuart; **569** Jack Davis (t.); Nancy Nash (t.r.); **570–590** Virginia Peck; **590** Jack Davis.

PHOTOGRAPHY: Background photograph for Silver Bookcase by Allan Penn for SBG. **4–5** Allan Penn for SBG, photo styling by Anne Bugatch and Lance Salemo (t.); **6–7** Denver Public Library Western History Department; **12–13** © Brian Parker/Tom Stack & Associates (t.); **16–19** Allan Penn for SBG, photo styling by Anne Bugatch and Lance Salemo; **17** © David Young-Wolff/PhotoEdit (inset); **19** Ulsaker Studio, Inc. (t., c.); **20** Ambrosi and Associates; **39** Farrar, Straus, and Giroux (t.l.); Ambrosi and Associates (t.r., c.r.); Doug Mindell (b.r.); **40** Mary Cassatt, *The Letter,* drypoint and aquatint, 1891, 34.9 x 23 cm. © The Cleveland Museum of Art, Bequest of Charles T. Brooks, 41.86 (l.); The Metropolitan Museum of Art, Gift of Arthur Sachs, 1916 (16.3.2) © 1995 by the Metropolitan Museum of Art (c.); National Gallery of Art, Washington, D.C. (photo by Dean Beasom), © 1994 Board of Trustees, National Gallery of Art (r.); **40–41** Sharon Hoogstraten for SBG; **41** Mary Cassatt, *The Letter,* 1891, drypoint and aquatint, 13 5/8 x 8 5/16", fourth of four states, Collection of St. John's Museum of Art, Wilmington, North Carolina, Gift of Therese Thorne McLane in honor of Samuel Hudson Hughes and Zelina Comegys Brunschwig; **44** Courtesy of Penguin Books Canada Ltd; **45** Ambrosi and Associates; **47** Courtesy of Penguin Books Canada Ltd; **48–49**

ACKNOWLEDGMENTS

Courtesy of Penguin Books Canada Ltd; **50** Courtesy of Penguin Books Canada Ltd; **53** Courtesy of Penguin Books Canada Ltd; **55** Courtesy of Penguin Books Canada Ltd; **56** Courtesy Jean Little; **57** Courtesy Jean Little (t.); Ambrosi and Associates (b.l., b.r.); **58–61** Sharon Hoogstraten for SBG; **62–63** Allan Landau for SBG; **65** Sharon Hoogstraten for SBG; **69** Sharon Hoogstraten for SBG; **73** Sharon Hoogstraten for SBG; **75** Sharon Hoogstraten for SBG; **80** Milton Pinkney (t.); **80–81** John Morrison for SBG; **81** © Roberta Herschenson/NYT Pictures (t.); Ambrosi and Associates (c.l., c.r.); **82** UPI/Bettmann (l.); **82–83** Sharon Hoogstraten for SBG; **83** © Roberta Herschenson/NYT Pictures (t.); Courtesy of The Schomburg Center for Research in Black Culture (b.); **92** © Rondal Partridge (t.); Ambrosi and Associates (b.); **93** © The Dorothea Lange Collection, The Oakland Museum, The City of Oakland. Gift of Paul S. Taylor; **95** © The Dorothea Lange Collection, The Oakland Museum, The City of Oakland. Gift of Paul S. Taylor; **96** Dorthea Lange/The National Archives; **97–101** © The Dorothea Lange Collection, The Oakland Museum, The City of Oakland. Gift of Paul S. Taylor; **102** © The Dorothea Lange Collection, The Oakland Museum, The City of Oakland. Gift of Paul S. Taylor (t.); Dorothea Lange/The National Archives (b.); **103** Catherine Noren (t.l.); Ambrosi and Associates (t.r., b.); **104–107** Allan Penn for SBG, photo styling by Anne Bugatch and Lance Salemo; **106** Ulsaker Studio, Inc. (t., b.); **107** Ulsaker Studio, Inc. (t., c., b.); **111** Ulsaker Studio, Inc. (t., c.); **112** Ambrosi and Associates (b.l.); **125** © David Maung/Impact Visuals (l.); Ambrosi and Associates (c., r.); **131** Ambrosi and Associates; **149** Marion Roth/Bantam Doubleday (l.); Ambrosi and Associates (c., r.); **152** Denver Public Library Western History Department (b.); **152–153** Sharon Hoogstraten for SBG; **153** Denver Public Library Western History Department (l.); © Smithsonian Institution (r.); **154** Denver Public Library Western History Department (b.); **154–155** Sharon Hoogstraten for SBG; **155** © Smithsonian Institution (l.); National Archives (r.); **156–157** Bentley Historical Society; **158** Reproduced from the collection of the Library of Congress (t.); **158–159** Sharon Hoogstraten for SBG; **159** UPI/Bettmann (b.); **160–161** Sharon Hoogstraten for SBG; **161** Courtesy of New York Public Library; **162** Reproduced from the collection of the Library of Congress; **162–163** Sharon Hoogstraten for SBG; **163** Courtesy of Penguin Books (t.); Ambrosi and Associates (c., b.); **164** Sharon Hoogstraten for SBG; **165–168** Jacob Lawrence/The Phillips Collection; **169–173** Jacob Lawrence/The Museum of Modern Art; **174** Jacob Lawrence/Eden Arts (t.); **174–175** John Morrison for SBG; **175** Jacob Lawrence/The National Academy of Design (t.); Ambrosi and Associates (b.c., b.r.); **176** Jacob Lawrence/The Phillips Collection; **177** Allan Landau for SBG; **178** © Norman McGrath; **178–179** Sharon Hoogstraten for SBG; **179** Collection of Whitney Museum of American Art, New York, gift of Julian Levy for Maro and Natasha Gorky in memory of their father, 50.17; photo by Geoffrey Clements, New York/© 1995 Estate of Arshile Gorky/Artists Rights Society (ARS), New York (t.); © Sandra Baker/ Gamma Liaison (b.); **180** John Morrison for SBG; **190–191** Sharon Hoogstraten for SBG; **191** © Lawrence Migdale (t.); Ambrosi and Associates (c., b.); **194** Ulsaker Studio, Inc. (t., b.); **195** Ulsaker Studio, Inc. (t., c., b.); **199** Ulsaker Studio, Inc. (t., c.); 201 Ambrosi and Associates (c.); 216 Courtesy William Morrow and Company (t.); **216–217** Sharon Hoogstraten for SBG; **217** Ambrosi and Associates (t.l., t.c., t.r.); **225** Ambrosi and Associates (r.); **237** Ambrosi and Associates (c., b.); **251** Courtesy of Ardath Mayhar (l.); Ambrosi and Associates (c., r.); **252–253** © Jules Frazier/West Stock; **254–255** Ken Marschall, Courtesy Madison Press; **256** Woods Hole Oceanographic Institute; **257** Pronk & Associates; **259** Pronk & Associates; **260** Ken Marschall; **261** Ken Marschall (l.); Woods Hole Oceanographic Institute (r.); **263** Ken Marschall; **264** Joseph Carvallo Collection; **265** Pronk & Associates (l.); Woods Hole Oceanographic Institute (r.); **266** Woods Hole Oceanographic Institute (t., b.); **267** Woods Hole Oceanographic Institute; **268** Painting by Ken Marschall; **269** Painting by Ken Marschall; Bill Sauder Collection (t.l.); Woods Hole Oceanographic Institute (t.c.); **270** Woods Hole Oceanographic Institute; **271** Painting by Ken Marschall; F. Browning/C. Hass (all inset photos); **272–273** Painting by Ken Marschall; Woods Hole Oceanographic Institute (inset photos); **275** Woods Hole Oceanographic Institute; **276** Pronk & Associates; **277** Perry Thorsvik/National Geographic Society (t.); Woods Hole Oceanographic Institution (l.); Ambrosi and Associates (c., r.); **278** Woods Hole Oceanographic Institute (t., b.); **279** © Joseph Bailey/The National Geographic Society 1985 (t.l.); © Brice Dale/The National Geographic Society 1985 (t.r., b.); **280** Courtesy of Haines Gallery (c.); **280–281** Sharon Hoogstraten for SBG; **281** Jasper Johns, *Numbers in Color,* 1959, encaustic and newspaper on canvas, 66 1/2 x 49 1/2", Albright-Knox Art Gallery, Buffalo, New York, Gift of Seymour H. Knox, 1959/© 1996 Jasper Johns/licensed by VAGA, New York, NY (t.); Courtesy of the Estate of Larry Beck (b.); **284** Ulsaker Studio, Inc. (t., b.); **285** Ulsaker Studio, Inc. (t., c., b.); **289** Ulsaker Studio, Inc. (t., c.); **291** Ambrosi and Associates (t.); **307** Courtesy of Simon & Schuster (l.); Ambrosi and Associates (r.); **308** Ambrosi and Associates; **324** Robert Ling (t.); **324–325** Sharon Hoogstraten for SBG; **325** Ambrosi and Associates (t., c.); **334** Fitz Hugh Lane/Bequest of Martha C. Karolik for the M. and M. Karolik Collection of American Paintings 1815–1865, courtesy Museum of Fine Arts, Boston; **336** Bowdoin College Museum of Art, Brunswick, Maine. Gift of Mrs. Charles Philip Kuntz; **338** Edward Thorp Gallery; **339** Courtesy of Barbara Toll Fine Arts (Photo by Zindman/Fremont); **340** Frank Stella, American, *Chocorua II,* 1966, fluorescent alkyd & epoxy on canvas, 124 x 120", Museum Purchase, 67.44, Collection of the J. B. Speed Art Museum, Louisville, Kentucky/© 1995 Frank Stella/Artists Rights Society (ARS), New York; **342** Hirshhorn Museum and Sculpture Garden, Smithsonian Institution, Gift of Joseph Hirshhorn, 1966. (Photo by Lee Stalsworth)/© 1995 Pollock-Krasner Foundation/Artists Rights Society (ARS), New York; **343** Courtesy of Random House (b.l.); Ambrosi and Associates (c., b.r.); **344** Courtesy of Fomento Cultural Banamex; **344–345** Sharon Hoogstraten for SBG; **345** Phillips, Bert, *Our Washerwoman's Family,* ca. 1918, oil on canvas, 40 1/2 x 41 5/8 in., Collection of the Museum of Fine Arts, Museum of New Mexico, Gift of Governor and Mrs. Arthur Seligman, 1922; **346** Private collection/ © Faith Ringgold, Inc.; **346–347** Sharon Hoogstraten for SBG; **347** photo by Jakrarat Veerasarn (l.); Marc Chagall, *I and the Village,* 1911, oil on canvas, 6'3 5/8 " x 59 5/8". The Museum of Modern Art, New York, Mrs. Simon Guggenheim Fund (t.r.); **348** Courtesy of Museo Nacional de Arte, INBA (l.); © Manuel Alvarez Martinez (t.r.); **348–349** Sharon Hoogstraten for SBG; **349** Courtesy of Fomento Cultural Banamex (t.); Courtesy of Museo Nacional de Arte, INBA (b.); **365** Courtesy of Lensey Namioka (b.l.); Ambrosi and Associates (b.r.); **370** Ulsaker Studio, Inc. (t., b.); **371** Ulsaker Studio, Inc. (t., c., b.); **372–375** © Brian Parker/Tom Stack & Associates; **375** Ulsaker Studio, Inc. (t., c.); **377** Ambrosi and Associates (t.); **391** Ambrosi and Associates (b.l., b.r.); Courtesy of Elizabeth Hall (t.l., t.r.); **420–421** Sharon Hoogstraten for SBG; **421** Ambrosi and Associates; **422–431** Sharon Hoogstraten for SBG (border); **432** © Marina Ancona (t.); **432–433** John Morrison for SBG; **433** Ambrosi and Associates (t.r., c.r.); Paul Buchbinder (l.); **440** Sharon Hoogstraten for SBG (l.); **440–441** © Kevin C. Rose/The Image Bank; **444** © Robert P. Carr/Bruce Coleman, Inc. (t.); **446** Anne Sager, National Audubon Society Collection/Photo Researchers, Inc. (t.); **447** © Kim Taylor/Bruce Coleman, Inc. (t.); **448** UPI/Bettmann (t.); **449** © Arthur Panzer 1979; **452** D. Brauning/© VIREO; **453** Doug Mindell (l.); Ambrosi and Associates (r.); **454** Fundacion Dolores Olmedo, Mexico City, Mexico/Schalkwijk/Art Resource, NY; **454–455** Sharon Hoogstraten for SBG; **455** © 1995 M. C. Escher/Cordon Art - Baarn - Holland. All rights reserved. (t.); Private collection/ Giraudon/ Art Resource, NY/© 1995 C. Herscovici, Brussels/Artists Rights Society (ARS), New York (b.); **456** Collection of the New-York Historical Society; **456–457** Sharon Hoogstraten for SBG; **457** National Gallery of Canada, Ottawa; **458–461** © Brian Parker/Tom Stack & Associates; **460** Ulsaker Studio, Inc. (t., b.); **461** Ulsaker Studio, Inc. (t., c., b.); **465** Ulsaker Studio, Inc. (t., c.); **466–467** Allan Penn for SBG; **485** Courtesy of Richard Berleth (t.); Ambrosi and Associates (b.); **486** Ambrosi and Associates; **492** Ambrosi and Associates (t.); **510** Courtesy of Dorothy Hoobler (t.l.); **510–511** Sharon Hoogstraten for SBG; **511** Courtesy of Tom Hoobler (t.l.); Ambrosi and Associates (t.c., t.r.); **512** Ambrosi and Associates (l.); **521** Courtesy of University of Nebraska Press (t.); Ambrosi and Associates (b.l., b.c., b.r.); **524** Courtesy of the Estate of Louis Carlos Bernal; **525** Courtesy of the Estate of Louis Carlos Bernal (c.); Sharon Hoogstraten for SBG (b.); **526** Courtesy of the Estate of Louis Carlos Bernal; **526–527** Sharon Hoogstraten for SBG; **527** Courtesy of the Estate of Louis Carlos Bernal; **528** Courtesy of the Estate of Louis Carlos Bernal (c.); **528–529** Sharon Hoogstraten for SBG; **530** Courtesy of the Estate of Louis Carlos Bernal (c); Sharon Hoogstraten for SBG (b.); **531** Courtesy of the Estate of Louis Carlos Bernal; **532** National Museum of American Art, Washington DC/Art Rescource, NY; **532–533** Sharon Hoogstraten for SBG; **533** Courtesy of Morning Star Gallery, Santa Fe, NM, photo by Addison Doty (t.); Solomon D. Butcher Collection, Nebraska State Historical Society (b.); **534–535** Topeka Women's Club, Courtesy of National Geographic Society; **561** Art Resource, NY; **563** Courtesy of Simon & Schuster (t.); Ambrosi and Associates (c., b.); **566** Ulsaker Studio, Inc. (t., b.); **567** Ulsaker Studio, Inc. (t., c., b.); **570** © A. d'Arazien/The Image Bank (t.r.); Sharon Hoogstraten for SBG (b.l.); **571** © Norm Thomas/Photo Researchers, Inc. (b.); **572** © Jeff Hunter/The Image Bank (t.); © Michael Melford/The Image Bank (b.l.); **573** © Gabriel M. Covian/The Image Bank (t.r.); © Joseph Van Os/The Image Bank (b.); **574** © Ralph A. Reinhold/Animals Animals (t.); **575** © Larry Gatz/The Image Bank (t.); © Gary Cralle/The Image Bank (c.); **576** © Terry Farmer/Tony Stone Images (t.); © Ross M. Horowitz/The Image Bank (b.); **578** © Fernando Bueno/The Image Bank (t.); Cosmo Condina © Tony Stone Images (b.); **579** © Chris Huss/The Wildlife Collection (t.); **580** © Onne Van Der Wal/Stock Newport (t.l.); © Adamsmith Productions/Westlight (r.); © Guido Alberto Rossi/The Image Bank (b.); **581** © Mercury Archive/Image Bank (t.r.); **582** © John Giustina/The Wildlife Collection (t.); Barros and Barros/The Image Bank (b.); **583** © Onne Van Der Wal/Stock Newport (l.); © Art Wolfe/Tony Stone Images (b.r.); **584** © Warren Morgan/Westlight (t.l.); © SIU Biomed Comm/Custom Medical Stock Photo (r.); **585** © Mark Adams/Westlight (t.r.); © Philip and Karen Smith/Tony Stone Images (b.); **586** © Rob Boudreau/Tony Stone Images (r.); © Leonard Lee Rue III/Tony Stone Images (b.l.); **587** © John Bova/Photo Researchers (t.); © Steve Smith/Westlight (b.l.); **588** © Ernst Hohne/Tony Stone Images (l.); **589** © Tony Stone Images (t.r.); © Murray and Associates/Tony Stone Images (l.).